Teaching Nutrition

Teaching

Ercel Eppright

Assistant Dean,
College of Home Economics,
Iowa State University

Drawings by *Harry Walsh*

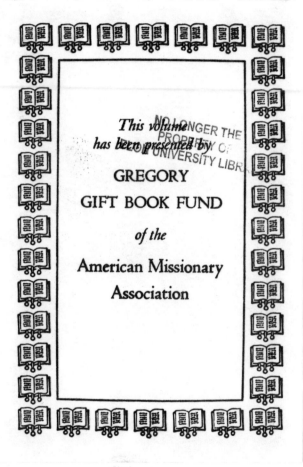

This volume
has been presented by

GREGORY

GIFT BOOK FUND

of the

American Missionary
Association

Basic to success in teaching
people to change their food habits
is an understanding of _why_
they eat as they do.

Nutrition

══ *Second Edition* ══

Mattie Pattison

Professor,
Home Economics Education,
Iowa State University

Helen Barbour

Assistant Dean,
College of Home Economics,
Oklahoma State University

The Iowa State University Press,
Ames, Iowa, U.S.A.

About the Authors

DR. ERCEL EPPRIGHT is Assistant Dean, College of Home Economics, and Assistant Director of the Agricultural and Home Economics Experiment Station, Iowa State University. She is nationally known for her work in nutrition education. In 1961 she received the Borden Award for her research contributions in nutrition with special reference to the nutritional status of children. Dr. Eppright holds the Ph.D. in physiological chemistry, Yale University. In 1957 she served as FAO consultant in Baghdad, Iraq, where she taught nutrition at the Tahrir College for Women.

DR. MATTIE PATTISON is Professor of Home Economics Education, Iowa State University. In 1963 Dr. Pattison was appointed to serve as chairman of the Baroda project, a program to develop graduate study and research in home economics at Baroda University, India. In addition to her teaching and research responsibilities, Dr. Pattison has served as consultant to the Iowa State Department of Education on the homemaking curriculum in Iowa secondary schools. She holds the Ph.D. in education from the University of Chicago.

DR. HELEN BARBOUR is Assistant Dean Coordinating Home Economics Research, and Head of the Department of Food, Nutrition, and Institution Administration, Oklahoma State University. Before her appointment there she was Head of the Department of Home Economics, New Mexico State University. Her doctoral study at Iowa State in nutrition and home economics education was done under the Mary Swartz Rose Fellowship from the American Dietetic Association. She conducted the initial experimental work in the use of generalizations in teaching nutrition to children.

© 1957, 1963 by The Iowa State University Press.
All rights reserved.
Composed and printed by
The Iowa State University Press,
Ames, Iowa, U.S.A.

First Edition 1957
  Reprinted 1958, 1959, 1961

Second Edition 1963
  Reprinted 1964

Foreword

AGAINST A BACKDROP of the world food situation, this expanded edition of *Teaching Nutrition* recognizes that nutrition educators play a responsible part in improving the nutrition of people everywhere and that improved nutrition is one factor involved in leading the way toward peace among nations.

Significant to this challenge is the authors' approach: nutrition education must convince the individual that his diet is a matter not only of personal health and vitality but, through its impact on others, is a matter of social concern.

The book points up the part nutrition plays in good health from childhood to old age. It does so within the framework of factors too infrequently recognized as potent influences in the state of nutrition — individual differences, environmental situations, group relationships, and quality of the food supply in a technological age. It emphasizes the effects that food eaten today may have on the individual years later.

By this painting of the picture of nutrition in all its complex and interrelated colors, *Teaching Nutrition* makes one of its most important contributions.

Based upon carefully selected and authenticated research, the material is timely, stimulating, and thought provoking. This book is primarily a handbook for teaching. It also provides a wealth of information helpful to workers in nutrition — those in extension, public health, dietetics, informational services, or homemaking.

The emphasis on the importance of using a variety of methods in the development of new concepts or "generalizations" in nutrition is good, for no *one* learning experience is adequate. The generalizations

[*v*]

and concepts developed in Chapter 6 may well serve as guides for any nutrition education program.

The elaboration of content and methodology in Chapter 7 and of evaluation of the learning processes in Chapter 8 will be helpful to any engaged in spreading nutrition information. From all the excellent suggestions provided, the nutrition educator should find appropriate methods to use with any particular group — youth or adult, elementary school or college, formal or informal, in the United States or elsewhere in the world.

Another value lies in the summaries which reveal the concerns of our government for the need of adequate nutrition education programs for the people of the United States. The story of the four national nutritional conferences and their impact on nutrition policies and education programs is told clearly. Educators also will appreciate the digests of the most significant information on national food consumption patterns from recent publications and the summaries of the cooperative nutrition researches conducted in the United States from 1947 to 1958.

It is with deep satisfaction that we, as colleagues of the authors, commend this enlarged and expanded book to all nutrition educators. We believe thoughtful use of its materals will widen the scope and increase the effectiveness of programs in nutrition education.

PEARL SWANSON

Professor of Nutrition, Iowa Agricultural and Home Economics Experiment Station and the Department of Food and Nutrition, Iowa State University

FLORENCE FALLGATTER

Professor Emeritus and former Head of Home Economics Education, Iowa State University

Preface

ONE OF THE MOST IMPORTANT responsibilities of the nutrition educator is to help the individual understand his changing nutritional needs, the choices he has for meeting them, the distractions he may encounter, and the long-time effects of the different patterns he may choose in his daily use of food.

Nutrition is a determining factor in the total health of the individual, and thus it can and does affect the attainment of goals. Because violations of nutrition principles usually do not produce immediately dramatic results, people find it difficult to establish in their minds convincing cause-and-effect relationships between eating and health. Therefore, motivation becomes an important aspect in nutrition education.

Every individual needs a practical working knowledge of nutrition. However, the application of nutrition cannot be couched in simple rules to be used by all people at all times. In this book we have taken into consideration the special needs of nutrition education for:

1. simplification of technical materials;
2. motivation of people to establish rational eating behavior.

From the mass of information in nutrition we have attempted to sift the doubtful and controversial, and to organize the working facts or principles for effective use. We have enlarged on certain aspects that seem to us especially important as a background for effective nutrition education. We have given emphasis to the present knowledge relating to what we eat and why, and to the evolution of current nutrition policies and nutrition education programs.

In our interdependent society, the maintenance of good nutrition depends on numerous environmental forces. Nutrition education, therefore, has a responsibility in helping people to understand these

[*vii*]

forces and to recognize the social action required to safeguard the food supply. It is essential for the citizens of our country to have some appreciation of the significance of nutrition to human welfare the world over.

Primarily this a handbook for teaching. It should be useful to those who know the facts of nutrition but have little experience in making them function for others. It is designed to be useful also to those with little education in nutrition. The "generalizations" are presented primarily for use in popular nutrition. They may, however, provide working guides for technical courses given for teachers, public health workers, or others engaged in applied nutrition. The book summarizes and gives examples of a wide variety of methods.

In addition, through its illustrations, it has attempted to emphasize the point that a seasoning of fun and good humor is generally an asset to teaching efforts, especially of a subject such as nutrition which is strongly related to human nature.

In our selections of emphases to be placed, we have been influenced by the results of investigations of several populations in Iowa over a twenty-year period. These studies were made under the auspices of the Iowa Agricultural and Home Economics Experiment Station by members of two departments of the College of Home Economics at Iowa State University: Food and Nutrition, and Home Economics Education.

Many people deserve our thanks for their assistance and encouragement during the preparation and publication of this book. We are especially indebted to Dr. Pearl Swanson, Professor of Nutrition, Iowa Agricultural Experiment Station and the Department of Food and Nutrition, and Dr. Florence Fallgatter, Professor Emeritus and former Head of Home Economics Education, both of Iowa State University.

ERCEL EPPRIGHT

MATTIE PATTISON

HELEN BARBOUR

Contents

Teaching Nutrition

*One of the few matters
of international agreement today
is the definition of health.*

Chapter One

Education: Cornerstone of Good Nutrition

BECAUSE NUTRITION is the foundation of good health, the food we eat today plays a major part in shaping our destiny tomorrow as an individual, as a family, and as a nation. "Good health" means more than just the physical well-being of a person. One of the few matters of international agreement in our world today is the definition of health which appears in the constitution of the World Health Organization of the United Nations and was agreed upon by the nations who ratified the WHO constitution (1):

Health is a state of complete physical, mental and social well-being and not merely the absence of disease or infirmity.

As nutrition is the foundation of good health, education is the cornerstone of good nutrition, because to attain good nutrition the individual must be *taught* to make good food selection and to maintain an environment conducive to the utilization of the nutrients provided by the food. Getting the proper nutrients every day is not achieved in man by instinct; it is accomplished through the application of knowledge. Thus man must know how to utilize the existing food supply so as to derive maximum nutritional benefit from it. "To establish good food habits, people must be able to learn, and nutrition educators must be able to teach." (2)

Our basic drive for food and the way we satisfy it are as personal as our fingerprints. Hunger is fundamental to life — it is a continuous drive from birth to death. From an infinitesimally small cell, an individual is produced who in about two decades will be twenty to thirty times as large as at birth. This miracle of growth results from a dynamic system in which substances are added to our bodies, used by them, and discarded.

[*3*]

How individuals satisfy hunger and appetite from day to day has a direct effect upon their well-being: our "nutriture" (health as it is affected by nutrition) depends upon the substances with which we were built before we were born, those we consumed in our growing years, and those we must rely upon throughout the adult life span. Patterns by which these nutrients are used in the normal course of events are determined by complicated systems of checks and controls.

FOOD AND SOCIETY

The immediate relationship of food to the health of the individual expands to become an influence upon the health of the society in which he lives. It has been said that nutrition is a science concerned with the movements of atoms in man to the movements of man in society. Because of the tremendous population explosion, the supply of food for all peoples of the world is indeed becoming more critical every year.

Wars have been fought over food — or lack of it. The concept of "lebensraum" (living space) and the need for land to grow more agricultural products have long been motives for conflicts ranging from neighborhood skirmishes between primitive tribes to world-wide wars among nations. Food and politics are more closely related than ever before in history.

Dr. C. G. King (3) has asserted that ". . . the growing interdependence of men in different fields of science, in different types of industry, and in different areas of responsibility stands out more clearly than ever before. . . . Voting and eating are close relatives in a very large family." The effective dissemination of nutrition information is vital in a democracy.

It can be further said that the nutrition problems of all the world's people are vital in the struggle between democracies and dictatorships, freedom and tyranny. Food has been a weapon in the hands of despots, but it can also be an instrument of peace in the hands of free peoples. The changing picture of the world's population and food supply might lead us to conclude that one way to a hungry man's

. . . . nutrition is a science concerned with the movements of atoms in man . . . .

*. . . one way
to a hungry man's politics
is through his stomach.*

politics is through his stomach. If he is restless, semistarved, and desperate for enough
food for survival, he is likely to accept immediate help now and pay the political price
later.

Lord John Boyd-Orr, first director-general of the Food and Agricultural Organization of the United Nations, aptly said (4):

> Food shortage with resulting land hunger in the overpopulated countries
> in Asia is a contributory cause of the unrest and revolt against the rule of the
> white man and the spread of communism, with its promise of land for the
> people and the production for consumption by the people and not for the
> profit of landowners and others.

He subsequently added,

> The masses of the people have little interest in politics, except in meas-
> ures which affect their interest. . . . Political freedom has little appeal for
> the poverty stricken illiterate masses which form nearly half of the world
> population, unless as a means of using a vote to get rid of the existing
> government. As an American visiting Asia is reported to have said, "If you
> offered a hungry Asian Roosevelt's four freedoms or four hamburgers he
> would choose the hamburgers."

Nutrition education carries much responsibility in acquainting
the public with the world food situation and with the meaning of
malnutrition, especially semistarvation, which is perhaps the most
prevalent form.

OUR NUTRITION PROBLEMS

It is hard to imagine that despite a surplus of food in the United
States we still have nutritional problems. We may not have starvation or semistarvation which is found elsewhere in the world, but we
do have poor food habits which, in as yet undisclosed ways, are under-
mining the longevity and productivity of many Americans. An im-

*. . . dietary patterns
may indeed be related
to the aging process.*

portant lesson yet unlearned is that of changing our way of eating
with the changing physiological needs of advancing age, changes in
economic status, and shifts in environment. For example, our inability
to adjust to these situations has brought upon us the problem of overweight — which is unique to our nation and other nations with a similar economic picture.

Various dietary abuses have created or contributed to other problems: dental caries and chronic disorders of body systems, such as the
vascular or skeletal. These problems occur despite the fact that the
body is apparently well equipped with reserves and safety devices.
Thus is indicated the cumulative effect of dietary abuse. In human
nutrition little is known about the delayed effects of early malnutrition, but we have reasons to believe they occur. Animal studies suggest the significance of poor nutrition in early years to degenerative
disorders which mark the onset of senescence. Long-time dietary patterns of human beings may indeed affect enzyme systems which undoubtedly are closely related to the aging process (5).

Freedom of Choice

Probably our precious freedom of choice precipitates many dietary
problems. Agricultural abundance, technological advances, and prosperity present us with a wide panorama of dietary items. Enjoyment
of eating is a part of the social way of life for many Americans; many
can afford to choose food for pleasure as well as for sustenance. Markets
present us with a bewildering array of foods, and advertisers often influence us to choose by emotion rather than reason. True variety in
food has repeatedly been shown to be a protection against a poor diet,
but, as pointed out by Dr. Margaret Lantis (6), an anthropologist with
the U.S. Public Health Service, the range of choices on our food

counters "is illusory and misleading. We are not nutritionally much better off for having three kinds of lettuce on sale at the same time in the same store . . . ."

This "supermarket complex" does lead to an infinite variety of choices, but too often a kind of variety that produces bewilderment, not better nutrition. In such a situation, one is called upon to make only a decision among many similar items rather than a selection of different kinds of food which would supplement each other nutritionally.

Our freedom of choice extends to the many opportunities to take meals away from home — in our schools, industrial plant cafeterias, institutions, and restaurants. These occasions often increase the number of decisions we must make as to what we eat. We can easily choose good diets at moderate cost, if we make intelligent use of our nutritional opportunities. *Quality* of diet in our nation is an easily attainable goal for most of the population.

In sharp contrast, survival of many of the world's peoples depends upon *quantity* of food: Whether a person can obtain enough nourishment every day to subsist. Even when food supplies are adequate for survival, the individual may have small variety from which to choose. Although good choices may be available, lack of nutrition knowledge or the presence of firmly established traditions may interfere with wise choices in food, which may ultimately result in dietary deficiencies. The health, productivity, and life span of the individual are thus determined by how he selects his diet — and what selections exist for him.

These occasions often increase the number of decisions we must make . . . .

We need to understand that because we in the United States are blessed with abundance and freedom of choice, we must be concerned about the education needed to direct our selections of foods in such a manner that they will contribute to health and productivity as well as to momentary satisfactions. The health and well-being of our citizens are an important part of our national resources now and in the future.

Education Is Important

How can the nutritional status of individuals, groups, and nations of people be improved? Answers to this question are not simple.

Education is important to many aspects of the problem. If incomes are adequate and foods plentiful, people must be taught how to choose wisely. If the problem is shortage of foods, remedies must be found for the root causes of those shortages before the dietary problems can be attacked. This, too, may be an educational matter.

We must teach other peoples of the world how to grow more and better agricultural products; how to process, distribute, and store them efficiently; and then teach them as we teach ourselves how to consume them advantageously.

As a comparatively young science, nutrition depends upon many specialists to apply their skills to the improvement of food supplies. When this is accomplished, nutrition educators must teach people how to build good diets for themselves. The educator must know *how* to teach the people — and *what* to teach them.

THE EDUCATOR AND THE SCIENTIST

The accumulation and dissemination of nutrition knowledge must go hand in hand, in a sort of team-like relationship as expressed in *Food for Life* (7):

Scientific knowledge did not happen; it was gleaned by continuing and patient effort, by study and experiment. In the realm of food, as in all others, support of such effort has paid rich dividends in human welfare. But knowledge of the scientists and technologists is not sufficient. To put it into action, there must be widespread understanding and support by the people. . . .

Obviously, nutritional science bears a large responsibility for future generations of men the world over . . . and it has begun to spread its newfound knowledge, as is shown by the improved nutrition of most Americans. At the moment, its immediate problem is to disseminate that knowledge so that every man, woman, and child not only has a sound understanding of what good nutrition is but also acts on it.

The greatest need of American nutrition today — and that means American health, too — is public education.

Nutrition education has made progress in the past. To a certain extent, we now know the roles of nutrients, the practical value of fortifying or enriching staple foods, the usefulness of food plans and guides, and how to help the individual become aware of his own nutritional status. But these things were not known 50 or 100 years ago.

The nutrition educator's task is twofold: first, to teach what is known and, second, to continuously study and critically evaluate new information. Modifying information presented in the light of new discoveries is a vital requirement for teaching.

. . . to critically evaluate new information.

SOURCES OF NUTRITION

1. MILK
2. COFFEE CREAM
3. BUTTERMILK
4. CHOCOLATE DRINK

The nutrition educator and the nutrition scientist share a common goal: to improve the nutritional status of people. At one time the same person combined the two responsibilities but now two separate specialists more often are needed. The scientist analyzes food and people; the educator relies upon the scientist's findings in order to teach people how to improve food habits; so the two are interdependent.

The scientist in nutrition research must analyze foods and investigate the metabolism of nutrients in relation to the functioning of body components. He must work in precise, disciplined techniques. Variables must be controlled insofar as possible. His results are then neatly tabulated, classified, and interpreted. They must be preserved for reanalysis and interpretation in the light of future discoveries. It is legendary that "a good set of data are eternal."

The findings, as reported by researchers, however, may appear to be far too formidable for the layman to understand, or to apply to his own food problems. Because the scientist is so busy with his specialized tasks, he may have little time or inclination to leave the laboratory in order to explain to laymen what he has learned and how it may help him. A good scientist often can present his findings and those of other researchers in a brilliant and convincing manner, but the day-to-day teaching, aimed at motivating people to change, requires special skills and techniques which the scientist may not have time to acquire.

The nutrition educator, however, has the necessary teaching skills and abilities, plus an understanding of nutrition research. The understanding should be broadly comparable with that of the nutrition scientist. The educator must use precise, scientific nutrition data to encourage flexibility and variability in the use of foods to meet physiological and psychological needs. The educator is a *translator* who carries the heavy responsibility of interpreting scientific evidence into meaningful facts which laymen can understand and apply to food selection in a wide variety of situations and to meal planning and preparation. Thus the nutrition educator has become the connecting link between the scientist and the layman; between the laboratory and the dinner table — whether that dinner table is in a home, a school or other institution, a restaurant, or a company cafeteria.

EDUCATORS MUST MOTIVATE

In motivating people to choose more nearly adequate diets for themselves, educators must arouse latent interest and enthusiasm, convincing people that nutrition does make a difference in the achievement of goals.

We cannot pass laws or issue edicts requiring every citizen to adhere to certain minimum standards of food consumption. Even if there were ways to interfere deliberately with the individual's food habits, we probably would meet stiff resistance and resentment, because the individual treasures his freedom of choice and his diet as a matter of personal privilege. People may guard more zealously their rights to choose what they put into their mouths than what they feed their minds — thus we observe the determined stands sometimes encountered in such projects as fluoridation of water supplies.

So we must convince the individual that his diet is a matter of personal responsibility, and that it also has social impact. For example a malnourished child can be a health hazard to his classmates. An industrial worker may have heavy responsibility for the safety of his co-workers: if he is poorly fed, his impaired physical and mental performance may endanger the lives of others. When a housewife has unsound eating habits the family may suffer from her apathy, fatigue, decreased efficiency, and hyperirritability, and from her example of poor food habits. Since we live in a highly interrelated society, our food habits do affect other people.

Hence the nutrition educator must persuade each person to evaluate his food habits in terms of optimum health and vitality, as a responsibility to himself and to others. But the nutrition educator must be cautious about the use of half-truths, oversimplification, and promises that cannot be fulfilled. Once the individual is convinced he needs to improve his diet, we may then teach him how to do it.

Unfortunately, we cannot offer everyone a thorough, complete course in nutrition, for once and for all time. New knowledge often replaces old; we must reach the public periodically with revised information as it becomes available. Then, too, every person needs to be reminded frequently of good food practices — just as he needs to be reminded of such things as traffic safety and routine dental or health care. We need better lines of communication — and they must remain open — if the individual is to be encouraged to open his mind to new knowledge and new habits.

The Educator's Ideal

If there were no impediments to the teaching of nutrition, we would begin by reaching all children with basic food facts at an appropriate age. We would encourage them to examine their food habits, to evaluate their daily diets, and to acquire some degree of understanding of the importance to their health of food selection and habits of eating.

Then we would continue to reach them often in their school years with broader and deeper concepts as new information is learned and organized. Most of all, we would remind them repeatedly to *alter their food habits with their changing food energy needs.* This is probably the most important lesson of all. If we succeeded in this, perhaps many of our middle-aged population might not have to cope with the problems of overweight.

. . . our middle-aged population might not have to cope with overweight.

Finally, we would have some direct, effective way to reach adults with continued learning based on new facts. In their later years, people would be helped to obtain nutritious diets despite such handicaps as poor teeth, inability to perform daily tasks of living, financial limitations, and the loneliness and boredom of old age which so often affect appetite and nutriture.

If we could follow a given individual from his childhood through his adult years with sound nutrition education, he would constantly be well equipped with a solid nutrition background, receptive to new facts and ready to utilize them.

Ideals Versus Actualities

We know, of course, the ideal situation seldom exists. That is true in nutrition education as it is in all other things.

When school curricula are crowded, nutrition education is sometimes covered perfunctorily and not so often or so thoroughly as we would like. Furthermore, outside influences often run counter to what is taught in school. Consequently, there are many young people and adults who have had little or no education in choosing good diets. This makes the educator's task more difficult: we must overcome fully established eating habits which have been re-enforced by traditional beliefs, cultural patterns, and even superstitions. We must first create a mental climate favorable to learning the basic facts of good nutrition; then we may begin to re-educate the individual with information based on sound knowledge.

EDUCATORS AS SPECIALISTS

Because food habits are so personal, nutrition educators must be concerned with the values, goals, attitudes, and beliefs of their students. They must tailor subject matter to fit the needs and abilities of students. Part of a teaching background lies in knowing what the sociologist, anthropologist, psychologist, and economist have revealed about people and their food habits — and then in being able to apply the information thus obtained to the task at hand.

The nutrition educator may be a specialist with nutrition education as a primary responsibility, or may be a generalist who integrates nutrition education into a diversified program. The level of information may cover a wide range from highly complex concepts to the very simple. Whatever the level, all are nutrition educators and all need a firm grasp of the knowledge of nutrition at the level they are teaching plus the techniques of reaching different groups of students effectively, evaluating their progress, and motivating them toward a lifelong interest in their diets.

The nutrition educator — whether man or woman — finds opportunities through many different avenues of teaching. As a woman:

● She may be a *home economist* in the teaching field, Extension Service, industry, or communications work — an informed, responsible citizen of her community. Her home economics predecessors pioneered in developing the science of nutrition, and their modern-era counterparts must continue to carry a large share of the teaching load, particularly in reaching homemakers through the media of magazines, newspapers, radio, television, and special publications.

● She may be a *public health worker,* who meets situations in which poor nutrition is one major facet of many circumstances affecting the health and welfare of individuals and groups.

● She may be a *dietitian* with the responsibility of planning meals for people who require intensive diet therapy as part of their treatment, and who may need individualized education to learn how to maintain special diet requirements after they have left the hospital or other institution. Dietitians may also provide instruction in nutrition to meet special conditions such as pregnancy, underweight, or overweight. One of the primary stated objectives of the dietetic profession is to promote nutrition education.

● She may be a *teacher* in a public or private school, college or university, or in an adult education class. Her job may require teaching nutrition as an independent subject, or as a special study unit in home economics, health and hygiene, science, or other courses.

● She may be a well-informed homemaker, sensitive to the needs of family and community, a willing cooperator in programs for the betterment of local environment.

The nutrition educator is aware that there is no one established method — or opportunity — to teach nutrition for everyone. Indeed, much nutrition education reaches the individual through one of many allied professional groups who work with the public, such as physicians or dentists. Nutrition is a subject that is taught at a variety of levels of complexity. At any level, the educator must have knowledge in greater depth than she is currently teaching. The lowest level may present the greatest challenge. Some nutrition education must of necessity be in the hands of essentially lay people. Nutrition education specialists have a heavy responsibility in providing materials and guidance to such people.

Because food habits are so personalized and individuals are so free to make their own choices, the educator must devise many approaches to suit an infinite variety of people and teaching opportunities.

A PRACTICAL APPROACH TO EDUCATION

Presented in this book are information and practical teaching methods which may be adjusted to fit the needs of schools and of special groups, including young people's clubs and organizations as well as adult groups. Material included here can be helpful for either a beginner's class in nutrition or an advanced course, and at varying age levels.

In Chapter 2, "The Framework of Nutrition Education," the scope of nutrition is examined as well as the danger signals of poor nutrition.

"What We Eat," Chapter 3, is based on extensive surveys which tell us much about our eating patterns on a national basis. In Chapter 4, "Factors Influencing Eating Behavior," emphasis is placed on the psychological, physiological, and cultural influences upon eating patterns of individuals and groups.

Chapter 5, "What Should You Teach," Chapter 6, "Generalizations and Facts," and Chapter 7, "Methods of Teaching" comprise a selection of helpful content and teaching techniques upon which the educator can base nutrition lessons.

Offered in Chapter 8, "Evaluation," are suggestions that will aid both students and teachers in discussing and assessing progress in nutrition education.

The historical background which underlies the philosophies we share in the field of nutrition is traced perspectively in Chapter 9, "Concern for Nutrition Education." This leads into Chapter 10, "International Nutrition — A Resource and a Responsibility," where world food problems as they relate to teaching nutrition in our present era and in the future are presented.

Finally, "The Challenge of Change," Chapter 11, is a discussion of the significance to nutrition education of change in the individual, within himself, and in his environment. Changing nutritional needs of people through their life stages are considered, and the possibilities of future developments in the science of nutrition as they might concern education are indicated.

THE IMMEDIATE TASK

The immediate task for nutrition educators is clearly defined: to take advantage of the wealth of information we now have in order to teach people to improve their eating practices. We cannot wait for a final solution of many controversial questions in nutrition or for "sure-fire" methods of changing food habits; we must make use of the large body of nutrition knowledge we possess.

Daniel B. Stone (8) reminds us that one of the most important problems of nutrition is the gap between existing information and applying that information to the daily diet. *We have acquired the facts, but they are not being fully used.* He compares research and teaching in nutrition to the wheels of a bicycle.

Both are essential. Both should be going the same way at the same speed. At present, research is the big wheel. I suggest not that we put the brake on this, but that we increase the size and speed of the teaching wheel. Our main business is not only to see what lies dimly at a distance, but also to do what lies clearly at hand.

We have enough knowledge to teach, and we can do the job which lies clearly at hand.

Sir Richard Gregory (9) said of knowledge:

Knowledge is like energy. It is capable of doing work but it must be changed from the potential state to the kinetic or moving state. Knowledge is like a rock set up on a shelf. It does no harm and it does no good so long as it rests there, but let somebody jar the shelf and let the rock fall off, and then something happens.

We may conclude that the main function of nutrition education is to "knock the knowledge off the shelf."

REFERENCES

1. Parran, T., and Boudreau, F., "The World Health Organization: Cornerstone of Peace." *Amer. Jour. Publ. Health*, 36:1267, 1315, Nov. 1946.
2. Babcock, C. G., "Attitudes and the Use of Foods." *Jour. Amer. Diet. Assn.*, 38: 546–51, 1961.
3. King, C. G., *Science and Food: Today and Tomorrow.* Proceedings of a Symposium, Dec. 8, 1960, Food Protection Committee, Food and Nutrition, Natl. Acad. Sci., NRC Publ. 877, p. 27.
4. Boyd-Orr, John, *Borden's Review of Nutr. Res.*, 15(No. 2):19, 20, March–April 1954.
5. Ross, M. H., "Protein, Calories and Life Expectancy." American Institute of Nutrition, Symposium on Protein Requirement and Its Assessment in Man, July 1959, *Federation Proceedings*, 18(No. 2): 66–83.
6. Lantis, M., "Cultural Factors Influencing Children's Food Habits." Nutrition Education Conference, Washington, Jan. 29–31, 1962. *Proceedings*, p. 27.
7. Gerard, R. W. (editor), *Food For Life*, p. 302. Univ. of Chicago Press, 1952.
8. Stone, Daniel B., *Nutr. Rev.* 19:1–2, 1961.
9. Gregory, Richard, quoted by John R. Murlin, Natl. Nutr. Conf. for Defense, 1941, p. 27.

Building the framework of nutrition education can be developed visually as a flannel graph, using photos, magazine illustrations, or drawings in the center, while segments of the framework are put in place as the theme progresses.

Chapter Two

The Framework of Nutrition Education

THE FOCUS of nutrition is on *people:* people of all ages, incomes, races, creeds, and nationalities. Our interest as nutrition educators is in helping them to develop good food habits which, in turn, will help them to become healthy, attractive, personable, and productive citizens.

As a result of the application of nutrition knowledge, we may visualize the ultimate development of a portrait of beautiful people. The portrait, let us say, is incomplete without a suitable frame. To the

nutrition educator, the frame may represent the various factors important to the development of the portrait. This, in a sense, shows the broad scope of nutrition education.

The frame consists of four major sides, each of which is a sort of mosaic consisting of important segments. The first major side of the frame relates to the individual; the second to the group or groups of which the individual is a part; the third to the maintenance of an adequate food supply; and the fourth to environmental conditions that affect nutrition (see Fig. 2.1).

Each segment is important and must be separately considered as we work toward the goal of helping people to achieve good nutrition. But without any one of the segments, the picture presents an unfinished appearance. Nutrition education therefore is concerned with the portrait itself and every part of the frame.

THE INDIVIDUAL

To many people, nutrition education involves mainly teaching the individual the essential nutrients in an adequate diet. The individual is indeed the focal point of nutrition education, but what he is taught about nutrition must include more than a list of dietary requirements or even the allowances for individual nutrients —

necessary as they may be. Because nutritional requirements are fulfilled mainly through *foods,* teaching people how to meet body needs through appropriate selection of foods is one of the main responsibilities of nutrition education. But this is not enough.

The individual must *accept* food which provides the nutrients required, must then *digest* it, and finally must *utilize* it to build the body and promote the proper functioning of its parts. Failure at any one of these steps leads to poor nutrition. For each step a large amount of knowledge exists.

Food acceptance involves appetite and preferences as well as hunger and the need for sustenance. It is concerned with attitudes toward food and eating, including the emotional, cultural, and traditional factors which influence choice of food.

After the individual has accepted food, his body then must perform the task of digesting it. Subsequently the utilization of nutrients by the body tissues occurs. In some ways, the utilization of nutrients may be regarded as following remarkably unerring processes, but the possible variations result in a wide range of individual differences in metabolic patterns and nutrient needs.

Nutrition educators must have an appreciation of the differences in needs of individuals, and it is a part of their responsibility to interpret to the public this concept of differences. Williams (1) has said that if large populations of individuals (both male and female) were studied, the range in calcium needs would be substantially larger than fivefold. On the basis of animal studies, he states that a tenfold variability, or possibly more, may be expected in the human needs for vitamin A. Similar observations have been made for other nutrients; for example, he states that the evidence indicates the requirement of human beings for ascorbic acid probably varies within a fivefold range.

The implications for nutrition education are highly important. They have been summarized by Williams as follows:

> One of the real difficulties in selling nutrition to the public . . . is the fact that there are individuals who seem to pay no attention to nutritional maxims, or to vitamins, minerals, et cetera, and yet remain healthy to advanced old age. . . . These individuals are very effective living denials of all the nutritionists have to say, and the public is not slow to see the difference between "theory" and "practice."

In continuing his discussion, Williams says these individuals "are not so phenomenal, actually" because they may have "unusually low demands for a number of crucial nutrients" which allows them apparently to violate nutrition laws. He concludes by emphasizing the need for more widespread recognition of the variations in nutritional needs among individuals.

food selection **food preparation** **food service**   **g r o u p**

THE GROUP

The nutrition of the individual is strongly influenced by the groups of which he is a part. Mealtime is mainly a group activity — whether it occurs within the family circle or in a public place. The same may be said for snack time. Usually we can be easily influenced by the attitudes of the people with whom we are eating. Furthermore, we are dependent on the knowledge and ability of those who plan, prepare, and serve our meals and who determine the quality of the food from which we select our diets. Perhaps the most important influence on the nutrition of our people is the skill of homemakers who hold in their hands the health of family members. The nutritional fate of the individual — especially in his early years — is determined by the mother-figure of the group.

Because an estimated 17 per cent of meals are taken outside the home in recent years, the quality of the nutrition of our people rests increasingly with those in the commercial or institutional food services. Children eating in the school lunch program, people who take their meals in industrial cafeterias, residents of sanitoria, and the aged in custodial homes are limited in what they can do for their own nutrition. Hence the nutrition educator carries a continuing responsibility to reach people in charge of group feeding, and to consider the possible influences of the group with which the individual is eating.

maintaining an adequate food supply — **production** **processing** **distribution**

MAINTAINING AN ADEQUATE FOOD SUPPLY

Maintaining an adequate food supply forms the base of the framework of good nutrition. This, of course, begins with *production* of food and continues through *distribution* and *processing*. Many contingencies affect food supplies, but probably the main one is the ratio of population to the available agricultural land. If population demands exceed the supply of food that can be grown, either food must be obtained elsewhere or the people must exist on reduced rations.

This segment of the framework may not seem important to the individual in a land of plenty, but it is so interrelated with our international affairs that nutrition educators need to view as one of their responsibilities the interpretation of the significance of an adequate food supply to world peace and the effect on people of the semistarvation that exists as a result of inadequate food supplies.

e same time such useful purposes are being served, the
s" prey upon the public with false claims and misleading
ng. A major problem for nutrition educators is helping
take advantage of the opportunities for better nutrition
by food industries, while at the same time aiding them to
e pressures of those who are in the competition for their food
The basic "defensive" tool for consumers is knowledge of
n, coupled with an understanding of the psychology of adver-
and quackery.
clearly evident that food processing plays an increasingly im-
t role in the affairs of man. If and when man gets to the
, food processing undoubtedly will have helped to make it
le.

NVIRONMENTAL INFLUENCES

The fourth side of the frame of our portrait of well-nourished
eople consists of important environmental influences which directly
r indirectly have a bearing on nutrition.

Sanitary Conditions

Such circumstances as poor sanitation or hygiene in homes or
public places are causes of various infectious diseases or infestations
by parasites in human beings. Illnesses caused by such factors will
greatly affect both the need for nutrients and the utilization of them.
If the amounts of the nutrients in the diet were marginal, the presence
of the infection or infestation may render the diet inadequate. An
environment in which children are exposed to repeated or chronic
infection may become a hazard to nutrition.

Social and Economic Conditions

A broad, over-all influence on the nutrition of an individual is the
social and economic situation in a nation, in a community, or in a
family. Wars and depressions have usually brought deterioration of the
diet and, ultimately, of the nutritional status of the population. As discussed in the first chapter, food supplies are closely related to political
conditions. Scarcity of food can create unrest and resentment toward
those who wield governmental power; history has shown repeatedly
that when harvests fail, revolutions may subsequently occur. The

Production

Here in the United States we h₁
resulting from agricultural surpl₁
other people of the world, howev
undernutrition and malnutrition re
ages. Not enough land, poor land, o₁
of modern equipment, inefficient labc
governments limit the possibilities of i.

Then, too, the physical or health sta
bearing on their ability to produce food
afflicted with disease, they will be unable
toward producing more food because t
vitality and ability have been impaired. I₁
and malnutrition form a vicious cycle, whe₁

Distribution

Problems of distribution relate directly to
adequate food supply. Food is not evenly disti
even when sufficient supplies are available on a
tions in harvest conditions during the year, cou₁
transportation or storage facilities for foods, m₂
feasts and famines. Statistics of the average amoun
in a nation may be misleading, because all indivi₁
access to those amounts on an equal basis the y
educator is challenged to help people to understand
distribution and ways to equalize the food supply b
plenty and scarcity.

Processing

Finally, problems of processing foods have a direct ₁
the maintenace of the food supply. Inefficient methods ₀
ervation often account for major losses in *quantity* as
quality of the food. If proper processing and storage fa
lacking, distribution of foods is adversely affected. Pr₀
related to transportation of food, too, because it is far easie
larger quantities of foods if they have been condensed and ₁
efficiently.

One unfavorable connotation of food processing exists
minds of many people. Often food processing is regarded as s₁
mous with the losses of nutrients which may occur in milling,
ing, and drying. To some extent, this is true, but processing
helps assure a safe and ample food supply the year round, and
food industry is continually at work to protect the nutritive value
food products.

At th
"huckste₁
advertisi₁
people
created
resist th
dollars
nutriti
tising
It i
porta
moo₁
possi

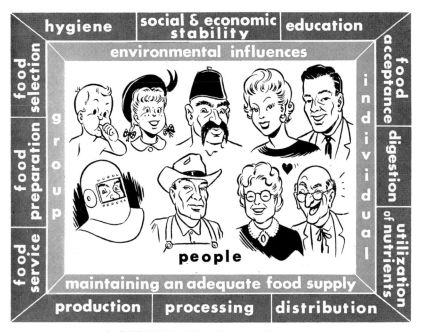

A PORTRAIT OF GOOD NUTRITION

socioeconomic status of a nation's people, particularly at the lower levels of the range, therefore is a strong determinant of the health of people as affected by nutrition.

Education

Perhaps the most important segment in the framework of nutrition is education. Actually, education of specifics overlies the entire structure of the framework, but education *per se* is also a discrete segment of the picture. Illiteracy and ignorance are usually equated with poverty and poor nutrition, while higher educational levels are likely to be associated with better diets.

The improved educational status of people in the United States has been cited as an important resource for health. The total of high school graduates, as a percentage of persons over 17 years of age, has increased fourfold since 1920, while the number of college degrees has jumped ninefold, according to *Health, Education, and Welfare Trends,* 1960 revision, Washington, D.C. With increasing education of our populace, the work of nutrition educators should be facilitated. It has been pointed out that nutrition education becomes more difficult as the gap widens between the literacy and culture of the educator and of the student. Therefore, as such a gap is bridged one of the problems of the nutrition educator is solved.

A BROAD PICTURE

The framework of nutrition portrays the complexities and the many facets of the field of nutrition. We can see in the over-all view the importance of the natural sciences of chemistry, biology, and physics to basic nutritional science. The social sciences — psychology, sociology, anthropology, and economics — play their part in furthering the application of facts discovered by nutrition science. Thus it is evident that education in nutrition must involve the *entire spectrum* of these various specialities if it is to achieve its goals.

To illustrate further the wide scope of nutrition, other areas of specialization which affect food supplies and diets must be considered. Specialists in agricultural, commercial, and governmental fields need to cooperate with scientists and educators in communicating ideas for better nutrition. As all the other specialists unfold the facts, nutrition educators must then proceed to organize and interpret them in relation to the needs of people, and proceed to disseminate them to the public.

NUTRITION IN THE UNITED STATES

It seems a contradiction that we have nutritional problems here in the United States, with our plentiful food supplies, a stable economy, many convenience foods of high quality, excellent facilities for food preservation and processing, and efficient distribution and storage.

In addition, meals are made conveniently available to many groups of people in our schools and colleges, industrial plants, public places, hospitals, sanitoria, and other institutions. Furthermore, we have established the custom of reserving time in midmorning and mid-afternoon for some kind of eating or drinking or both.

Despite all these opportunities and advantages, however, *the status of our health and nutriture though generally good is not as high as it should be.* Certain barriers to health have been removed and, con-sequently, cannot be blamed: rampant communicable diseases, ex-ploitation of child labor, unhealthful working conditions for adults, and poor sanitary facilities in homes and communities. For many people the greatest remaining hazard is the assault on health made from three to five times a day, sometimes seated at the meal table, but occasionally eating on the run at a snack bar or restaurant. Coffee breaks too often are attempts to make up for missed breakfast or lunch; late afternoon snacks too frequently are high in calories and low in needed nutrients. Much more attention is directed toward social than nutritional values of snacks. These and many similar dietary abuses can adversely influence the health of our people.

. . . attention is directed toward the social rather than the nutritional values of coffee breaks.

LONG-TIME TRENDS IN HEALTH AND NUTRITURE

To evaluate the nutrition problems of a people, the first step is to take a look at the vital statistics, preferably over a long period of time.

One of the first publications of the Food and Agricultural Organization of the United Nations (2) made the following statement:

Food consumption is directly correlated with health. As diet deteriorates in quality, health and physical abilites decline and length of life decreases. In communities where the diet is adequate, the average length of life is nearly seventy years compared with thirty to forty in the worst fed communities. Unfortunately, poverty is associated with other conditions adverse to health, and it is difficult to assess the relative killing power of the different disease-producing factors. But the remarkable improvements in health and physical well-being following an improvement in diet show that inadequate food is one of the main causes of the preventable diseases, misery, and premature death which afflict the majority of mankind.

In the first World Food Survey of 70 countries whose people represented 90 per cent of the world's population, poor nutrition was observed to be associated with high death rates and low expectation of life; high mortality in infancy and early childhood and among women during the child-bearing period; increased susceptibility to many diseases such as tuberculosis; and impaired working capacity. Evidences of the high state of health and nutrition in the United States are that the life expectancy has been extended by more than 20 years during the first half of the century. Further, nutritional deficiency diseases have been substantially wiped out, national average height and weight charts of the younger generation have been revised upward, and athletic records of youth continue to be improved. We are considered to

TABLE 2.1

Age-adjusted Death Rates for United States Per 100,000 Population*

Year	Heart Disease	Cancer and Other Malignan- cies†	Tubercu- losis	Influenza and Pneumonia	Gastrointes- tinal Inflamma- tory Diseases
1900..........	167	80	199	210‡	113‡
1950..........	300	126	15	24‡	4‡
1959..........	291	127	6	24‡	4‡

* Adapted from: Lindsay, D. R., and Allen, E. M., in *Science* 134:2017–24, Dec. 22, 1961.
† Including leukemia.
‡ Exclusive of newborn.

TABLE 2.2A

Life Expectancy at Birth (Age-adjusted Rates for the Continental United States, Exclusive of Alaska)*

	Total Population	Males	Females
	(*Yrs.*)	(*Yrs.*)	(*Yrs.*)
1900....................	47.3	46.3	48.3
1950....................	68.2	65.6	71.1
1959....................	69.7	66.5	73.0

* Source: Same as Table 2.1.

TABLE 2.2B

Age-adjusted Death Rates for the Continental United States, Exclusive of Alaska for Deaths From All Causes*

Year	Deaths per 100,000 Population
1900..............	1,778
1950..............	840
1959..............	770

* Source: Same as Table 2.1.

have stronger, healthier, better informed individuals than ever before and, in addition, we have social and community health resources of an extent and variety never before available (3).

Nevertheless, some of the trends in the incidence of certain diseases are not wholly reassuring. (See Table 2.1.) Data for life expectancy and total deaths per 100,000 population are given in Tables 2.2A and 2.2B.

The United States Public Health Service is the watchdog of the nation's health. Dr. James Hundley (4) has reaffirmed that conditions are good with the people of this country, but he points out that pockets of malnutrition still exist, due largely to poverty, ignorance, misguided dieting, food faddism; and, secondary, to other causes such as alcoholism.

He states further that as older health problems have come under control, new problems have arisen to take their places. A large segment of adults, perhaps 10 to 20 per cent, are obese. Senior citizens, according to Hundley's statement, have special health problems, notably coronary heart disease and cancer. He states that there are indications that health progress has reached a plateau in this country. A number of countries have less heart disease, and some countries have better infant mortality rates than we have in the United States; the general death rate here has not changed since 1956.

We cannot afford to be complacent about our national health picture, however, for Hundley adds that if further substantial health progress is to be achieved we must find ways to control cardiovascular disease and cancer; furthermore, that there is some evidence that a "break through" may be achieved through diet.

Olson (5) has said:

Nutrition has been implicated as etiologic in a variety of chronic diseases in which the threat appears to be overnutrition rather than undernutrition. These diseases include obesity, diabetes, coronary artery disease, and certain types of neoplasm. The particular role of nutrition in causation of these diseases is not entirely clear, but certainly no less clear than was the etiology of pellagra when Goldberger carried out his classic studies.

PUBLIC HEALTH NUTRITION PROBLEMS

A listing of the public health problems of the country may vary somewhat with the judgment of those who are making the analysis, though the general agreement is striking. Excerpts from the summary by Daft (6) are given as a guide to the nutrition educator in interpreting current nutrition problems in the United States.

1. Dietary deficiency diseases have largely disappeared from the country.

2. Despite the virtual disappearance of frank deficiency disease in this country, the margin of safety is not large. Complacency is not justified. We should not feel that the newer nutritional problems of public health importance have been substituted for deficiency disease but rather that they have been added to our field of responsibility.

3. In many parts of the world, deficiencies . . . remain as an extremely important public health problem. This constitutes an important challenge to us as well as to the citizens of the countries directly involved. In addition, it presents an opportunity for training of nutrition personnel.

4. Obesity is one of the most important public health problems in this country today. Our attack on this problem leaves much to be desired.

5. The chronic diseases are widely recognized, not only as public health problems of tremendous and increasing importance but also as related in various ways to nutrition. Atherosclerosis is rightly occupying a great deal of our attention today. In relation to many other chronic diseases there are also important nutrition problems deserving attention.

6. Lastly, there is another important group of diseases in which dietary factors are of great and, in some instances, paramount importance. These are hereditary or familial diseases, sometimes called "molecular" diseases. Diabetes, where the importance of diet is widely recognized, has an hereditary component.

In Dr. Stare's discussion (6), he for the most part agreed with Daft's analysis of current nutritional problems and reaffirmed the importance of obesity, atherosclerosis, and the need for fluoridation as public health concerns. He re-emphasized their importance along with the possible future role of nutrition in diseases in which hereditary and genetic factors are important. In addition to diabetes, Stare stated that most cardiovascular diseases and dental caries can involve strong genetic factors.

Overnutrition is considered by Stare as an important problem today. With respect to food energy, the effect of excesses is obvious. In addition, some concern exists about excesses of vitamin D and calcium. A considerable controversy, however, centers upon the true calcium need. Data still seem to point to a greater frequency of diets containing too little calcium than too much.

In the so-called molecular diseases, poor nutrition is not regarded as a causative factor, but drastic dietary adjustment may help to offset the abnormality.[1]

*Overnutrition
is considered an
important problem* . . .

---

[1] For a more recent discussion of current nutrition problems in the U.S.A., the reader is referred to "The Changing Face of Nutritional Disease in America," by John B. Youmans, M.D., *Jour. A.M.A.*, 189:672–76, Aug. 31, 1964.

FINDING OUT ABOUT OUR PROBLEMS

Neither guesswork nor idle opinion determines the nature of our dietary and nutritional problems, because many techniques are being developed in research to assess the nutritional state, or nutriture, and to detect evidence of nutritional problems. Among them are these:

We weigh and measure individuals, to determine body size and weight in relation to the need for nutrients. Simple records of weight and height, kept for persons or for groups over a period of time, can show important trends which may reflect the effects of good or poor nutrition. Measurements usually include standing heights; additional measurements may be helpful in determining body build, which should be considered in the interpretation of actual weight. Schools should be encouraged to standardize methods for obtaining information on body size of children and to keep consistent records throughout the years, because changes in trends in weight and stature may signal adverse effects of over-all dietary practices of populations as well as individuals.

A continuous check of the nutritional status of a population is a first step toward ensuring a high state of health. A good example of such a program is that of the Netherlands, described by C. Den Hartog (7) at the Fifth International Congress on Nutrition. With the co-operation of school physicians a census is taken every year of the food consumption by school children and of their growth and development. In consultation with the statistician the 8-year-old children to be included in the investigation are chosen. They should be well dispersed over the country according to town, village, and rural district.

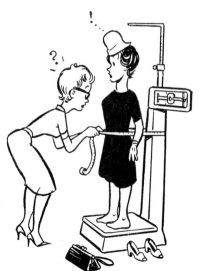

We weigh and measure individuals.

Simple dietary records are obtained together with measurements of weight, height, sitting height, and subcutaneous fat. The data are compared from year to year. Changes in nutritional status which may accompany unfavorable economic developments are expected to show up in the changing trends of body measurments. A decrease in the annual rate of growth is a danger signal.

Similar data are compiled in the centers for prenatal care. This repeated "transversal" investigation of diversified groups — as infants, school children, and pregnant women — may be expected to render a "proper idea" of the nutritional status of a population.

Such a systematic and ongoing check of the nutrition of peoples everywhere could be of great value not only in checking the progress of maturation but in preventing overnutrition, in the form of a growing tendency toward overweight.

Knowledge of body composition is important in interpreting the information obtained from the scales. Is the observed increase in body weight an increase in fat, bone, or muscle? This information may make considerable difference in deciding whether a change, if any, is desirable. Various methods have been developed for getting this information, and some can be easily applied. For example, skin folds in specific parts of the body can be measured by suitable instruments, providing an index of the thickness of the fat layer under the skin. The procedure has been described as "taking a pinch," but certainly it is an educated, carefully measured pinch.

We take X-ray pictures of bones to determine their density which is related to their mineral content. In addition, the X-ray pictures reveal important facts about the total maturation of an individual: whether his bones have developed as might be expected for his chronological age. It is an important index of the physiological age and, when considered with menarche for girls, can help to pinpoint the stage of maturation.

We study diets and food habits . . .

Physicians take a careful look at many facets of the physique. Are the eyes clear, with surrounding tissues free of infection? Is the tongue free of cracks and fissures, and of proper color? Is the skin smooth and resilient, with the "bloom" of good health? Is the hair glossy? Are there cracks about the corners of the mouth? What about the general posture and appearance of the individual? The absence of any of these positive signs can indicate health problems other than poor nutrition, of course, but viewed collectively such indicators can be significant in determining a person's total nutriture.

Dentists examine teeth and oral tissues to find signs associated with malnutrition, including faulty tooth structure, dental caries, fluorosis, and redness, swelling, and bleeding of the gums.

We analyze blood samples because "blood will tell." It will tell a great deal about what has been eaten recently, as well as the status of our body stores of certain nutrients. It will reveal how we are utilizing important building stones and chemical substances essential to health. In analyses of blood, indications of defective body structure and impaired function may be found.

We analyze physical fitness — the ability to perform standard physical tasks, both for children and for adults. We know that exercise alone will not guarantee physical fitness; nutrition is an important companion part. People in poor nutritional status are seldom outstanding examples of fitness. Any coach or athletic director knows the importance of nutrition and encourages his athletes to build their health and physical abilities upon a foundation of good nutrition. The role of nutrition in the physical fitness program has not been clearly defined; further research is needed to show the relationship between the two.

We study diets and food habits because we know that improper eating for the individual, after a period of time, leads to faulty body structure and function. Diet and nutrition are not synonymous, but poor diets are a first step toward poor nutrition. Body reserves and adaptations may serve to delay the effects of poor food habits, but if inadequate diets are continuously followed, body functions will be impaired and body tissues affected. What people eat and how they utilize their food must be studied in order to forecast the possible effects of what they are doing to their health. Within the past 10 or 15 years, scores of studies have been conducted in all sections of the United States which tell much about diets and food habits.

For better understanding of methods of detecting poor nutrition, the reader is referred to two publications: *Nutritional Diagnosis,* by Grace A. Goldsmith (published by C. C Thomas, Springfield, Ill.) and *Control of Malnutrition in Man,* a 1960 publication of the American Public Health Association, 1790 Broadway, New York City 19, N.Y.

DANGER SIGNALS

Studies of nutritional status and of diets of individuals have uncovered some specific danger signals which indicate the dietary and nutritional problems which exist for people of the United States. These are warnings. If they are heeded, our vital statistics could be favorably modified and many nutrition problems prevented. It is particularly important that these signals be noted in youth:

1. *Failure to regulate food energy intake to meet body needs.* This is particularly difficult for many people in our country today who are overweight because they consume more food than they need for the energy required for maintenance and activity. Conversely, some individuals consume too little food to meet their energy needs, resulting in underweight — a hazard to health because in this condition nutrient reserves may be depleted or impaired and body defenses diminished. The problem for every individual is to adjust his food energy intake to the level appropriate for maintenance of body size compatible with his health and vitality. Proper intake varies through the life cycle, but, unfortunately, food habits are not automatically adjusted. (See Chapter 11, "The Challenge of Change," for a discussion of changing calorie requirements in the various stages of age.)

2. *Low blood concentrations of certain substances.* The hemoglobin level in the blood is regarded by nutrition researchers as an indicator of nutritional status. In the main, the concentrations of this constituent for the sample populations studied in the U.S.A. were satisfactory. But there are always some people with low values, and these cannot always be accounted for by diet. Serum concentrations for vitamin C and carotene are indicative of the content of those substances in the recent dietary intake. The levels of these have been shown to be low for many people studied. This observation confirms the dietary shortages observed in the use of foods which are rich in these nutrients. The full implications of these findings for health are not entirely clear.

3. *Dental caries and poor oral conditions.* Dental caries are prevalent among the people of the United States. Although we do not know the exact part played by the different nutrients in protecting the teeth against decay, it is reasonable to believe that this body structure, like all others, must have the proper building materials. The situation is complicated by the fact that the formation of the tooth took place long before its eruption. But the tooth is a dynamic structure with an ebb and flow of metabolic changes such as are characteristic of all kinds of body tissues. Environment of teeth is largely determined by what is taken into the mouth, intermingled with saliva. Thus food and drink undoubtedly are involved in creating an environment which may or may not be detrimental to the teeth. Individuals, communities, and nations differ distinctively in their susceptibility to caries.

4. *Lack of physical fitness.* Many of our young people would not rate an "A-plus" in a test of physical fitness; nor, for that matter, would adults. But we expect youths — with their younger and less worn body machines — to be more fit than adults. Yet in any schoolroom of youngsters, most would seem what we would term "average" in health and fitness. Too few would have the buoyance and vitality of the ideal. In contrast, some would be below average, tending to be apathetic, listless, and difficult to motivate. We seem to be content to regard average health as a normal state of affairs — and seldom question the meaning of "average" or the difference between "average" and "ideal." We need a public demonstration of the effects of better over-all nutritional status in order to determine the extent to which good nutrition can improve the now prevalent "average." The average may be laudable in some endeavors, but should it be the goal in human health and achievement?

5. *Embezzling nutrition reserves.* Most people pay close attention to their bank accounts, protecting reserve funds for use in emergencies while budgeting day-to-day assets for most effective use. Few pay attention, however, to *nutritional* reserves and dietary *"budgets"* or allowances. Some seem to be on a long-term program of "deficit

eating," taking out of their bodily reserves more than they replace, while others misappropriate dietary allowances by overspending and neglecting to set aside reserves for basic needs or unexpected demands.

There is nothing so obvious or regular as a bank examiner to detect depletion of stored nutrients. Unfortunately we have few ways by which we can identify and measure the body reserves, so that the "overdrawn accounts" are unobserved. Eventually, they may become evident under stress of illness or accident, when demands are too great to be met. This of course could be disastrous, depending upon the extent of the demands of the emergency.

Teen-age mothers, especially in the lower social and economic levels, are likely to be in this group of "embezzlers." Dr. Genevieve Stearns (8) has said:

The girl who marries during her mid-teens is apt to be a girl poorly nourished through most of her lifetime and to be equally ill-equipped to meet the many psychological problems inherent in establishing a successful marriage and a new family. It is not surprising, therefore, that she is the least successful mother in producing a healthy full-term infant. These young adolescent girls greatly need counseling in nutrition and in the whole area of preparation for successful family life."

6. *Ailing and aging are considered synonymous.* We naturally expect the number of ailments to increase with age. Facts show that as people grow older the number of ailments does increase.

The following data were obtained in a study of Iowa women (9):

Age in years	Number of ailments per person
30–39	1.9
40–49	2.4
50–59	2.8
60–69	3.1
70 plus	3.6

At the Workshop on Aging sponsored by the American Home Economics Association in April 1962, Edna Nicholson (10) pointed out the need to distinguish between age and illness. When people after age 65 are sick or disabled, she explained, it is because they are suffering an illness or the results of an accident, just as is true at any other time in life. Although nothing can be done to change the *age*, she continued, a great deal can be done to prevent and relieve illness and disability. However, the prevalence of chronic illness among old people is indeed a danger signal. Prevention rests largely on changing the habits and living patterns of people, preferably before they become old. Nutrition education can play a major role in improving their health, thus prolonging their enjoyment of a useful life and perhaps lessening the need for custodial or institutional care.

THE POWER OF GOOD NUTRITION

The nutrition educator must convey to her students that there is *power* in good nutrition. If the body's needs are met in childhood and adulthood, the person can normally expect:

1. To have good health, vitality, and energy.
2. To mature at the proper time.
3. To withstand stresses of the environment.
4. To fulfill his biological role in life.
5. To enjoy an extended prime of life.
6. To withstand many of the hazards of aging.

Knowledge is power, particularly in nutrition. And there is much power in good nutrition.

REFERENCES

1. Williams, R. J., "Human Nutrition and Individual Variability." *Borden's Review of Nutr. Res.* 17(No. 2): 11–26, Jan.–Feb. 1956.
2. "Proposals for a World Food Board and FAO." *World Food Survey*, Rome, Italy, Oct. 1, 1946.
3. Mattison, B. F., "Organization for New Responsibilities in Public Health." Part II: Health Resources and Developments, *Amer. Jour. Publ. Health* 52:791–99, May 1962.
4. Hundley, J., *U.S. Publ. Health Reports*, p. 277, Apr. 1962.
5. Olson, R., Food and Nutrition Newsletter, No. 1, American Public Health Association, Jan. 1961.
6. Daft, F. S., "Nutrition and Public Health." American Institute of Nutrition, *Federation Proceedings*, 17(No. 2): 740–45, July 1958.
7. Den Hartog, C., "Public Health Indices of the Nutritional Status of Man." American Institute of Nutrition, *Federation Proceedings*, 20, Part III, Suppl. 7:19–25, March 1961.
8. Stearns, Genevieve, "Nutritional State of the Mother Prior to Conception." *Jour. A.M.A.*, 168:1655–59, 1958.
9. Swanson, P., Roberts, H., Willis, E., Pesek, I., and Mairs, P., "Food Intake and Body Weight of Women." *Weight Control*, p. 85. Iowa State University Press, 1955.
10. Nicholson, E., "Physical and Psychological Adequacy." Amer. Home Econ. Assn., Workshop on Aging, Apr. 29–May 2, 1962, *Proceedings*, pp. 36–45.

BOIN-N-NG!

To withstand the stresses of the environment.

Chapter Three

What We Eat

DEFINING THE GOALS and objectives of nutrition education depends in a large part on knowing what people eat. The United States Department of Agriculture is, in a sense, the watchdog of the diets of the nation. Faithful since the beginning of the century, this branch of the government has been continuously at work to find out about our food supply through studies of food disappearing through retail channels, surveys of household food consumption, and dietary records of individuals. These studies have been supplemented by regional research with the cooperation of many universities and experiment stations and a number of state agencies.

As knowledge of food composition has developed, more nearly accurate estimates have been made of the nutrient supply. For determining the needs of educational programs we should have more than national averages. Researchers with colleges and universities (both public and private), industries, and various foundations have studied food and nutrient consumption of specific groups of people throughout the land. From these sources have come many types of data to help nutrition educators toward a better understanding of what we eat.

The net result is that we have acquired much information about trends in food consumption over the years and about differences among groups, defined by such characteristics as age, sex, place of residence (rural or urban) socioeconomic level, region, and even employment of homemaker. It should be remembered, however, that changes in society result in changes in food habits. Hence the food and nutrient supply of a people must be under constant surveillance. Nutrition education programs must be based on up-to-date information on food practices, not what was done 15 or 20 years ago — unless, of course, there has been no change.

Three publications of much significance to educators are the Yearbook of Agriculture, 1959, entitled *Food,* published by the United

[*36*]

States Department of Agriculture; *Nutritional Status, U.S.A.,* Bulletin 769 published by the California Agricultural Experiment Station; and the *Agricultural Outlook Chartbook,* issued annually by the USDA. These publications are readily available to nutrition educators, but since the findings of these reports are basic to nutrition education programs, some will be highlighted in this chapter. Certain tables and figures merit repeated study and consideration by the educators.

RECENT TRENDS IN FOOD CONSUMPTION

Nutrition educators are not expected to be experts in all phases of food economics, but it is important for them to know what is going on in the market places of our nation. Reliable wide-scale surveys furnish indications of trends and changes in food consumption. As we walk down the aisles of any supermarket, we can easily observe that our food supplies are constantly improving: new products are competing for the food dollar, although many emphasize convenience and attractive packaging at higher cost and with little improvement in nutritive quality.

New products emphasize convenience with little improvement in nutritive quality.

Trends in consumption of certain groupings of food between 1940 and 1960 are clearly shown in Figure 3.1. Despite fairly large increases in income, fewer pounds of food were used per person in the United States in 1960 than in 1940. Experts in the USDA attribute this shift in food consumption to such factors as changing population, lighter physical work loads, knowledge of developments in nutrition, concern about obesity and overweight, and technological advancements affecting food products. These factors, they say, are expected to continue to modify our diets for years to come.

Further analyses reveal some data that are of particular interest to the nutrition educator: in 1960 Americans appeared to consume 33 pounds more of red meat and poultry per person than in 1940, 28 pounds less of potatoes, and 55 pounds more of processed fruits and vegetables, but 111 pounds less of the fresh. Since 1955, consumers have been eating more beef than pork per person.

To the nutritionist, changes in consumption of dairy products and of vegetables and fruits as shown in Figures 3.2, 3.3, and 3.4 are of special interest.

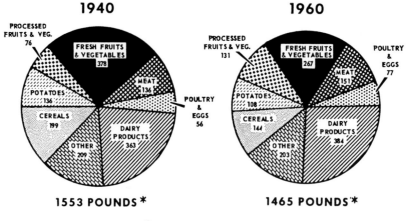

Fig. 3.1 — Changing tastes put emphasis on different foods. (Source: USDA, **Agricultural Outlook Chartbook**, 1962, p. 9.)

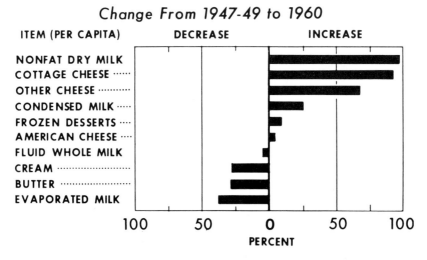

Fig. 3.2 — Consumers shift to greater use of dairy products rich in solids-not-fat (1947—49 and 1960). (Source: USDA, **Agricultural Outlook Chartbook**, 1962, p. 16.)

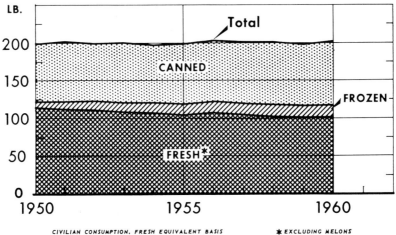

Fig. 3.3 — Use of vegetables per person has remained nearly stable since 1950. (Source: USDA, **Agricultural Outlook Chartbook**, 1962, p. 30.)

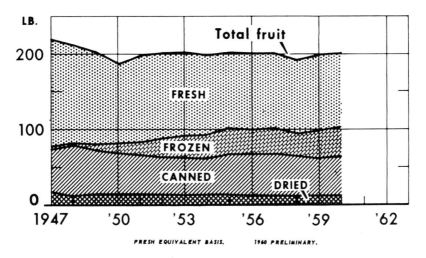

Fig. 3.4 — Large gain in frozen items marks per capita fruit use. (Source: USDA, **Agricultural Outlook Chartbook**, 1962, p. 32.)

To some extent consumers have changed their use of dairy products rich in fat to those rich in nonfat solids. According to agricultural
economists, the reduction in per capita consumption of milk fat has
been due both to competition from products made from lower priced
vegetable oils, and to a conscious effort on the part of many consumers
to restrict their intake of certain fats. Because of population increases,
the aggregate consumption of milk fat has changed very little, while
that of nonfat solids has increased. The extended use of nonfat dry
milk solids is gratifying to nutritionists, who have long appreciated the
value of this food in enriching the diet. A fair share of the increment
may be attributed to the use of the dried product in prepared foods.
Much remains to be done to educate the individual homemaker to the
importance and use of nonfat dry milk.

Total consumption of vegetables over the last decade has remained
surprisingly stable as shown in Figure 3.3. The same can be said for
fruits as shown in Figure 3.4. These statistics may be somewhat discouraging to nutritionists, who for years have been teaching people
that diets in general would be improved by the use of more vegetables
and fruits, particularly of certain types. Figure 3.4 shows an increased
use of frozen fruits, with waste reduced to a minimum, and of frozen
concentrated juices which may represent an upgrading of the diet
not revealed in the poundage trend. To be effective in increasing the
use of fruits and vegetables, it appears that new approaches are needed.
The shift from fresh to processed varieties of fruits and vegetables
has been spectacular (see Fig. 3.5).

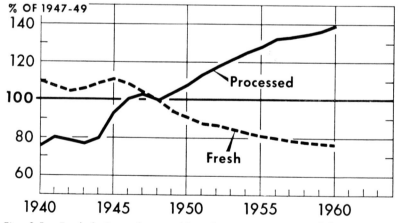

Fig. 3.5 — Fresh fruits and vegetables give way to processed forms. (Source:
USDA, **Agricultural Outlook Chartbook**, 1962, p. 9.)

Consumers have reduced the per capita consumption of eggs; according to the USDA, this is largely due to the declining importance of breakfasts in the diets of urban families. Use of eggs in prepared foods, however, is helping to support the intake of this important food.

Probably one of the most pronounced changes in food consumption since the early 1940's has been the reduction in use of potatoes and cereals (see Fig. 3.6). However, the decline in per capita use of potatoes has recently been checked as people have begun to consume more frozen French fries, chips, and dehydrated potatoes. This indicates that trends in our food consumption appear to rest more and more in the hands of the food processors, who can influence consumer preferences through the development of attractive and convenient products.

Reasons for the decrease in use of cereals include increased incomes, greater availability of other foods, concern about overweight, reduced work loads, population shifts to urban areas, and a decrease in home baking.

Any realistic approach to nutrition education requires a consideration of significant trends in food consumption (see Fig. 3.7) and the reasons for them in so far as they can be determined. This approach represents the tide with which nutrition education must flow. If new directions in food consumption are to be sought, the obstacles affecting them may be detected by paying careful heed to these trends.

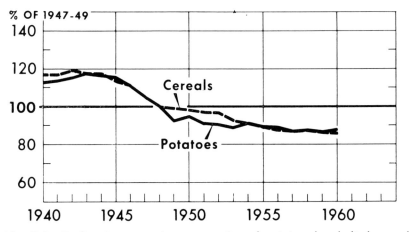

Fig. 3.6 — Decline in per capita consumption of potatoes has halted; cereal decline has continued. (Source: USDA, **Agricultural Outlook Chartbook**, 1962, p. 10.)

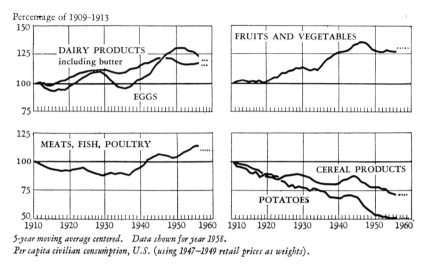

5-year moving average centered. Data shown for year 1958.
Per capita civilian consumption, U.S. (using 1947–1949 retail prices as weights).

Fig. 3.7 — Trends in food consumption. (Source: USDA, **Food**, The Yearbook of Agriculture 1959, p. 592.)

The distribution of calories among the food groups in family diets is shown in Figure 3.8. This is not to be regarded as a standard, but if the distribution differs greatly from this, one may expect some deviation in nutritive value from that which typifies the national dietary picture.

FOOD, MONEY, AND THE NUTRIENT SUPPLY

Consumers spent $62.2 billion for domestic farm-produced foods in 1961 — a $20.7 billion increase over 1950.[1] This is a fantastic figure which we can hardly comprehend, and it signifies the importance of food to our economy. The increase between 1950 and 1961 can largely be accounted for by rising costs of marketing. Competition for retail food dollars creates some of the major problems confronting the nutrition educators, who bear heavy responsibility in directing people to food expenditures that will yield optimum returns in terms of individual and national health.

The stability of our economy in recent years has brought expanded purchasing power, which has encouraged many improvements in our food marketing system. Countless attractive and convenient products have been introduced within amazingly short periods of time. Advertising has gone hand in hand with supermarkets and their distribution systems to popularize these products rapidly and thus create a large impact upon food habits and preferences.

Per capita consumption of food rises slightly as income increases: for each 10 per cent increase in income per capita, economists have noted a rise of about 2 per cent in food consumption. In general,

[1] USDA, *Agricultural Outlook Chart Book*, 1962, p. 11.

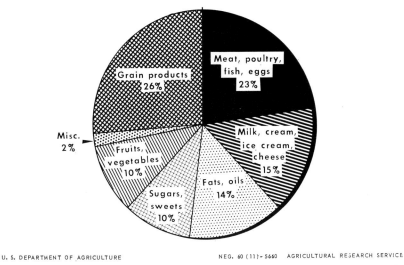

U. S. DEPARTMENT OF AGRICULTURE   NEG. 60 (11)- 5660   AGRICULTURAL RESEARCH SERVICE

Fig. 3.8 — Sources of calories in family diets, spring, 1955. (Source: USDA, **Household Food Consumption Survey 1955**, Report No. 16, p. 6.)

more food in the presence of what already is sufficient cannot be considered an asset to health. Higher incomes usually mean better diets. Yet increased expenditures for food do not necessarily insure improved diets for *all families.*

Figure 3.9 shows that between 1948 and 1955 the average family spending for food in a week increased from $25.50 to $32.00. This $6.50 increase represented higher prices for food, the needs of larger families, the use of more expensive foods at home, and more meals

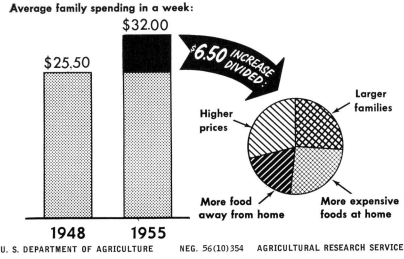

U. S. DEPARTMENT OF AGRICULTURE   NEG. 56(10)354   AGRICULTURAL RESEARCH SERVICE

Fig. 3.9 — Changes in urban food expenditures. (Source: USDA, ARS, Oct. 1956.)

This $6.50 increase represented higher prices for food . . .

eaten away from home. Relatively little improvement of diets was apparent, which emphasizes again the continuing need of nutrition education for homemakers.

Expenditure of the food dollars is readily apparent in Table 3.1, showing how it is distributed among food groups, as determined by the 1955 Household Food Survey. Figure 3.10 shows the relationship of income to food consumption.

One very significant change in our way of life is the increasing practice of eating meals away from home. In 1929, 13 per cent of food was eaten outside the home; in 1958 the percentage had risen to 17. Prices of food away from home have increased much more than the cost of food at home (see Fig. 3.11); this difference is due more to the increased costs of labor than of food. Whether or not meals are actually taken outside the home, prices of many food items will include the cost of services as well as of food, because of the popularity of prepared convenience products.

In these years of prosperity, little attention has been paid in nutrition education to the true costs of food — the "raw material" — as compared with added costs of processing and packaging. Nutrition educators are therefore responsible for interpreting to the public the criteria for determining the *actual* value of food items, with consideration of the proportion of waste and the amounts of food energy and nutrients obtained for money spent. During the depression and World War II, nutritionists paid close attention to the problem of "what a

TABLE 3.1

SHARES OF THE FOOD DOLLAR AS DISTRIBUTED AMONG THE MAJOR TYPES OF FOOD*

Meat, poultry, fish, or eggs ....35 ¢
    (24 ¢ for beef, pork, veal, and lamb
      5 ¢ for poultry
      4 ¢ for eggs
      2 ¢ for fish)
Vegetables and fruit...18 ¢
    (More than half for fresh produce)
Milk and milk products...14 ¢
Flour, cereals, bread, baked goods....................................11 ¢
Beverages...10 ¢
    (About one-third for alcoholic beverages, as reported by householders)
Fats and oils, sugars and sweets, and miscellaneous items such as condiments,
    seasonings, mixtures, soups.......................................12 ¢

* Data from *Household Food Consumption Survey, 1955.*

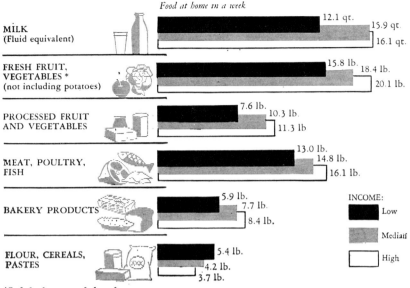

Fig. 3.10 — Income and food consumption per city family, spring, 1955.
(Source: USDA, **Food,** The Yearbook of Agriculture 1959, p. 610.)

dime will buy." Recalculation in the light of today's dime and today's
food market would be illuminating to many consumers. Money spent
for saving time and effort in food preparation must be reconciled with
the capacities, values, and goals of the individual and the family, too.
Table 3.2 shows an analysis made of nutrients available per dollar

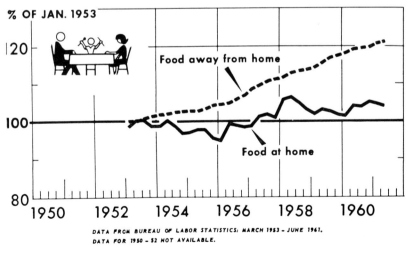

Fig. 3.11 — Prices of food away from home increase more than food at home.
(Source: USDA, **Agricultural Outlook Chartbook,** 1962, p. 39.)

TABLE 3.2

Nutrients Per Dollar

Average Quantity and Nutritive Value Per Dollar of Money Value¹ of Food Used at Home in a Week, by Food Group

(Housekeeping households of 1 or more persons in the U.S., April–June 1955)*

Food Group (1)	Quantity of Food (2)	Food Energy (3)	Protein (4)	Calcium (5)	Iron (6)	Vitamin A value (7)	Thiamine (8)	Riboflavin (9)	Niacin (10)	Ascorbic acid (11)
		calories	gm.	gm.	mg.	International Units	mg.	mg.	mg.	mg.
Milk, cream, ice cream, cheese	3.9 qt.	2,900	140	4.5	3	7,300	1.2	6.3	4	40
Milk, fresh and processed	4.8 qt.	3,200	160	5.6	3	7,300	1.6	8.1	5	60
Cream and ice cream	2.3 lb.	2,200	40	1.2	1	6,500	.4	1.8	1	10
Cheese	2.0 lb.	2,600	180	3.7	6	8,400	.1	3.1	1	†
Meat, poultry, fish, eggs, dry legumes, nuts (including mixtures and soups)	1.9 lb.	2,000	120	.2	19	5,300	1.1	1.5	23	†
Meat, poultry, fish	1.7 lb.	1,700	120	.1	16	4,900	1.0	1.3	25	†
Bacon, salt pork	1.9 lb.	5,600	70	.1	6	†	1.4	.9	15	0
Eggs	2.0 doz.	1,800	140	.6	30	12,700	.9	3.1	1	0
Dry beans and other legumes	4.6 lb.	6,800	440	2.7	142	†	6.3	4.3	44	40
Nuts, peanut butter	1.6 lb.	4,100	170	.6	16	†	1.4	.9	99	†
Vegetables (including mixtures and soups)	6.6 lb.	1,500	50	.7	22	28,700	1.7	1.4	19	340
Potatoes	11.8 lb.	4,200	90	.5	33	†	3.8	1.8	50	470
Dark green and deep yellow (including sweet potatoes)	5.5 lb.	800	40	1.6	30	168,700	1.2	2.1	12	590
Other green	5.7 lb.	700	50	.8	23	10,300	1.5	1.5	11	300
Tomatoes	5.1 lb.	700	30	.3	13	27,600	1.3	1.0	20	390
Other vegetables	5.7 lb.	1,000	30	.6	15	3,300	.8	1.0	9	180

TABLE 3.2 (*continued*)

Food Group (1)	Quantity of Food (2)	Food Energy (3)	Protein (4)	Calcium (5)	Iron (6)	Vitamin A value (7)	Thiamine (8)	Riboflavin (9)	Niacin (10)	Ascorbic acid (11)
		calories	*gm.*	*gm.*	*mg.*	*International Units*	*mg.*	*mg.*	*mg.*	*mg.*
Fruits................	6.3 lb.	1,500	20	.4	11	6,400	1.1	.7	8	610
Citrus...............	6.9 lb.	1,600	30	.7	11	4,300	2.2	.7	8	1,520
Dried................	3.0 lb.	3,700	40	.9	48	16,600	1.2	1.8	15	40
Other................	5.8 lb.	1,400	10	.3	10	6,800	.7	.7	7	230
Grain products (including mixtures and soups)........	3.6 lb.	7,200	190	1.6	44	400	5.2	3.3	47	†
Enriched, restored, or whole grain...............	4.3 lb.	8,100	240	2.1	62	†	7.7	4.7	67	
Not enriched, restored, or whole grain.............	2.7 lb.	6,400	130	.8	18	900	1.6	1.2	17	†
Fats and oils..........	2.7 lb.	9,200	10	.1	1	18,500	.1	†	†	0
Butter and margarine........	2.1 lb.	6,900	10	.2	†	31,600	†	†	†	0
Other (including salad dressings).	3.5 lb.	12,400	10	.1	3	800	.1	.1	†	0
Sugars and sweets...........	3.7 lb.	6,200	10	.3	8	200	.1	.4	1	10

[*47*]

[1] Based on food used and prices paid by households surveyed in 1955. Price changes since 1955 would affect the absolute quantities of foods and nutrients but would have little effect on the interrelationships between the broad groups of foods.

* Source: USDA, *Household Food Consumption Survey 1955.*

† Less than 50 International Units of vitamin A value, 5 milligrams of ascorbic acid, 0.5 milligrams of iron or niacin, 0.05 milligrams of thiamine or riboflavin.

from the different food groups. This is a significant guide in teaching the true economy of foods in terms of nutrients supplied.

The following summary of observations from the 1955 Household Food Consumption Survey by the USDA should be of help to nutrition educators as they work with people of varying income levels:

1. Income *does* affect the type and amount of food used by a family, hence the nutritive value of the diet is influenced by it, although it is a difficult matter to assess the effects of income *per se.*
2. Diets of higher income families contain larger quantities of nearly all nutrients than do those of low-income groups, as shown in Figure 3.12.
3. The nutritive value of the diets of farm families is less closely related to income, particularly in a single year, than is that of urban families.
4. The nutrient with the closest relationship to income is ascorbic acid. People with more money to spend buy more fruits and vegetables, which provide nearly all of the ascorbic acid in the diet. The key food illustrating this tendency is the citrus fruit group.
5. Thiamine is the nutrient least related to income level. Families with high incomes are as likely to fall short in the supply of this nutrient as families of low incomes. Use of pork and grains greatly influences this picture.
6. The beneficial effect of enrichment programs has been noted most dramatically for low-income families. Their diets showed in 1955 that they consumed more grain products; consequently, enrichment greatly improved their intakes of iron, riboflavin, thiamine, and niacin.

That increased purchasing power does not ensure good diets is illustrated in Figure 3.13. At the top-income level, the percentage of family diets not meeting the Allowances is considerably reduced for all nutrients studied except thiamine. But even at this income level, problems related to dietary adequacy in calcium and ascorbic acid are fairly common.

People with more money to spend buy more fruits . . .

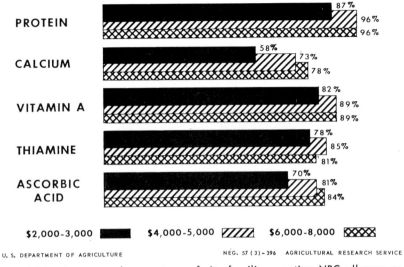

U. S. DEPARTMENT OF AGRICULTURE   NEG. 57 (3)–396   AGRICULTURAL RESEARCH SERVICE

Fig. 3.12 — Income and percentage of city families meeting NRC allowances, 1955. (Source: USDA, ARS, Mar. 1957.)

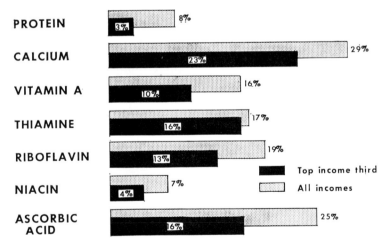

U. S. DEPARTMENT OF AGRICULTURE   NEG. 57 (3)–397   AGRICULTURAL RESEARCH SERVICE

Fig. 3.13 — Need for changed food habits, 1955, showing family diets not meeting NRC allowances. (Source: USDA, ARS, Mar. 1957.)

FOOD AND NUTRIENT CONSUMPTION DIFFERENCES AMONG GROUPS

The Household Food Survey of 1955 has helped pinpoint some of the differences to be found among population groups in our country. These differences may be useful in selection of appropriate educational emphases, but it must be kept in mind that it is difficult to isolate and separately consider the many factors that influence the food supply. Complete details on survey data may be obtained from a series of publications entitled "Household Food Consumption Survey, 1955," published by the United States Department of Agriculture.

Regional Variations

Regional differences in food consumption practices existed but were not great in 1955. In fact, they were usually less than income differences within a region.

Of the four regions, Northeast, North Central, South, and West, the South generally differed more from the other three regions than these regions differed from each other. In southern states, food expenditures were lower, relatively less of the dollar went for food away from home, and, because southern families were larger, differences per person were relatively greater. A little less food was produced at home in the South. Greater use of grain products and more home baking have been traditional features of southern diets, along with use of more fats and more sugars — at least in the cities.

Regional differences in food consumption can be associated with levels of nutrients in the diet. For example, low levels of milk consumption in the South would account for the relatively low intakes of calcium. Similarly, smaller consumption of citrus fruit and tomatoes and of fruits and vegetables of all kinds resulted in lower ascorbic acid levels for southern diets.

Another regional deviation of interest is the lower level of thiamine in household diets of people in the Northeast region. This difference is associated with the relatively smaller consumption of pork and grain products in this region.

Regional differences may be linked with such factors as income, basic food habits, and the ratio of rural families to urban.

City-Farm Differences

Farm families in 1955 generally had more food than city families, but city families ate out more often. Farm diets made greater use than city diets of milk, grains, sugars, and fats. But farm families, surprisingly enough, consumed less meat. As a group, farm people produced 68 per cent of their milk, using a larger proportion in its original form and less as processed milk and cheese than families who bought their milk.

Farm families consumed more eggs than city families and a larger proportion of such grain products as cereal and the flour used in home baking. Nonfarm families used more vegetables, fruits, and potatoes than did farm families.

Measured in terms of calories, rural people consumed more food. The 1955 Survey showed that in the North, a few more farm than city families had diets meeting the allowances for all of the nutrients. When their diets failed in any nutrient, however, farm people tended to fare worse than city families. Investigators pointed out that the 1955 study was made in the spring. Although this season is considered most typical of the year-round diet, different results might have been noted at other seasons.

Size of Family

The food budget takes more of the family funds in larger than in smaller families, but the expenditure per person is less. This is apparent in Table 3.3 which shows city families of six members in the median-income class spent an average of nearly half their income for food, while families of two spent only a fourth. The money value of food per person in the 6-member families was less than two-thirds as much as in the 2-member families.

Large families eat fewer meals away from home; members of large families who do eat out usually spend less than members of small families.

Trends in food consumption by size of family were similar for both farm and urban families. The value of home-produced food tended to be greater for farm families with more members. Extending home production is apparently one way the large family augments its food budget.

TABLE 3.3

PERCENTAGE OF INCOME SPENT FOR FOOD AND MONEY VALUE OF FOOD; CITY FAMILIES IN MEDIAN INCOME GROUP

Family Size	Per Cent of Income Spent for Food	Money Value of All Food Eaten at Home and Away in a Week (per family member)
2-member families............	26	$11.54
3-member families............	35	$10.30
4-member families...........	39	$ 8.74
5-member families...........	46	$ 8.20
6-member families............	48	$ 7.10

These observations were based on the 1955 data:

1. Households with six or more persons found it difficult to meet allowances for protein. About the same proportion of families with 2, 3, 4, or 5 members had diets containing enough protein.
2. Larger households had the most difficulty in providing enough calcium in the diet. Nearly all of the larger households included children.
3. Larger households did just about as well as small households in providing recommended amounts of thiamine, because per person they used as much enriched or whole-grain bread, flour, and cereals.

Peak expenditures for food were made by families in which the housewife was between 30 and 50 years old. The 30- to 49-year group, with an average household size of 3.96, was most significant in regard to its total consumption and the consequent size of its food bill.

Age of Homemaker

For dietary adequacy, households with homemakers 60 years of age and older did not fare as well as households of younger homemakers regardless of income. Table 3.4 shows, in relation to the age of the homemaker, the percentages of households in which the food used at home in one week failed to meet the recommended amounts of nutrients.

The relatively poorer nutritional position of older persons can be related to their lower consumption of major food groups. Meat consumption was higher for each successive age group up to 60, but was less for households with homemakers over 60 than for those in their 50's. Similarly, consumption of all fruits and vegetables, whether fresh or processed, was greater for households in each successive group up to those with homemakers in their 50's, but less for the oldest group.

Homemakers over 60 years of age provided poorer diets for their families than did younger women. In the older group, families consisted of 2.58 persons; only 10.2 per cent had children under 16 years of age. Forty-two per cent of the households represented by this group had incomes of $2,000 per year or less, as compared with 10 to 20 per cent in the others. Average level of food consumption of the over-60 age group reflected the pattern of households of the lowest economic class.

This study has pointed to age differences and what would seem to be dietary inferiority in households in which the homemaker is 60 years or older. Similarities among age groups, however, are greater than differences with a specific age group, and the diets in the United States, as shown by the USDA interpretation of its data, do not have clearly defined subcultures according to age. Older homemakers ac-

TABLE 3.4

	Under 30 Years	30–49 Years	50–59 Years	60 Years and Over
Protein..............	5	7	8	13
Calcium..............	28	30	25	31
Iron.................	5	9	10	16
Vitamin A value........	15	17	15	20
Thiamine.............	13	17	19	19
Riboflavin............	14	19	20	27
Niacin...............	5	7	6	10
Ascorbic Acid..........	24	24	24	29

* Source: "Dietary Evaluation of Food Used in Households in the United States," *Household Food Consumption Survey, 1955*, Report No. 16, USDA, Washington, 1955, p. 5.

cepted relatively new foods such as frozen vegetables and fruits – an encouraging point for nutrition educators. A summary in the Household Food Consumption Survey (1) stated:

Traditional consumption patterns may be more accessible to change than some had supposed. Scientifically sanctioned food innovations seem to find a place in the households of older homemakers as well as of younger ones.

Living Alone

Persons living alone spent a fifth more for food than those in households of two people or more, using a tenth more food per person, measured in calories. They used more of all food groups except milk, yet their diets were no better. Half did not reach recommended amounts in one or more nutrients. More had diets lower in iron than was observed for persons in large families; a few more had diets low in protein and the B vitamins. Nearly three-fourths of those who lived alone were women; half were women 55 or more years old.

Employment of Homemaker

The percentage of women employed outside the home is mounting. The 1955 Survey sought to find out whether employment made any difference in the quality of food provided in the household. Of all homemakers reporting, more than one-fourth were employed outside the home, and of these 70 per cent had full-time rather than part-time jobs.

There was little indication that more of the households with employed then unemployed homemakers had diets falling below the recommendations of the National Research Council. However, food patterns for the two groups did differ somewhat. Money value of food used *per person* in households of employed homemakers was generally greater than in the households of the nonemployed. Families of non-employed homemakers included 3.7 persons, while those employed had 3.08 persons. The result was that in households with nonemployed homemakers (with larger families), the total money value and quantity of food used were greater.

Interestingly enough, in 1955 there was no evidence that employed homemakers used more convenience foods of the older or newer types than did nonemployed homemakers.

In general, families with working homemakers spent more for all food away from home — meals and snacks — than did the others. In many of the classes, differences ranged from fifty cents to a dollar per family per week. Later studies on the food practices of employed homemakers in different sections of the United States agreed with the results of this survey.

No difference relating to the employment status of mothers was noted in the use of convenience foods among 104 families with pre-school children in Columbus, Ohio. A slightly greater percentage of the children of employed mothers had diets rated as good. (2)

In Louisville, Kentucky, the food patterns of 90 families with working wives were analyzed and compared with 482 families in which the wife was not employed. This 1958 survey showed no striking dif-ferences in buying practices and food use of the working wife. She apparently did not spend more money for food and did not use significantly more short cuts in shopping and preparation. Thus she apparently did not take full advantage of what was available to her. More working than nonworking wives indicated that the pressure for time at breakfast was felt in their homes. (3)

A few studies have been reported on the relation of employment of mothers to diets of adolescent girls. No significant differences have been observed in either the adequacy or the inadequacy of diet which could be attributed to the employment of the mother. Daughters of working mothers in one study were shown to be more independent, to like a greater variety of foods, and to take more responsibility for the preparation of meals than daughters of nonworking mothers. (4)

In a study of 140 young adolescent girls in Iowa, employment of the mother was not related to diet adequacy, to missing meals or eating snacks, or to enjoyment of food. Daughters of employed mothers tended to have more responsibility for family meals than daughters of nonemployed mothers. (5)

Education of the Homemaker and Quality Food Supply

This relationship has been under study for many years. In food con-sumption studies as far back as 1930 it was pointed out that at every level of expenditure for food, some families succeeded in obtaining better diets than others. Even at the lowest income levels, some families succeeded in having good diets.

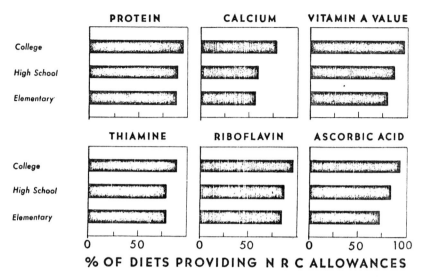

Fig. 3.14 — Education of homemaker and adequacy of diets of city families with incomes of $3,000 to $4,000, spring, 1948. (Source: USDA, **Proceedings of National Food and Nutrition Institute,** Agr. Handbook No. 56, Dec. 8, 9, 10, 1952, p. 38.)

However, the general level of formal education of the homemaker does show up in dietary adequacy. Findings from the 1948 study of the food supply by the Bureau of Human Nutrition and Home Economics are shown in Figure 3.14. Nutrients for which the intake is most likely to be associated with the level of education of the homemaker were calcium, ascorbic acid, and the vitamin A value.

More recent household food consumption studies, made in 1955, yield less conclusive evidence of relationships between the over-all adequacy of diets and formal education of the homemaker when place of residence and income levels are considered. Although data shown in Figure 3.15 do suggest that general formal education at the college level is associated with better diets in most groupings considered, they also suggest that something more than general education is needed to bring the diets of both farm and city families with incomes of $4,000 to $6,000 a year up to a high frequency of adequacy. This interplay between education and income in achieving dietary adequacy is of interest.

Young has noted in the cities of Rochester and Syracuse, New York, some interesting interrelationships among education, income, and the use of all seven basic food groups. The percentage of homemakers using all seven of the basic food groups increased with the amount of education in all income levels. However, with increased

Percentage of Diets Meeting Allowances of National Research Council in All Nutrients

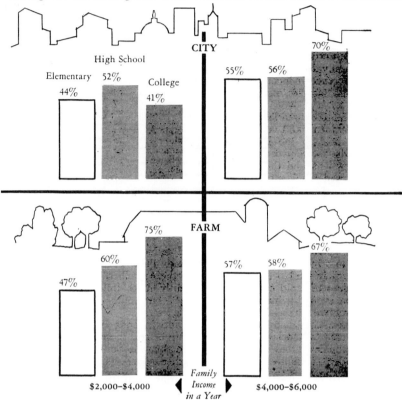

Fig. 3.15 — Diets and education of wives. (Source: USDA, **Food**, The Yearbook of Agriculture 1959, p. 624).

income, the percentages of homemakers with the lowest level of education (eighth grade or less) showed no tendency to increase their coverage of the seven basic food groups. (6)

EVALUATING THE NUTRIENT SUPPLY

Nutrients available per person per day in our food supply, as shown by the survey of 1955, have reassured us of the adequacy of the diets we enjoy in the United States. However, a critical study of the data made by R. S. Goodhart (7) raises some questions important for consideration by nutrition educators.

Comparisons of food energy and nutrients available in our food supply have led many people to believe that it is practically impossible for Americans to consume inadequate diets if they make full use of the available foods. This is not the case.

The apparent abundance of nutrients is associated with a large overabundance of calories. Goodhart estimates that at least a third of the calories must be wasted; otherwise, we would expect more obesity than we have. By reasoning and calculation, he showed that this waste cannot be attributed solely to discards of drippings, fats cut off meat, or waste in cooking fats and oils. Inevitably, the waste must involve a loss of essential nutrients. Excesses over the recommended allowances are least for the intakes of calcium, thiamine, and riboflavin. The distribution of ascorbic acid in foods is uneven; the same may be said for carotene in foods which provide a substantial portion of our vitamin A.

We may therefore expect dietary inadequacies among these nutrients to be the most common observed. Whether or not they are of serious nutritional consequence awaits further research defining the true requirements and the amounts of nutrients needed by individuals.

In nearly half the families surveyed in 1955, the food supply did not reach the Recommended Daily Allowances for one or more nutrients. Here are a few of the significant observations from this study:

1. Three out of 10 households did not have recommended amounts of calcium.
2. One in four did not meet the allowances for ascorbic acid.
3. Fewer than one per cent of families in the nation had enough calcium without using milk products in their original forms.
4. Families whose diets attained recommended levels for ascorbic acid used more than twice as much fresh fruits and vegetables per person as did families who did not reach the allowances.
5. From 15 to 20 per cent of families had less than the recommended levels of vitamin A, thiamine, and riboflavin. Fewer than 10 per cent, however, had diets inadequate in protein, iron, or niacin.
6. Nearly all diets low in protein were also low in at least three other nutrients.

Figure 3.16 summarizes the need for improved diets in the United States as indicated by the 1955 Survey.

Dietary Studies

Dietary studies of some 10,000 individuals in parts of the United States present about the same picture as did the 1955 Survey. *Nutritional Status U.S.A.* (8) presents information based upon different procedures from those used to acquire the 1955 household consumption data. A critical analysis of these findings has led to the following conclusions, which confirm and expand the results of the national food consumption studies:

Family Diets Not Meeting Allowances of National Research Council

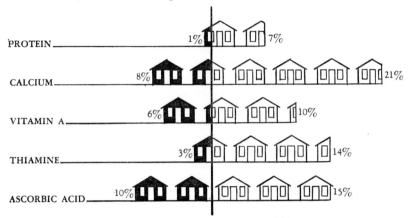

Each unit represents 5% of the households.

Fig. 3.16 — Need for improved diets. Black figures on the left show percent-ages meeting less than ⅔ NRC; those on the right show percentages meeting ⅔ NRC, but less than 100 per cent. (Source: USDA, **Food**, The Yearbook of Agriculture 1959, p. 622.)

1. The nutrients most often found to be lower than the recommended amounts in the diets of children and adults in all four regions were vitamins A and C, calcium, and iron.
2. Diets of teen-age girls presented the least favorable picture of all those examined.
3. Caloric intakes were low for many groups, but they were not con-sidered deficits, since people were by no means underweight on the average.
4. The nutritional status (i.e., health as conditioned by choice and amount of foods or nutrients eaten) on the whole was found to be good, probably the best that has ever been reported for any similar population groups.

Recommendations for dietary improvement which have grown out of these nationwide studies have been variously stated. Dr. Agnes Fay Morgan (8) has said:

The one major recommendation might be the inclusion of more fruits and vegetables. The choice should be in favor of the dark green and deep yellow vegetables, and tomatoes, berries, citrus fruits, and melons. These are sources of vitamins A and C, iron, and some calcium. Milk and cheese con-tribute much calcium and riboflavin, and milk fat contributes vitamin A. Milk solids (nonfat) offer a premium value in nutrition if increase in calorie intake is undesirable.

This recommendation rests on a sound scientific basis, but certain points should be kept in mind. First, some selectivity is required if fruits and vegetables from the so-called "green and yellow group" are to contribute appreciably to the iron intake, which is one of the possible deficit areas. A glance at a table of food composition will show a high degree of variability in the iron content of the foods of this group and will indicate that the members of the group which are richest in this nutrient are the dark green, leafy ones. Unfortunately, these are perhaps least often selected. Most of the deep yellow vegetables and fruits (except the dried) are not rich in iron. Teenage girls, the one group of people probably most in need of additional iron, may not fulfill this need through their selection from the dark green or yellow varieties of vegetables.

A second point is that general dietary guidance, in terms of the addition of more of any foods, may be questioned as we struggle to regulate energy intake to output in this era of labor-saving devices and spectator sports. Goodhart (7) states that educational programs designed to increase the consumption of particular foods are not the answer to existing dietary problems. He continues to say that any nutritionist attempting to design a successful public health nutrition program must remember that addition of certain foods to the diet must be accompanied by the substraction of an equivalent number of calories in the form of other foods. He concludes:

> Consumer purchasing power and educational level remain, as they always have been, important determinants of the incidence and distribution of dietary inadequacies in the United States.
>
> Dietary inadequacies do exist and are common in the United States where there is a plethora of food and where obesity is considered to be a public health problem of the first order. They are particularly prevalent and serious among adolescent girls and young women. This problem cannot be solved simply by encouraging an increased consumption of food.

DIETARY ERRORS

The human element in eating is most important to the nutrition educator; she must be a keen observer of the ways of life of different groups of people. Part of her job in motivating persons toward a continuing interest in their own nutrition lies in encouraging them to examine their own eating patterns. Group discussions, for

example, should include such everyday pitfalls as dietary fads, "crash" diets, poor snacks, and undue haste in eating. (See Chapter 7, Methods of Teaching, for discussion techniques.)

The *when* and *where* of eating are important for students to consider, just as is the *what* of eating. Dietary habits of a given individual cannot be completely charted or equated in scientific terms; nevertheless, such habits do have direct bearing on his total nutriture.

Casual Versus Regular Eating

Preserving the regularity of meals has been a basic and traditional tenet of nutrition education and of our culture. Convenience, custom, working conditions, habit, and "togetherness" have contributed to the belief that regular meals are a practice to be perpetuated. There is reason to believe that some nutrients, the essential amino acids, for example, should all be available for absorption in sufficient amounts at the same time if they are to be best utilized.

However, there is a growing trend toward casual eating and some research to support the idea that body composition is favorably influenced by nibbling as opposed to spaced meals. In experimental animals, spaced meals, as compared with frequent small feedings, have resulted in increased body fat and decreased body protein and water. It is suggested that spacing-of-eating habits may play a role in the pathogenesis of metabolic diseases. Researchers in this field, however, call attention to the fact that the experimental nibbling has been such that every morsel consumed was complete from a dietary standpoint, whereas in our human society, current practices of nibbling would scarcely meet that criterion. The matter of casual, frequent eating versus fewer spaced meals may be expected to occupy a considerable amount of attention of both researchers and educators in the future, for our society today seems pointed more and more toward casual and, perhaps, irregular eating.

Poor Breakfast Habits

Either skipping breakfast entirely or eating breakfasts of questionable nutritive value are dietary errors common to both adults and children. A midmorning lag and a noticeable decrease in efficiency at the office or in school may be traced back to a poor choice of food or complete lack of it at breakfast time. Some obese persons often mislead themselves into believing that skipping breakfast entirely "saves" calories. The truth is that usually such people more than make up for any calorie "savings" with later snacks or at other meals. In the end they are thus nutritionally much worse off than if they had eaten an adequate breakfast in the beginning.

. . . . breakfast hour in many homes is chaotic rather than leisurely.

In our present social structure, missing meals generally is regarded as a poor dietary practice. At Iowa State University a study of the eating behavior of 140 teen-age girls showed a high negative correlation between missing meals and the level of dietary adequacy (9).

Another significant observation of the changing breakfast habits of Americans is their pace of living. People from other countries comment, "Americans are always in a hurry." They marvel at our drive-in snack bars and the "quick service" emphasized in many of our restaurants. Their leisurely patterns of eating are a sharp contrast to our "eat and run" philosophy.

The morning breakfast hour in the United States is chaotic rather than leisurely in many homes. Employment of homemakers may contribute in some degree to the rush; this problem may be expected to increase in the future as more homemakers are employed.

Many families are wise to insist on sitting down together for a leisurely and carefully planned morning meal. They are off to a much better start each day than families whose breakfast habits are helter-skelter. One need not conduct scientific research to reach such a conclusion; common sense serves adequately.

Poor Snacks

Particularly for teen-agers, snacks can comprise a large share of the day's nutrient intake. Studies at Iowa State University have shown that, on the average, snacks may furnish as much as 15 per cent of

. . . snacks may comprise a large share of the day's nutrient intake.

the total calories of the day for teen-aged girls. Many of them tend to consume carbohydrate-rich foods at snack time, with heavy emphasis on carbonated beverages and sweet dessert-type foods. Snacks ideally should complement the day's meals, augmenting the intake of essential nutrients. It is generally assumed that the practice of snacking results in poor diets but this has not been proved.

Lack of Variety in Diets

Variety in the diet has long been recognized as a safeguard against poor nutrition. The previously mentioned study at Iowa State University showed the summer menus of 140 teen-aged girls to average 14.8 servings of food daily which provided 8.9 different food items a day. Corresponding averages for winter menus were slightly higher. The range was fairly wide. One girl had only 4.6 different items of food daily while another had 14.4. Both the number of servings and the number of different food items were significantly related to the adequacy of the diet.

When one considers the vast number of different kinds of food available, the limited variety that appeared on the menus of these girls seems very small. In a long-time study of girls in one county of Iowa (at intervals over a 2-year period), identical meals — particularly breakfasts — were repeated. In one instance the same breakfast was listed for *every one of the 20 days* for which records were kept. Lack of variety in the diet undoubtedly is caused partly by unwillingness to try new food. U.S. Army studies have mentioned that 14 per cent of a large number of men surveyed had not tasted tomato juice and 30 per cent had never tried broccoli. In every food class a considerable number of items were found that had not been sampled. Investigators in this quartermaster food preference study concluded that part of the problem in changing food habits is familiarizing people with different foods.

Fads and Quackery

We have observed many food fads which seem to reap meteoric success and, like a meteor, soon burn themselves out and fizzle into oblivion. There have been vinegar-and-honey concoctions, blackstrap molasses tonics, various herb and spice combinations, kelp and seaweed preparations, plus myriad other cure-alls for supposed nutritional deficiencies. All of them have shared one essential quality: they promised to do wonders with little effort on the part of the consumer, who has been advised that "calories don't count" or that he "can do it the easy way." Most of these supplements were based upon heavily promoted commercial schemes designed to sell books or products at inflated prices. And they sold well.

Many consumers have put their hard cash and misguided faith into these nutritional tonics and supplements, believing that they then would immediately gain in health, strength, and vitality. Salesmen of such products have even hinted broadly at the possibility of curing such dread diseases as cancer, arthritis, and ulcers through the use of these concoctions. It is regrettable that basic nutrition facts cannot be promoted so intensively and believed so completely by the same persons who accept the nutrition nonsense promoted by quacks and charlatans. In recent years an estimated 10 million Americans spend half a billion dollars annually on nutritional quackery: the useless, wasteful food supplements and "tonics" (10).

The nutrition educator knows that good diets with proper nutrients — including vitamins and minerals — can be achieved relatively easily, and at low cost. An adequate nutrient intake cannot be dispensed by the pill or by the pound, or in "quick and easy" doses, however. Purveyors of the food fads are much more interested in reaping a fast profit than in promoting long-range good nutrition.

Purveyors of food fads reaping fast profits . . . .

The powerful influence of advertising maintains and encourages many worthless food-supplement products. Advertising messages entice a potential buyer to try "the magic way" to lose weight, gain weight, regain pep and energy, "feel ten years younger," "build up good red blood," and so on. These appeals are based on emotions and human frailties. They hold out promises of easy solutions to complex problems of appearance or psychological insecurity. Nutrition educators must be aware of the techniques used in such advertising and utilize them as discussion topics which can be countered by sensible nutrition.

Unsound Weight-reduction Diets

Women's magazines have often featured what are termed "crash" or "blitzkrieg" diets, designed to help men and women lose a good deal of weight rapidly. Despite being cautioned to consult a physician before embarking on such a program, many women eagerly follow unwise regimens. If pounds are lost, they are soon regained and "diets never do me any good" becomes the conclusion.

There are good diets, to be sure, published in the women's magazines. But does the public have the knowledge to differentiate between these and the nutritionally unsound ones? Here is another "entering wedge" for the educator who can capitalize on magazine promotions in order to focus the attention of students on sensible weight-reduction diets.

Twelve reducing diets recently published in magazines and papers were subjected to critical study. Table 3.5 shows the estimated daily nutritive value as compared with the allowances for a 25-year-old woman. Needless to say, prolonged subsistence on some of these diets would be deleterious to health. Fortunately, most of them are such that they can be endured for only a very short time. The discouragement and intermittency of reducing, however, may have adverse effects.

Failing To Have Plans or Guideposts of Nutrition

The Basic Four food plan offers a dependable, easily understood approach to good nutrition. (See Chapter 5 and Appendix A for explanation of the plan.) This might well be regarded as a daily philosophy of eating: instead of "something to *live* by," it is "something to *eat* by."

Along with such a basic plan, the individual should have his own blueprint or guideposts for nutrition, tailored to fit his needs. Such a frame of reference could insure that each person would:

TABLE 3.5

NUTRITIONAL VALUE OF 12 REDUCING DIETS COMPARED TO RECOMMENDED DIETARY ALLOWANCES FOR A 25-YEAR-OLD WOMAN

Diet	Calories	Protein	Calcium	Iron	Vitamin A	Thiamine	Riboflavin	Vitamin C
		gm.	mg.	mg.	I.U.	mg.	mg.	mg.
1.	927	25	661	9.3	2,795	.7	1.2	98
2.	1152	138	732	5.5	2,160	.4	2.2	87
3.	900	22	765	.5	1,250	.15	1.1	4
4.	860	60	865	10.7	8,425	.4	1.1	99
5.	1053	50	596	9.0	16,408	.6	1.4	82
6.	1270	102	2,064	6.0	19,490	1.0	3.7	63
7.	945	67	303	16.5	12,570	.8	1.5	114
8.	769	25	661	4.4	2,870	.5	1.2	71
9.	850	50	468	15.6	8,540	1.6	2.3	156
10.	900	84	969	12.7	8,461	1.4	1.7	185
11.	720	64	588	11.5	2,287	.7	1.3	7
12.	748	46	170	8.2	12,245	.6	.9	203
Recommended Allowance Woman—25.	2300	58	800	12.0	5,000	1.2	1.5	70

1. Adjust amounts of nutrients as his bodily needs change. (See Chapter 12, The Challenge of Change, for a discussion of changing calorie requirements.)
2. Supply daily the foods needed for building, maintenance, and protection of the body, plus adequate reserves.
3. Use food which brings the greatest satisfaction psychologically, socially, economically, and nutritionally.

Developing a personal food plan does not mean adhering to a rigid regimen. It has quite the opposite effect, because a sensible personal food plan or "budget" provides for the necessary dietary adjustments to meet new demands in a changing individual. A diet plan actually *creates* flexibility by *planning* for it. This, of course, results in more freedom to enjoy food. The more we know and understand about our nutritional needs and composition of foods, the more we can obtain enjoyment from a wide variety of foods to satisfy those needs.

REFERENCES

1. *Household Food Consumption Survey, 1955,* Report No. 14, p. 6.
2. Metheny, N., Hunt, F. E., Patton, M. B., and Heye, H., "The Diets of Preschool Children." *Jour. Home Econ.,* 54:297–303, Apr. 1962.
3. Wrightman, M. R., and Roberts, J. B., "Comparison of Working and Non-Working Wives in Food Shopping Preparation." Progress Report 106, Univ. of Ky., Agr. Exp. Sta., Lexington.
4. Lollis, E. S., "Some Factors Influencing the Dietary Habits of Adolescent Girls." Unpubl. M.S. thesis, University of Oklahoma Library, Norman, 1960.
5. Hinton, M. A., Chadderdon, H., Eppright, E., and Wolins, L., "Influences in Girls' Eating Behavior." *Jour. Home Econ.,* 54:842–46, Dec. 1962.
6. Young, C. M., *et al.,* "Description of Studies in Rochester and Syracuse, N.Y." *Jour. Amer. Diet. Assn.,* 32:214–18, Mar. 1956.
7. Goodhart, R. S., *Amer. Jour. Clin. Nutr.,* 7:508–13, 1959.
8. "Nutritional Status, U.S.A." Agnes Fay Morgan, ed. Calif. Exp. Sta. Bul. 769, Oct. 1959.
9. Hinton, M. A., "Factors Related to the Eating Behavior and Dietary Adequacy of Girls 12 to 14 Years of Age." Unpubl. Ph.D. dissertation, Iowa State University Library, Ames, 1962.
10. Mitchell, H. S., "Don't Be Fooled by Fads." *Food,* USDA Yearbook of Agriculture, 1959, pp. 660–68.

Chapter Four

Factors Influencing Eating Behavior

BASIC TO SUCCESS in teaching people to change their food habits is an understanding of *why* they eat as they do. The common idea is that eating behavior is dominated by food habits, although the meaning of "food habits" is not entirely clear. To what extent do people habitually eat the same foods or combinations of foods repeatedly at similar time intervals? Because little is known about variation of an individual's eating behavior from day to day and year to year, we need longitudinal studies of eating behavior as well as of growth and other forms of biological and psychological development.

One of the main obstacles faced by nutrition educators is the general impression that "food habits," like most habits, are inflexible and unchanging. Perhaps we need to divorce the two words separating "food" from "habits." Together, they imply an idea which may operate as a handicap to progress in nutrition education. Despite the efforts of nutritionists to establish the connotation of "good" to habits relating to food, "bad" seems most likely to be the popular association with the idea of "food habits."

The first step toward the development of these habits, whether good or bad, is food acceptance, which is primarily an act of the individual. The two essential elements are the individual and the food. Even so, this situation is not simple because of countless variations within the individual — physical and psychological — that may influence his behavior toward food. The act of acceptance may be further complicated by many secondary elements belonging to the environment.

Food habits, therefore, are a much more complicated form of eating behavior than food acceptance because from the first reaction to tasting a food it is a long step to the later incorporation of that food into the regular diet.

[*67*]

Although research in eating behavior is fragmentary, it is sufficient to give us some important insights into teaching nutrition. Fortunately, too, expanding knowledge regarding eating behavior presents a truly interdisciplinary challenge. Information has been supplied through research in many areas, such as the biological sciences, psychology, cultural anthropology, sociology, economics, history, and also philosophy and literature.

What people believe and have written about food in the past have strong implications for nutrition education. In addition, our knowledge of eating behavior has widened with the great expansion of our international interests and endeavors in the realm of nutrition. Developments in the area of human ecology — the interrelationship of man with his environment — offer broad bases for increasing our understanding of eating behavior.

Eating behavior will be discussed from two standpoints: (a) what we have learned from various disciplines or approaches, and (b) what we know about certain age groups. This is not an attempt at an exhaustive study, but a summary of some observations which may help nutrition educators better to understand eating behavior.

THE BIOLOGICAL SCIENCES

The taste of food is probably the most important factor in its acceptance. People say they like a food because it "tastes good." It is reasonable to believe that eating behavior must be closely related to taste sensitivity, although the exact relationship has not been established. Literature on this subject was reviewed in 1962 by Korslund (1).

The individual is endowed, probably at birth, with taste receptors or sense organs. Sensitivity to the basic tastes of sweet, sour, bitter, and salty has been measured for many subjects, and wide individual differences are indicated. Identical foods may even taste different to the same person on different days. Some people are known to have a "taste blindness" to certain substances; this trait is perhaps genetically controlled.

Age differences in taste sensitivity have been studied, but there is no general agreement on the significance of such differences. Sweetness has been observed always to be acceptable to infants, while sour and salty tastes are acceptable only in dilute concentrations. Bitter flavors are rejected by infants, but may later become acceptable through training.

Sex differences in taste sensitivity do seem to exist. Most results indicate that women have lower taste thresholds (that is, are more sensitive to taste) than men. However, one study showed that women, in comparison with men, were more sensitive only to sweetness and saltiness, not to sourness in taste. The reaction of subjects toward bitterness is different from the reaction to the other three basic tastes. People tend to rate either high or low in sensitivity to it, not intermediately. The relationship of taste sensitivity to food likes and dislikes and to other types of eating behavior has been studied, but with inconclusive results. Evidence may favor the idea that taste-acute individuals have more food dislikes than those people who are less sensitive to taste.

Indications that vitamin A may be related to taste sensitivity have been produced from laboratory work with rats. In vitamin A depletion experiments, taste sensitivity of the rats decreased. Upon repletion with vitamin A, sensitivity returned. A logical explanation rests upon the fact that vitamin A is needed for maintenance of epithelial tissues and that taste buds consist largely of epithelial cells.

TEXTURE AND FOOD PREFERENCES

The accent in much of our food advertising is on textures which are bland, smooth, creamy, or soft. Food choppers, blenders, mixers, and grinders for home use have become increasingly popular.

It is true that objectionable textures can affect food preferences, for we know that outer peelings of some fruits and vegetables are unpleasant to many people. Yet removing skins — such as on apples — may also remove much of the chewing pleasure and taste appeal and some of the nutritive value.

Therefore, while it seems appropriate to widen food acceptance by removing objectionable textures, it is important to remind individuals that complete absence of texture may be depriving them of important nutrients as well as chewing exercise.

The question of "built-in" tendencies for people to select appropriate food has been the subject of much conjecture and of some study. Animals seem to have drives or urges to seek nutrients they need. This characteristic has been observed with range cattle, and in the laboratory with small animals.

People with certain metabolic diseases have been reported to crave substances they lack, such as salt in the case of Addison's disease, liver in conditions of pernicious anemia, and sweets in cases of hypoglycemia. How universally these tendencies may exist in people with deranged metabolism is not known, but the probable existence of these tendencies is nevertheless interesting. For example, why do some pregnant women eat clay, and what, if anything, is the advantage?

A classical example of the theory that people originally have some protection against the selection of a poor diet lies in the well-known account of the study of babies by Davis (2). When offered a variety of foods, largely in their natural form, the babies she observed made selections which apparently sustained them fairly well. Today, however, we would want to know much more about the outcome of the experiment than was possible then. We would like a control group, and also we might wish to know the concentration of blood constituents, and the body composition. It has been largely conceded that if such a mechanism ever exists in the individual as an infant, it soon becomes ineffective in the environment in which he finds himself.

The inability of individuals to regulate food energy intake to their needs has been cited as the root of most crucial nutrition problems in the United States. The extent to which the problem has a psychological, physiological, or biochemical basis is not known.

Certain mechanisms do exist within the body that influence the urge to eat. How these are mediated has not been established, but we recognize them in the form of hunger pangs, feelings of satiety, and appetite. Blood chemistry, metabolic rate, temperature regulation, and nerve impulses, along with glucoreceptors possibly situated in the hypothalamus, may all play a role in the complicated regulation of intake of food energy to output. Mayer (3) has described the situation as follows:

> . . . in all higher animals and particularly in man, the basic physiologic regulation is topped by complicated, partly conscious, cerebral integration. While the basic mechanism "sets the stage" for feeding behavior, it does not necessarily lead to it; conversely, in some cases, feeding will take place or be continued while there is no longer any physiologic basis for it.

While the search continues for the truth about body mechanisms involved in energy intake regulation, the nutrition educator is challenged to supply information and motivation needed to enable the individual to exercise the so-called "conscious integration."

The interrelationship between periodicity of eating and body chemistry is also of interest. To what extent have physiological needs dictated the evolution of our regular meal-eating pattern? Is casual eating of well-planned food more compatible with our physiological well-being than regularly spaced meals?

PSYCHOLOGY AND EATING BEHAVIOR

The classical contribution of psychology to our knowledge of eating behavior was the discovery of the ease by which behavior of an animal could be changed through the use of food as the primary stimulus. The principle has been applied over and over again, and because of its potency as a factor in behavior, food acquires many meanings other than those related to health.

Babcock (4) has described symbolism of food as follows:

> Food is, from the day of birth, associated with intimacy. Buttressed by other life essentials, it carries not only the feelings of security, protection, love, and developing strength, but also sense of pain, rejection, deprivation, and the potential terror of starvation.

She also adds that it carries the projection of power, " . . . power for the mother who feeds; power of nations to starve those they perceive as their enemies into a rebellious and implacably hungry submission."

Kaufman (5) has classified food likes and dislikes by common, emotionally determined reactions to symbolic or sensory values of specific foods. This useful classification is shown in Table 4.1.

TABLE 4.1*
SOME MEANINGS OF FOOD

Food Likes	Food Dislikes
Security Foods	Cultural Taboo Foods
Reward Foods	Religious Taboo Foods
Fetish Foods	Familial Taboo Foods
Show-off Foods	Individual Taboo Foods
Grown-up Foods	
Advertised Foods	
Pleasurable Association Foods	Unpleasurable Association Foods
Familiar foods prepared in familiar ways	Familiar foods prepared in unfamiliar ways
Easy-to-prepare foods	Hard-to-prepare foods
	Foods with built-in anxiety
	Foods from filthy sources
	Unfamiliar foods
Foods With Agreeable Sensory Properties	Foods With Disagreeable Sensory Properties
Unspoiled foods	Spoiled foods
Proper color foods	Off-color foods
Proper odor foods	Off-odor foods
Proper taste foods	Off-taste foods
Proper texture foods	Off-texture foods
Proper temperature foods	Off-temperature foods

An individual's attitudes toward foods are constantly changing in accordance with his current emotional needs as these can be expressed or satisfied through the use or avoidance of specific foods.

Any food may belong to more than one category in this formulation at any one time or at different times. For example, for a given person milk may be both a security and a reward food. At picnics, for exhibitionistic purposes, he may drink huge quantities of milk, thus using milk as a show-off food. If he then gets sick from drinking too much milk, he may develop an aversion to it, and eliminate it from his diet.

*Source: Wm. Kaufman, "Some Psychosomatic Aspects of Food Allergy," *Psychosomatic Medicine*, XVI (No. 1), p. 11, 1954.

This tendency for foods to acquire a specific "reputation" is often a problem in nutrition education. For example, it is not infrequent to encounter adults who avoid the use of milk because they regard it as a food "only for children." Some men regard salads as "foods fit only for women" or will label fresh vegetables as "rabbit food."

Such attitudes toward food items — and there are countless examples which may come to mind — create obstacles and offer challenges for the nutrition educator, who must encourage students to evaluate foods in terms of what they actually *are,* not what they are *reputed to be.* The "image" of a food is a factor to be reckoned with in nutrition education.

VARIETY AND MONOTONY IN THE DIET

Variety in choice of foods has been shown in studies to bear a high correlation to adequacy of diet for all ages. Among teen-age girls, the number of different food items eaten in a day correlated positively with adequacy of diet. The relationship was highly significant (6). Among a sample of aged people, higher "variety scores" in foods have been observed for those who are working, married and living with their spouses, and who have higher incomes (7).

Monotony in selection of food seems to characterize the diets of many people. Countless examples could be supplied from many dietary studies. To a certain extent, self-imposed monotony is a way of life for many people. Self-imposed monotony in eating may have far different effects on the individual than enforced monotony, however. The enforced limitation of variety is of special interest to the armed forces, possibly to the civil defense program, and to space scientists who deal with the problems of suitable diet for astronauts who must subsist for long periods in space vehicles.

The effect of repeated eating upon the rejection of a limited number of food items in preference ratings was investigated by Pilgrim and associates in their work with the armed forces (8). Eighty army men, maintaining a high activity level in a cold climate, subsisted for six weeks on a fixed diet of four daily menus. With repetitive consumption, some foods rose in preference, some remained unchanged, and some declined. The more a food was liked initially, the less was its decline in preference. Most canned meats and vegetables declined in acceptance, while dry cereals rose in preference, and fruits, desserts, and staples showed little change.

Further reports from the study with the armed forces have shown that a combination dish, consisting of both a "liked" and a "disliked" food, will probably be unpopular. Moreover, these investigators noted that the more complex the dish, the less it will be liked.

Pilgrim has also reported observations regarding the effect of participation of men in selecting their food. He concluded that men who designed their own menus from a fixed and limited supply of items were more satisfied with their meals than were those men for whom menus had been planned by others.

FOOD MISINFORMATION

Allusions have been made to various tonics and food and nutrient supplements in the realm of quackery. Of similar interest are the myths, fallacies, and misinformation about *food* items which often influence food preferences and have been variously classified.

1. Attaching special virtues to foods at the expense of others which are equally nourishing. The yoghurt, blackstrap molasses, and wheat germ fads undoubtedly led some of the public into believing

An apple a day doesn't necessarily keep the doctor away.

all these items possessed nutritional virtues far beyond their actual values. Similarly, advocating an apple a day to keep the doctor away or eating carrots to improve eyesight are examples of overemphasizing values of foods which may be nutritionally beneficial, but which cannot work miracles.

2. Distorting the value of vitamins and minerals (which often occurs in advertising) by implying that they may ensure adequate nutrition without regard to dietary habits.
3. Classifying foods or combinations of them as harmful: "tomatoes cause cancer" or "oranges cause ulcers."
4. Overemphasizing "natural foods" grown on special soils, with "natural fertilizers," implying that foods grown otherwise do not contain the same nutrients.
5. Special devices designed for appetite control or weight loss, such as cellulose crackers which "fill the stomach."
6. Special "disease diets" which advocate foods as cures for ulcers, arthritis, or cancer.

Many of these myths and fallacies regarding food values are the result of honest but misguided efforts. But probably the larger share of them are the result of deliberate deception through advertising and promotion of specific "brands" of foods. Such deception must be countered by legal action in cases where there are clear-cut infractions of laws, but many of them can be dealt with only through nutrition education. Thus it is up to educators to be alert for food misinformation and to convert it into a tool for teaching established food facts.

Emotional entanglements with food greatly complicate nutrition education. The nonpsychiatric-trained educator cannot probe far into the reasons why neurotic aversions or eating patterns exist, but it is nevertheless necessary to be aware of their existence. It is well to remember that people who are reasonably secure, constructive, and open minded in their outlook on life may be expected to accept a wide range of changes and limitations in their eating habits. Deep-seated emotional problems which result in neurotic food preferences usually cannot be treated on the same plane as the normal likes and dislikes of fairly well-adjusted people.

WHAT WE HAVE LEARNED FROM THE SOCIOLOGISTS

Family situations may influence attitudes toward food. One may expect children to have different attitudes toward food and different eating behavior in households with varying family situations or conditions such as these (9):

1. Economically-deprived households, where food has great survival or social value.
2. Immigrant families, where food may reflect strong emotional ties to the native land.
3. Families in which illness may put the main emphasis upon food for the sick person.
4. Very religious families, where food rituals or taboos are strictly observed.
5. Broken homes or families with conflicts resulting in unhappy mealtimes.

The possibility of changing a family's use of a food is influenced by the extent to which the food is firmly placed in the "core" diet (10). "Core" items are the staple foods universally and regularly used by a population. This would mean, for example, the combination of meat, bread, and potatoes favored by most people in a community. Foods termed as "secondary," which are widely but not universally used, are more easy to change than "core" foods. A third group — "peripheral" foods — includes those that are characteristic of groups but not of individuals in a population. Such foods are the most easily changed of the three categories.

The degree of urbanization in relation to economic conditions may also affect the difficulty of changing food patterns. Where urbanization is *high* and economic conditions are *favorable,* people are more ready to accept change. Where urbanization is *high* but economic conditions are *poor,* the desire for change may be present, but the actual diet depends on what can be bought with the money

. . . families with conflicts resulting in unhappy mealtimes.

available. When urbanization is *low* and economic conditions *favorable,* diets tend to be traditional and people are resistant to change. Our prosperous, midwestern rural areas would fit the description of this group; i.e., low urbanization and good economic conditions. Perhaps as a group they do tend to retain the traditional, but to add new foods. This situation might account for a seemingly high percentage of overweight in such areas. There is, however, a fairly ample supply of additional items in the so-called secondary core and in the peripheral group of foods. Thus the possibility exists of changing foods in the latter two categories for purposes of weight reduction.

When urbanization is *low* and economic conditions *poor,* diets are resistant to change. They are meager, described as virtually without innovation, and notably like the historic core diet for the community. These are trends which may be significant for nutrition educators who work in rural communities.

The social status of people, which usually includes their economic situation, has been shown to be closely related to eating behavior in a number of studies. Analyzing the various aspects which may be involved and deciding how to deal effectively with them presents a perplexing problem for nutrition educators. One sociologist posed this question: "How can you change the food habits of a southern sharecropper whose diet is tied into a one-crop method of production and the type of credit allowed by the stores, along with habits of catering to individual preferences, assigning ill health to particular foods, and rejecting any food that may be identified as animal food?"

CONTRIBUTIONS OF THE CULTURAL ANTHROPOLOGIST

Dorothy Lee (11) has summarized the following ways in which cultural influences affect food habits. In her book, *Freedom and Culture,* she gives many interesting examples.

Cultural influences determine:

1. The way of feeding the baby.
2. The emphasis on family meals.
3. The kinds of foods people will eat, or what they consider as food.
4. The whole attitude toward eating, whether it is to still hunger, to acquire health, to perform a duty, or to be sociable.
5. The form in which food can be consumed.
6. The morning appetite.
7. The amount of foods eaten and the attitude toward getting fat.
8. The part of a plant or animal that will be eaten.
9. Values placed on monotony or variety.
10. Appropriateness of foods for different occasions.
11. Food taboos.
12. Symbolic values of food.

In the American culture, Dr. Lee has observed tendencies to place a *high value on newness, change, and variety.* In some other societies, sameness is valued — monotony is sought. *Speed and efficiency* are also highly valued in the United States. Thus we find our preference is for juice rather than the whole fruit, and for sandwich lunches.

Remoteness from sources of food has been cited by anthropologist Margaret Lantis (12) as another factor in our culture that may affect nutrition education. Developments in our society are such that the businesses of food production, processing, and marketing have become far removed from the consumer's experience. Most of us cannot watch the strawberries ripening on the vine or the watermelon growing; nor can we collect the fresh eggs from the henhouse.

Dr. Lantis points out that many city and even farm children have no knowledge of the labor and organization required to bring food to them. Hence they do not appreciate the intrinsic value of food, unless they happen to have been deprived and hungry, either physically or psychologically:

They do not know in their own bones and nerves the physical danger of fishermen, the agonizing "stoop labor" of vegetable pickers, the anxiety of citrus fruit growers when a freeze threatens. . . . We seem also to have a decrease in appreciation of the work and skill involved in good cooking. If a child does not feel — I do not mean "know cognitively," but "feel emotionally" — that food is precious, one wonders whether the child can readily understand that any specific food, or food element, is vital to him.

Such developments as the vending machine, the coffee break, TV meals, and convenience foods may make major changes in our eating behavior. These changes may come so gradually that we may fail to take note of their full effect. Constant vigilance, therefore, is needed on the part of nutrition educators, who must be alert to the impact of such changes on the nutritive value of the diet.

We have had some valuable lessons from anthropologists on the general problem of changing food habits. The following is a partial summary:

1. Food habits are deeply rooted in a culture. Because their origins may be completely unknown, they may have become intertwined with superstition, tradition, and custom.

TV meals may make major changes in our eating habits.

2. Time and patience are usually required to change food habits, especially by means of education. Through technology, however, a change may occur at a rapid rate if a new product appeals to some major desire of the people.
3. Changing a single food habit may involve many other changes; the net result may be less desirable than the original state. Therefore, a careful analysis of the total impact of a contemplated change should be made.
4. The fact that people do not possess the nutrition educator's knowledge does not mean that they have no knowledge of their own.
5. The world over, there are many ways to obtain a good diet; judging the adequacy of diets in other cultures requires a careful look at methods used in processing and preparing food. Efforts to effect an improvement sometimes have resulted in a change in practice which, in turn, has led to deterioration of the nutrient supply.
6. As the cultural and educational gap between the teacher and learner widens, the process of education becomes more difficult.

EATING BEHAVIOR OF AGE GROUPS

The nature of foods described as "liked" or "disliked" from preschool age through later years shows a surprising similarity. Table 4.2 shows foods preferred by various age groups, as noted by several researchers. Foods *least* liked or most often rejected by preschool children in the nursery school at Iowa State University, as observed by Korslund (1), were mustard, sour and dill pickles, olives, fresh grapefruit, fresh tomatoes, broccoli, cooked carrots, sweet potatoes, liver, spinach, and grapefruit juice. Somewhat similar are the food likes and dislikes as reported by Pilgrim (8) for men in the army. He observed in studies of army men that foods least liked were, in order mentioned, mashed turnips, broccoli, baked hubbard squash, fried parsnips, cabbage baked with cheese, asparagus with hollandaise sauce, iced coffee, cauliflower with cheese sauce, and candied parsnips.

In general, the most acceptable foods — beginning at an early age — are mild flavored and colorless. Some may have a textural quality of crispness, such as cereals and potato chips, but more of the favorites are soft, perhaps even mushy.

Throughout the age range, among the most generally disliked common foods listed are the flavorful, colorful vegetables including the green and leafy variety. *The roots of food dislikes are, therefore, apparently planted at an early age.* Pilgrim has stated that if we wish to increase the consumption of this group of foods, we must have something more than a nutrition campaign.

Although the attitudes toward specific food groups show a fair degree of constancy from one age to another, an interesting difference in attitude toward specific meals has been observed between preschoolers and teen-age girls. Preschool children were described by

TABLE 4.2

COMPARISON OF FOOD LIKES OF DIFFERENT AGE GROUPS

Investigator	Date of Study	Age of Subjects	Foods with Largest Percentage Described as Liked
Korslund..........	1962	4–5 yrs.	Dry cereals Potato chips Milk Ice cream Apples Candy Hamburgers Peanut butter White bread and butter
Breckenridge........	1959	5½–11½ yrs.	Meat Ice cream Potatoes Bread and crackers Raw fruits Cereals
Adams.............	1949	Grades 4–12	Meat Milk Eggs Bread Cereals Fruits, esp. fresh Vegetables, a few
Pilgrim.............	1960	Army men	Fresh milk Hot rolls Hot biscuits Strawberry shortcake Grilled steak Ice cream Ice cream sundae Fried chicken French fried potatoes Roast turkey
Eppright............	1950	Adults in Iowa	Butter Beef steak Potatoes Ground beef Fruits Eggs Citrus fruits and tomatoes Pastry

their mothers as always being hungry for breakfast and as enjoying this meal perhaps most of all. In the same locality 44 per cent of a sample of teen-age girls said they were not hungry for breakfast, and 37 per cent said they did not enjoy it, whereas only 12 and 15 per cent said they did not enjoy the other two meals of the day.

For 181 Iowa girls, age 8 to 15 or 16 years, foods listed as disliked by the highest percentage were the following in the order mentioned: dark green leafy vegetables, 45 per cent; winter squash, 45 per cent;

liver, 41 per cent; cottage cheese, 28 per cent; sweet potatoes, 28 per cent; canned tomatoes, 27 per cent; tea and coffee, 26 per cent; tomato juice, 20 per cent. Of the 181 girls, only 18 were reported as having no food dislikes. The mean number of food dislikes for the girls in each of the four schools in which the study was conducted were: 3.1, 4.8, 3.8, and 3.5. The range in number of food dislikes for individual girls was from 0 to 16.

Because nutrition educators often work with individuals by age groups, it may be well to consider some of the information available from studies of people of various ages. Since most studies of eating behavior involve small numbers of subjects, not selected to be representative of populations, the results cannot be considered as typical of specific groups. Moreover, there are usually more variations within a specific age group than between ages. For example, differences among teen-agers may be greater than differences between teen-agers and adults.

Although consideration of the individual is of paramount importance in nutrition education, some degree of understanding of differences among age groups may serve as useful guideposts.

Infants

Our knowledge of the nutrient needs of infants has reached a high stage of development. In the beautiful, healthy, and well-developed babies of the United States we have a good example of what can be accomplished through the application of the science of nutrition and related health fields.

Despite the scientific excellence of infant feeding, there is some concern about the fact that in the United States feeding the infant seems to be tending toward a highly impersonalized experience. The prevalence of breast feeding appears to be rapidly declining. Prepared formulas — even boiled water — may be easily purchased. These preparations undoubtedly are sometimes given to infants without the warmth and the personal attention which quite naturally accompany the breast feeding experience. The outcome of such impersonal, routinized feeding in regard to the emotional well-being of both mother and child would be difficult to evaluate.

Prepared formulas may be easily purchased.

Many facts argue for a concern about the influence that early feeding experiences may have on the reactions a child may develop toward food and eating. Food is the first link for the child with the outside world. The early eating situation has great potential in shaping later eating behavior; even in lower animals, conditioned behavior is readily established through the use of food and the power of association between emotions and feeding.

Paul György (13) estimates that in the United States at least 90 per cent of infants are receiving supplemental food below the age of three months, often during the first weeks of life. The manner in which food is presented may be significant. Early and protracted spoon feeding may elicit responses in infants which conceivably could lead to frustrations that might manifest themselves later in neurotic reactions.

To the adult, the potential shock of thrusting a hard spoon into the infant's mouth is incomprehensible. Primitive peoples tend to be extremely gentle in their infant feeding practices, even to the extent of masticating food and using the fingers as a means of conveying food into the mouths of infants.

The life-long significance of social and emotional factors in infant feeding was recognized at the Fifth International Nutrition Conference, when F. W. Clements (14) stated that the dominance of the stomach in early infancy as a sensory organ makes infant feeding the primary variable in child rearing practices which affect nutrition.

Each feeding occasion should be, in its entirety, pleasant and satisfying for the infant and mother. Not only must the supply of food be adequate, easily obtained, and fully digestible, but, as advocated by Clements, the mother must have the time and opportunity to give the baby the satisfying human contact which gratifies his need for clinging and support. This is a note of warning to our increasingly time-conscious people, particularly those who are tempted to seek the most convenient, rapid methods for feeding infants.

The far-reaching effects of two opposite kinds of mothering were described by Clements in examples drawn from the Okinawans and the Alorese. The Okinawan infants are described as "well-mothered." Directly after birth, these infants are offered "well-nippled breasts that are copiously filled with milk." They are offered the breast whenever they are hungry and disturbed, thus their anxieties are allayed and they are afforded a sense of protection and security. The Okinawan mother does everything in her power to prevent early frustrations, so that the outcome is observed to be an "unspoiled child, capable of self-discipline and harmonious social cooperation." Physical and emotional breakdown rates in later years have been extremely low. As a group these people were observed to withstand the stress of World War II extremely well.

The young Alorese, in contrast, are cared for exclusively by mothers for only the first four to six days. From that time on, the infant is given premasticated foods in addition to human milk. When the mother returns to work on about the 14th day after birth, the infant is left during the day in the care of an older child or a relative. Thus there is great variation in the amounts of attention children receive. The infants have been described often as "nourished but not nurtured." During the period of infantile helplessness and similarly throughout childhood and adolescence, maternal care is said to fall short for the Alorese; and the basic personality of these people, according to the observer, is characterized by anxiety, suspicion, and distrust.

Preschool Age

A high degree of individuality in nutrient intake has been stressed by Beal (15) as a result of her observations of children who served as subjects in the long-time investigations of the Child Research Council at the University of Colorado School of Medicine. Most children, according to Beal, show a characteristic pattern of intake for each nutrient and remain within their own channels with remarkable constancy. A few shifts from one channel to another have been observed. These may be associated with marked change in diet due to illness or simply to an unexplainable change in appetite. It is significant that in the latter observation the appetite changes occurred some time before the actual shift in intake.

In general, a smooth curve of increase in intake was noted in the first months of life and also between 4 and 8 years of age, but there were irregularities in intake between late infancy and the early preschool years. Almost from birth, the intakes of boys exceeded those of girls. Apparently boys are innately prepared to provide for a larger organic structure than are girls.

Beal observed a decrease in milk consumption for both boys and girls beginning at approximately 6 months. Boys, however, maintained a higher intake to 18 months, with an abrupt decrease during the next year. Beal further observed that girls never reached as high or low a level of milk consumption as boys, on the average, but the decrease extended over a longer period of time and it was not until the age of 7 or 8 years that the median for girls approximated that for boys. Meat intake for boys and girls was alike during the first year, but thereafter boys maintained a higher level than girls. Egg intakes were similar for boys and girls, except between ages 1 and 3, when girls tended to consume more eggs than did boys.

Beal's observations suggest that some kind of relationship may exist during this period between changes in children's nutrient intake and their growth patterns. Because the preschool period is a time of relatively slow growth, smaller increments are noted in stature and weight than in any other time during childhood. There was also a strong suggestion of a relationship between the decrease in milk consumption and the timing of certain psychological and emotional changes in the child's development. Mothers commented that the decrease in milk consumption came at a time when the child was showing independence from the mother in other areas of behavior, at a time when toilet training was being conducted, or when there was other evidence of emotional turmoil.

Beal also showed the wide difference in food intake of siblings. It is erroneous to assume that within a single family group the individual members will have similar intakes.

The influence of family members on the food consumption of young children has been studied. Bryan and Lowenberg (16) noted a significant relationship between the attitudes of the father and the preschool child toward vegetables. The greatest influence of the father on the food eaten by the child was indirect, because the limitations of his likes and dislikes had an effect on the food served in the home.

Research conducted at the Ohio State University (17) showed that with few exceptions, foods disliked by both parents were either disliked by the child or unfamiliar to him. The social influence of peers is also an important factor in food selection; the greatest influence is exerted upon a younger child by a close friend or older child.

Dudley (18) studied the acceptance by preschool children of four vegetables: green beans, asparagus, carrots, and rutabaga. Frozen asparagus and green beans were prepared four different ways: au gratin, creamed, buttered whole, and buttered pieces. Fresh carrots and rutabagas were prepared as raw sticks, buttered and grated, buttered julienne, and creamed. The children preferred raw preparations of carrots and rutabagas more than any other style. They ate larger amounts and left smaller portions uneaten for the raw than for any other preparation of these vegetables. Of the green vegetables served, the au gratin preparation was preferred to the creamed, which differed only by the addition of crumbs on top. Some children had definite preferences, choosing either of two or three preparations almost every time they were offered. Because the children did vary widely in their choices, the conclusion was that one should be cautious in making general statements about preferences of children for certain types of preparations, and perhaps even for certain foods.

Studies on taste sensitivity of preschool children indicate that while the levels for recognition of basic tastes of sweet, sour, bitter, and salty are similar to those of adults, in this characteristic preschool

children also differ widely among themselves. Some indications were
obtained of relationships of keenness of taste to food likes and dislikes and to enthusiasm about eating. If any differences existed, it
was that the *keen*-sensed children had more food dislikes than others
and were less enthusiastic about meals (1).

School-age Children

Since the late 1940's, repeated studies of the diets of Iowa school
children have indicated that the general type of eating behavior has
not changed. Food groups most often below the recommendations
are the dark green leafy and yellow vegetables, milk or its equivalent
in other dairy products, and the fruits and vegetables rich in vitamin
C. Fluctuations in intakes for the latter group have been more evident than in the other two food groups. The major physiological
finding is a persistent tendency, on the part of girls, toward heavier
weights for height, probably accompanied by an increasing tendency
toward earlier maturation. Concern about overweight or generally
increasing heaviness among Iowa girls is therefore entirely justified.

Over a 2-year period, observations were made intermittently of
the acceptance by Iowa girls 8 to 13 years old of foods included in
two types of supplements, one rich in nutrients and the other poor
(19). Menus for the nutrient-rich supplement were selected from
orange or tangerine juice, limeade, apricot nectar, grapefruit sections,
canned and dried apricots, carrot sticks, a cracker, and a milk drink
— one serving equivalent to a pint of fluid whole milk — made from
frozen milk concentrate and flavored with chocolate, vanilla, straw-
berry, or peanut butter. The snack-type menu usually consisted of a
serving of juice, piece of fruit or vegetable, and a cracker; the milk
was given as a separate feeding.

Menus from the less nutritious foods were similar in type but
were chosen from pineapple juice, grape juice, lemonade, pear and
peach nectar, apple juice, dried prunes, fruit cocktail, canned pears,
fresh apples, applesauce, and celery.

Although both types of snacks were well accepted, foods which
included the less nutritious items were much better accepted than
were the highly nutritious snacks. Of the foods offered in the nutrient-rich category, the acceptance was highest for orange juice,
chocolate malted milk, and tangerine juice. Most poorly accepted
were tomato juice, grapefruit sections, and milk flavored with peanut
butter.

These supplements were administered to girls in four neighbor-
ing schools in one county. Acceptance of both supplements was much
higher in one school than in the other three. In the school where
acceptance was highest, girls were youngest and they ranked lowest in
sex-role identification. This school also ranked highest in percentage
of fathers who were farmers. No other significant differences were

*To increase use of
eggs in diets
of growing girls* . . .

noted among the girls when they were divided into three groups according to food refusal rates: low, medium, and high.

The nutrient-rich supplement was effective in decreasing the number of girls who had diets rating low in calcium, vitamin A, and ascorbic acid. However, the supplement did not alleviate dietary inadequacies in iron, a nutrient often short in diets of teen-age girls. It is well to note that the over-all general recommendation of increasing intake of milk, fruits, and vegetables will not automatically solve the dietary problems of girls. Attention must be given to the *kinds* of fruits and vegetables. Increasing the use of eggs in the diets of growing girls might be a good measure to promote. In the selection from the group of colorful vegetables, special attention should be given to the dark green and leafy as well as the yellow.

It was found that some adjustments were made in the basic self-selected diets of the girls in order to accommodate the food offered in the nutrient-rich snack, which furnished food energy to the extent of about 500 Calories. Nevertheless, the rich supplement did increase the total intake of the girls by 200 Calories or more a day. The result was a slight tendency toward increase in body weight even though the supplement was administered on school days only. Nutrition education of girls, therefore, should *place emphasis on readjustment of diet in order to attain nutrient standards, rather than addition of foods.*

It must be kept in mind that dietary excesses may be as much a matter of concern as are deficits. We are oriented in our thinking toward deficiencies, but trends in statistics of body size — at least in Iowa — plus increasingly earlier maturation suggest that the scope of nutrition education should include both excesses and deficits. Much emphasis should be placed on adjustments to meet changes in nutrient needs.

Focus on Teen-age Girls

Observations of the eating behavior of teen-age girls have brought to light certain relationships significant to nutrition education.

Though these findings are not of sufficient scope to apply with certainty to the entire population of teen-age girls, they pinpoint some of the problems involved in nutrition work with girls in their early teens, and they suggest some directions of efforts which may prove fruitful.

PHYSIOLOGICAL MATURATION

In the study of Iowa girls conducted by Iowa State University (6), girls who matured either early or late were conspicuous for their poor eating behavior, as shown by such factors as meals missed and low scores in dietary adequacy. For earlier maturing girls, the picture was further complicated by a tendency toward overweight. Later maturing girls were not overweight for their age group, although their food practices were similar to those of early maturing girls. It is logical that both extremes of maturation should affect eating behavior similarly if one accepts the possibility of interrelationships between emotional state and eating. Jones and Mussen (20) have observed that girls whose maturational status is at one extreme or the other may have feelings of inadequacy and isolation. These authors postulated that early maturation created a hazard to social adjustment, while late maturation was characterized by less adequate self-concepts and slightly poorer parent-child relationships.

VALUES CONSIDERED IMPORTANT IN FOOD SELECTION

When health was considered important in the selection of food, girls in the Iowa studies (6) tended to miss fewer meals, to select more adequate diets, and to enjoy food more. Fewer of the girls who valued health highly were overweight. The values held by all these girls appeared to influence their eating behavior. Convincing girls that health is an important value in their lives should be a fundamental effort in nutrition education.

Use of food to enhance social occasions is not to be discouraged, but the educational problem is to accomplish this goal without sacrificing health. Girls whose eating is highly motivated toward being sociable, asserting their independence, or acquiring status have been shown to have poor diets. It is highly probable that the same observation would apply to all segments of the population.

KNOWLEDGE OF NUTRITION

Girls who scored higher on tests of nutrition knowledge (which were set up particularly to ascertain choices in certain situations) missed fewer meals and selected more adequate diets than others. This observation, in connection with the relationship of the value of health to the selection of a good diet, indicates that nutrition education for teen-age girls should have a sound, rational basis. Appeals to emotions may improve the effectiveness of education, but they should not replace the basic appeal to reason (6).

PERSONAL RELATIONSHIPS

In the Iowa study, peer-group relationships seemed less important in eating behavior than did family relationships. Girls who scored high in a cluster of items in personal adjustment and family relationships missed fewer meals and selected better diets than those who scored lower. Their social status was higher.

Conditions favoring good family relationships seem to bring better eating practices on the part of teen-age girls, at least as shown in this sample of Iowa girls. An important deduction is that nutrition education can best be pursued in a framework which considers more than just diet *per se*.

It may be of interest to note that in the personality traits investigated, conformity was included. Results of one study (21) have suggested that this is a personality trait associated with the selection of an adequate diet. Emotional stability and good adjustment to reality seem to characterize girls with better food habits. Similar observations have been made by others who have viewed poor psychological adjustment to be related to poor food habits; in fact, the number of food aversions has been postulated as one way to measure neurotic tendencies of an individual (22).

SOCIAL STATUS

In the Iowa study there was a strong interaction between eating behavior and social status of teen-age girls. Social status rating was shown by factors related to the father's occupation and the education of parents. The range of income was more narrow than the range in education. Problems were more evident among the girls in the lower than in the upper social status segment. This factor needs to be considered in nutrition education. Burgess (23) has pointed out that difficulties in nutrition education increase as the social and cultural gap between the teacher and the learner widens.

CONCERN ABOUT OVERWEIGHT

Iowa girls classified as overweight were inclined to have poorer diets than others, to miss more meals, to enjoy food less, and to value health less than others in selecting foods. Three-fourths of the girls who were concerned about overweight actually were overweight; 65 per cent of heavy- or very-heavy-for-age groups were concerned about overweight. Contrary to popular opinion, few girls not actually overweight were concerned about overweight.

Different amounts of energy often are required to accomplish the same task.

No significant relationships were observed between weight status and gross activity, but the latter may be extremely misleading as to the actual energy expenditure of the individual. Tension, drive, and mannerisms may result in differences between energy required by two people to accomplish the same task. Also, in the total energy consumed to accomplish the same task, the steady worker may differ from the one who works in spurts.

Both overeating and undereating have been related to the emotional state of the individual. Undoubtedly such relationships exist, but as yet they are too complex and ill-defined to permit general statements. In a study of heavy, medium, and thin girls in four Iowa schools, no differences were noted in the psychological characteristics of the three groups (24). The only significant difference was in the weight of the parents. It may add to the anxiety of parents, and of the girls themselves, if they accept indiscriminately the idea that obesity invariably has a psychological basis and, to make matters worse, if they too often regard overweight and obesity as identical.

Observations in California (25) of 25 girls who were 16, 17, and 18 years of age are in striking agreement with the findings of the Iowa study. Over a fourth of the girls (29 per cent) were in the obese classification. These had poorer diets than the others. They showed a preference for less active types of leisure activities. Like the Iowa girls, the obese girls in the California sample were aware of their obesity and would like to correct it. Many of the California girls in the normal group had unrealistic ideas about a desirable weight for themselves.

Dealing with overweight in all segments of the population is one of the most difficult problems faced by nutrition educators in the United States. Effectively checking the trend toward heaviness throughout childhood, which is apparent from data in a long-time study of body measurements of Iowa children, presents a challenge. Iowa girls are apparently becoming heavier for their age and height as shown in Figures 4.1A and 4.1B. If this is not a desirable situation, then we must find ways to alter it. Indications are that the heavy girls become heavy adults.

Eating Behavior of Boys

Sex differences in eating behavior have been noted, according to Beal (15), to start almost at birth. In children of preschool age, boys have been shown to be less sensitive than girls to the tastes of sweet, sour, bitter, and salty. In general, boys seem to have fewer food dislikes than girls, although there are undoubtedly exceptions to this.

As a rule, boys eat more than girls. Consequently, their diets usually show fewer nutrient inadequacies than do those of girls. Boys tend to use less fruit, especially of the citrus variety, than do girls. Hence their diets may be more often inadequate in ascorbic acid than those of girls. Their more rapid growth rate, particularly at the time of the adolescent spurt, may be a factor related to the differences in eating as compared to girls.

However, in view of the shorter life span of men than of women in the United States and the greater incidence of coronary heart disease among middle-aged men than middle-aged women, one must not ignore the possibility that food habits of boys need close scrutiny. Although overweight among teen-age boys seems less frequent than among girls, Hundley (26) has presented data to show that overweight is becoming more frequent in white men and less frequent in white women.

Adults

Extensive studies have been made of food preferences among men in the armed forces (8). Results are perhaps typical for much of our adult population. Food preferences are said to account for a large proportion of the plate waste in army mess halls. These preferences follow certain trends reflecting influences of region, education, and urban or rural living. Investigators noted that food preferences are "not capricious," but that they fall into distinct patterns, so that persons with similar backgrounds have similar reactions to food.

A study of food habits and preferences of two groups of Iowa people, male and female, in the age groups of 17–19 and 46–58, showed food habits and preferences to be closely related (27). Preferred menus, i.e., menus given as those desired if there were no restrictions of any kind, did not differ markedly from the actual. In general, the backbone of diets was meat, bread, potatoes, dessert, and beverage — other than milk — and this was the plan preferred at the time of the study, in 1948. Such preferences seem to continue to exist.

What the family *likes* to eat — more than the cost, health value, or "convenience" — dominated the diets of California people as shown by foods purchased by homemakers in the Berkeley area (28).

Food preferences of the father in the family play a dominant role in food prepared for the entire family. The homemaker herself and the teen-age girl are usually considered to have the poorest diets of

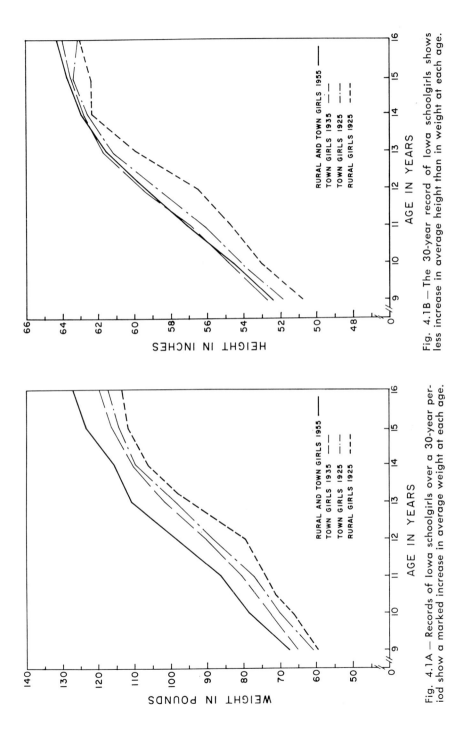

Fig. 4.1A — Records of Iowa schoolgirls over a 30-year period show a marked increase in average weight at each age.

Fig. 4.1B — The 30-year record of Iowa schoolgirls shows less increase in average height than in weight at each age.

*Casual eating
may partly account
for poor dietary habits
of homemakers.*

all family members. Casual eating while the family is away at work or school may partly account for poor dietary habits of homemakers.

Eating behavior of women during pregnancy is another matter of special concern in nutrition education. Stearns (29) has shown particularly poor practices to exist among young pregnant women on low economic levels. She has stated that the young woman is considerably influenced by food preferences of her husband, although during pregnancy she may try to follow carefully the dietary directions of a physician. Lapses between pregnancies should be considered in the total educational program of women during the reproductive period. If the woman is to benefit fully from the science of nutrition, a high level of nutriture should be maintained throughout the period of reproduction, not just during pregnancies. The lack of interest which is prevalent regarding breast feeding is questionable. Should women in the United States desire this method of feeding infants, they need considerable help in understanding dietary adjustments necessary for successful breast feeding. It is probable that few women embarking on the period of lactation have diets that conform to the recommendations for that period.

Eating Behavior of the Aged

Eating behavior of older persons is a complex result of lifelong habits, pronounced physiological changes, income changes, and profound alterations in their ways of life. Some changes are gradual; others may come precipitously.

Types and amounts of foods eaten have been shown to differ for women in the two different areas in three successive decades: 50–59 years, 60–69 years, and age 70 and above (30) as shown in Table 4.3. For all food groups except milk and cereals, the number of pounds used per person per week was smaller in the group over age 70 than in the two preceding decades. The decrease was especially marked in the consumption of protein-rich foods: meat, poultry, fish, eggs, cheese, and legumes.

The decreased food consumption is reflected in a generally decreased nutrient intake of women over seventy in the North Central Region as shown in Figure 4.2.

TABLE 4.3

SUMMARY OF AVERAGE AMOUNTS OF FOODS CONSUMED BY WOMEN AGED 50 YEARS OR OLDER*

(*Pounds per Week*)

Region	Age	Number of Die- taries	Meat, Fish, Poul- try	Eggs, Cheese, Le- gumes	Milk	Cereal Prod- ucts	Fats	White Pota- toes	Vita- min- rich Fruits and Veg.	Other Fruits and Veg.	Sweets and Desserts	Total Fruits and Veg.
	years	*lbs.*	*lbs.*	*lbs.*	*lbs.*	*lbs.*	*lbs.*	*lbs.*	*lbs.*	*lbs.*	*lbs.*	*lbs.*
North Central.	50–59	406	1.63	0.74	2.10	2.04	0.84	1.98	4.39	2.34	1.49	8.71
	60–69	271	1.32	0.72	2.24	2.22	0.87	1.97	4.40	2.43	1.31	8.80
	70 plus	193	0.93	0.51	2.11	2.10	0.73	1.78	3.71	1.78	1.10	7.27
California.	50–59	95	1.80	0.80	2.86	1.62	0.47	0.71	4.05	3.07	2.09	7.83
	60–69	106	1.78	0.81	3.56	1.69	0.59	0.76	4.21	2.90	1.95	7.87
	70 plus	73	1.48	0.72	3.99	1.60	0.45	0.67	3.53	2.71	1.75	6.91

*Source: *Nutritional Status, U.S.A.*, Calif. Agr. Exp. Sta. Bul. 764, p. 25.

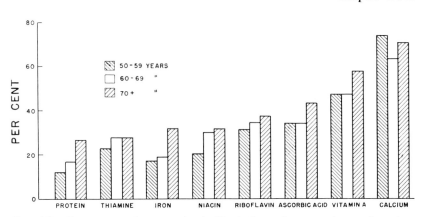

Fig. 4.2 — Percentage of women in six North Central states who ate less than two-thirds the recommended amounts of mentioned nutrients. (Source: **Nutritional Status, USA,** Calif. Exp. Sta. Bul. 764, p. 44.)

A survey of aging persons in one Iowa county (31) revealed that they liked to eat and that most of them regarded their diets as "good" or "very good," although nutritionists rated a majority of the diets poor in quality. This comparison is shown in Figure 4.3. Ninety-three per cent of these elderly people ate three regular meals a day, but a high proportion of single persons living alone ate only two meals a day.

More than 40 per cent of people in their early 60's included snacks in their diets, compared with 27 per cent of those over 75. Many snacks included calorie-rich foods, such as cake and cookies, or breads. Beverages, including tea, coffee, or Postum, were used often as snacks. Milk was more popular as a snack for people living in cities than it was for those who lived in towns or open country.

Older people who did not enjoy their meals usually were in the upper age grouping. Enjoyment of meals by most of the elderly people suggest that they may afford a receptive audience for nutri-

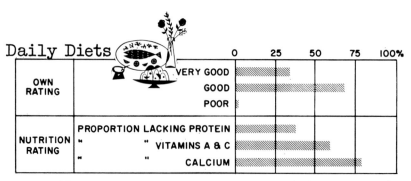

Fig. 4.3 — Elderly people of one Iowa county gave a higher rating to their diets than did the nutritionists who made the study. (Source: **The Aging Persons,** Iowa Home Econ. and Agr. Exp. Sta. Bul. RS—355, p. 17.)

tion education. However, the attitude of food enjoyment may not characterize all groups of elderly people.

In a study of a number of elderly people at the Age Center of New England (7), appetites were generally good or excellent, but many subjects thought of eating as a necessary activity rather than as a pleasure.

Nutrient intake of oldsters has been shown to be influenced not only by social and economic factors, but by difficulties in obtaining food, preparing it, and storing it. Variety of foods used by older subjects was studied. For both sexes, those who were working, married and living with their spouses, and who had higher incomes showed higher variety scores than those who were retired, living alone, and who had lower incomes.

Food habits of more isolated members — those living alone — were compared with those described as "gregarious" or "social." The more isolated members ate far less a variety of foods than the more gregarious. For all nutrients except iron, the mean daily intake was lower for the isolated than for the social group.

Food faddism among older subjects in the New England Age Center was also observed. Diets of the 10 members most addicted to faddism were compared with the 10 least interested. Food faddism was not associated with a reduced nutrient intake; in fact, it appeared to augment it. This observation was not interpreted to mean that food faddism for oldsters is good, but that it apparently represented an interest in food that did not reduce nutrient intake, at least for this group or subjects. Many old people reduce their usual intake of milk, eggs, meat, and fish, but this usually occurs because of changed circumstances of living which were related to aging.

Oral status, function, and chewing efficiency have a decided effect upon the eating behavior of older people; consequently, such difficulties affect the nutritive value of the diet. Twice as many of the subjects of the study at the Age Center who had "poor" oral function had low protein intakes, compared with those who had "good" function. Only those who had "good to excellent" chewing efficiency had a high protein intake.

Income undoubtedly places a limitation upon foods used by older people. It was estimated in 1962 that the median income of couples

. . . chewing efficiency has a decided effect upon the eating habits of older people.

past 65 in the United States was $2,530 per year. At the same time, based on costs in 20 cities of the United States, an income of $2,600 to $3,200 was considered necessary for older couples to maintain minimum standards of living (32).

Babcock (33) has observed that because aging is associated with loss, it is one of the stress periods in life, in which internal tension and conflict are heightened. Both the anxieties and emotional needs of an older person are frequently demonstrated by changes in his attitudes and habits regarding food. Anxiety and stress may be expressed in terms of loss of appetite, overeating, or highly selective eating. The older person may speak fondly of dishes that are primarily associated with his earlier life.

Decreased perception, hearing, and seeing may also have a definite impact upon the eating situation of oldsters. Brighter, more attractive dining rooms may contribute to a greater enjoyment of mealtimes than quiet, drab places which are dimmed even more by decreased powers of perception. Babcock reminds us that when perception is decreased, the world becomes quite dull.

The health and happiness of the older person is closely allied with his ability to change food habits, not only after old age has arrived, but during the earlier decades. Ailing and aging need not be synonymous, for it is possible to be healthy in old age. Important to the attainment of this goal is the prevention of obesity in earlier years, coupled with proper dietary management of such handicaps as diabetes, hypertension, or other chronic diseases. Knowledge of nutrition is not enough to ensure a lifetime state of good nutrition. The ability to change food habits in accordance with changing physiological needs throughout the life span is indeed the crux of the problem.

Dietary habits may be tools for good nutrition, but they may also be obstacles preventing needed dietary changes for people of all ages. Nutrition knowledge can transform habits from liabilities to assets, if such knowledge is applied.

Concern for the welfare of our older population has focused attention on the philosophy that sensible preparation for old age does not begin in the later years; it is a lifelong process. In no area is this more true than it is in nutrition. Griffith (34) has said:

Certainly, better education in nutritional know-how is a necessity, and renewed efforts must be made to improve knowledge of foods in the home and in the school. Especially it is important that parents use the "family table" as a means of furthering family unity, family strength, and family motivations, including the interest in nutritional fitness. Trite as it may be, it is still true: today's children are tomorrow's senior citizens.

. . . today's children are tomorrow's senior citizens.

REFERENCES

1. Korslund, M. K., "Taste Sensitivity and Eating Behavior of Nursery School Children." Unpubl. M.S. thesis, Iowa State University Library, Ames, 1962.
2. Davis, C. M., "Self Selection of Diet by Newly Weaned Infants." *Amer. Jour. Diseases of Children,* 36:651, 1928.
3. Mayer, J., "Regulation of Food Intake and the Multiple Etiology of Obesity." *Weight Control,* p. 34. E. S. Eppright, P. Swanson, and C. A. Iverson, eds. Iowa State University Press, Ames, 1955.
4. Babcock, C. G., "Attitudes and the Use of Food." *Jour. Amer. Diet. Assn.,* 38:546–51, 1961.
5. Kaufman, W., "Some Psychosomatic Aspects of Food Allergy." *Psychosomatic Medicine,* 16(No. 1):10–40, 1954.
6. Hinton, M. A., "Factors Related to the Eating Behavior and Dietary Adequacy of Girls 12 to 14 Years of Age." Unpubl. Ph.D. dissertation, Iowa State University Library, Ames, 1962.
7. Davidson, C. S., Livermore, J., Anderson, P., and Kaufman, S., "The Nutrition of a Group of Apparently Healthy Aging Persons." *Amer. Jour. Clin. Nutr.,* 10:181–99, March 1962.
8. Pilgrim, F. J., "What Foods Do People Accept and Reject?" *Jour. Amer. Diet. Assn.,* 38:439–43, 1961.
9. Hamburger, W. W., "The Psychology of Dietary Change." *Amer. Jour. Public Health,* 48:1342–48, Oct. 1958.
10. Passin, H., and Bennett, J. W., "Social Process and Dietary Change," pp. 113–23, in: "The Problem of Changing Food Habits." Natl. Res. Council Bul. 108, Oct. 1943.
11. Lee, D., *Freedom and Culture.* Prentice-Hall, 1959.
12. Lantis, M., "The Child Consumer." *Jour. Home Econ.,* 54:370–75, May 1962.
13. György, P., "Orientation in Infant Feeding." Fifth International Congress on Nutrition, *Federation Proceedings,* 20(No. 1): Part III, March 1961.
14. Clements, F. W., "Nutrition in Maternal and Infant Feeding." Fifth International Congress on Nutrition, *Federation Proceedings,* 20(No. 1): Part III, March 1961.

15. Beal, V., "Dietary Intake of Individuals Followed Through Infancy and Childhood." *Amer. Jour. Public Health,* 51:1107–17, Aug. 1961.
16. Bryan, M. S., and Lowenberg, M. E., "The Father's Influence on Young Children's Food Preferences." *Jour. Amer. Diet. Assn.,* 34:30–35, 1958.
17. Metheny, N. Y., Hunt, F. E., Patton, M. B., and Heye, H., "The Diets of Preschool Children." *Jour. Home Econ.,* 54:297–310, May 1962.
18. Dudley, D. T., Moore, M. E., and Sunderlin, E. M., "Children's Attitudes Toward Food." *Jour. Home Econ.,* 52:678–81, Oct. 1960.
19. Unpubl. research, Iowa State University.
20. Jones, M. C., and Mussen, P. H., "Self-conceptions, Motivations, and Interpersonal Attitudes of Early- and Late-maturing Girls." *Child Development,* 29:491–501, 1958.
21. Ohls, G. I., "Factors Related to Diet of Freshman Women at Iowa State University." Unpubl. M.S. thesis, Iowa State University Library, Ames.
22. Wallen, R., "Food Aversions of Normal and Neurotic Males." *Jour. Abnormal and Social Psychology,* 40:77–81, 1945.
23. Burgess, A., "Nutrition Education in Public Health Programs . . . What We Have Learned." *Jour. Amer. Public Health,* 51:1715–26, 1961.
24. Burchinal, L. G., and Eppright, E. S., "Test of the Psychogenic Theory of Obesity for a Sample of Rural Girls." *Amer. Jour. Clin. Nutr.,* 7:288–94, 1959.
25. Hampton, M. C., Shapiro, L. R., and Huenemann, R., "Helping Teen-age Girls Improve Their Diets." *Jour. Home Econ.,* 53:835–38, 1961.
26. Hundley, J. M., "Need for Weight Control Programs." *Weight Control,* pp. 1–15. E. S. Eppright, P. Swanson, and C. A. Iverson, eds. Iowa State University Press, Ames, 1955.
27. Eppright, E. S., "Food Habits and Preferences; A Study of Iowa People of Two Age Groups." Iowa State Exp. Sta. Bul. 376, 1950.
28. Shapiro, L., Huenemann, R., and Hampton, M. S., "Dietary Survey for a Local Nutrition Program." U.S. Dep't. HEW, *Public Health Reports,* 77:257–68, March 1962.
29. Stearns, G., "Dietary Habits of Pregnant Women of Low Income in a Rural State." *Jour. Amer. Diet. Assn.,* 28:27–34, 1952.
30. "Nutritional Status, U.S.A." Agnes Fay Morgan, ed. Calif. Agr. Exp. Sta. Bul. 769, pp. 25, 44, Oct. 1959.
31. "The Aging Persons of Linn County, Iowa . . . A Study of the Characteristics, Situations, Problems of Persons 60 Years of Age and Over." Agr. and Home Econ. Exp. Sta. Bul. RS-355, Iowa State University, Ames, Aug. 1960.
32. Tibbits, C., "Economic and Social Adequacy of Older People." Amer. Home Econ. Assn., Workshop on Aging, Apr. 29–May 2, 1962, *Proceedings,* pp. 26–35.
33. Babcock, C. G., "What Is the Older Person Saying?" Unpubl. paper presented at Second Public Health Nutrition Inst., University of Pittsburgh, June 5–10, 1960.
34. Griffith, W. H., "Senior Citizens." Borden Centennial Symposium on Nutrition, *Proceedings,* pp. 85–97, 1958.

Chapter Five

What Should You Teach?

TECHNOLOGY IS AFFECTING the form and quality of food so that adequate and attractive meals are easily available to most families. However, it is a mistake to assume that diets will be improved automatically. Well-planned nutrition education is as important now as it always has been.

There are many ways to teach nutrition and all of them can make important contributions to nutrition education. Whether you publish articles, books, or pamphlets; give talks or teach lessons to organized groups — you are teachers concerned with changing members of your audience in various ways. This is education: the process of changing behavior in desirable directions.

Behavior as defined here refers to all forms of activity: it includes such processes as thinking and feeling as well as more visible activities; it applies to covert as well as overt actions. When objectives are stated as behaviors, attention is focused on what you hope will happen to students as a result of your teaching.

. . . attention is focused on what you hope will happen as a result of your teaching.

There are four parts to a plan for teaching: objectives, generalizations or concepts, learning experiences, and evaluation. Each of these has a unique function:

Objectives guide the selection and use of the other three
Generalizations or concepts indicate content
Learning experiences describe opportunities for learning so that objectives may be reached
Evaluation indicates how well learning is taking place

You are most likely to educate people as you desire if you find answers to four questions:

1. What educational objectives should guide my teaching?
2. What generalizations or concepts do I want learners to know and be able to apply as one means of reaching objectives?
3. What opportunities can I provide for learners to reach the objectives? [1]
4. How can the effectiveness of these learning experiences be evaluated? [2]

SELECTING AND WRITING OBJECTIVES

The ways in which you wish to change people are your objectives and so, to be most useful, they are stated as desirable behaviors of learners. When objectives are stated as broad educational outcomes they can give you a sense of direction for your teaching. The objectives indicated by Roman numerals I through VI on the following pages are examples of this type of objective.

When, however, objectives are stated only in broad general terms, they have limited use when selecting generalizations or when planning for experiences and evaluation. You need to know what students can *do* when they have achieved the objectives. The more specific behaviors are illustrated by the objectives indicated with italicized letters following each Roman numeral.

As a result of your teaching do you expect people to be better able to think for themselves? You cannot be sure to reach this goal unless you know the behaviors to expect when one has learned to think. These behaviors range from the simplest, such as recall of facts, to complex intellectual abilities and skills, such as ability to solve problems or to evaluate a plan.

Even when you believe that knowledge of nutrition is important, would you be willing to accept this as the primary goal of your teaching? Probably not. You will want individuals to plan for good nutrition in whatever situation they may find themselves. To do this they must be able to find and use appropriate information and techniques

---

[1] This question is discussed in Chapter 7, "Methods of Teaching."
[2] This question is discussed in Chapter 8, "Evaluation."

to solve their problems. It is the specific kinds of information or the specific techniques needed to solve the problems selected for consideration that will be useful when planning for teaching.

This belief about objectives guided the preparation of those suggested on the following pages. In order to identify the behaviors which would indicate that individuals were reaching each of the objectives I through VI, answers were found to the following questions:

What knowledge is needed to develop each ability?
    What facts? What terminology? What criteria? What generalizations? What techniques?
What intellectual skills and abilities are needed?
    What must be comprehended? To what situations should generalizations be applied? What planning is necessary? What judgments are desirable? What evaluation is needed?

As you answer these questions, you identify the kind of competence you expect. The behaviors suggested in the following objectives are relatively simple because they indicate the kind of competences you might expect of students with limited background for understanding nutrition. When planning for individuals with an extensive background you would expect different kinds of behavior. For example, instead of knowing how to use a food guide as a basis for planning, you might desire ability to calculate the amounts of nutrients in a day's dietary.

In nutrition education, changing the way people think is not enough. The food practices of people may be influenced more by the way they feel than by what they think. How well an individual uses what he has learned about nutrition is influenced by his attitudes, his interests, what he appreciates and enjoys, his values, and the goals he has for reaching values. Since these behaviors influence what a student is likely to learn, they are important in any set of objectives.

... using what he has learned about nutrition ....

OBJECTIVES FOR NUTRITION EDUCATION

As a result of nutrition education, people will be better able to:

I. Appreciate the relationship between goals of individuals and the kind and distribution of foods which they eat because they:

    A. Comprehend how nutrition influences different parts of the body and the characteristics which relate to personal appearance.

    B. Comprehend how nutrition influences personality.

    C. Comprehend how nutrition influences efficiency.

    D. Comprehend how nutrition influences growth and development through its interplay with heredity and environment.

    E. Know the characteristics which reflect nutritional state.

    F. Comprehend how physical condition influences utilization of nutrients.

    G. Accept the validity of findings that result from sound research.

II. Extend the variety of foods eaten and enjoyed by themselves and others when they:

    A. Comprehend how such factors as customs, nationality, and religion influence food preferences and practices.

    B. Comprehend how age, physical state, and emotions influence food preferences and practices.

    C. Are willing and able to identify probable causes of refusal to eat rejected foods.

    D. Comprehend ways to overcome food dislikes of themselves and others.

    E. Are willing to experiment with ways to overcome food dislikes or to improve distribution of foods in meals and snacks.

    F. Develop skill in food preparation to increase acceptance and conserve nutrients.

    G. Are willing and able to assume responsibility for their own nutrition.

III. Plan and prepare nutritious meals and snacks because they:

    A. Know how to use a food guide as a basis for planning.

    B. Know the foods that are classified in each food group.

    C. Comprehend the functions of nutrients and chemical substances in the body.

    D. Know contributions of usual servings of foods to daily requirements of nutrients.

    E. Know how to adjust calorie intake to needs of individuals.

    F. Comprehend how nutrient requirements change with age.

    G. Can judge the adequacy of meals by sound criteria.

IV. Plan the use of resources for providing food for themselves and others because they:

    A. Comprehend the relationship between a food budget, nutritious meals, and food preferences.

    B. Know relative costs of foods which contain comparable nutrients.

    C. Develop skill in planning meals that can be provided within limitations of time, energy, and money.

    D. Develop judgment in buying foods of suitable quality for use.

    E. Can evaluate the worth of processed foods such as packaged mixes, frozen foods, and ready-prepared meals.

    F. Can evaluate the usefulness of vitamin supplements.

    G. Know how to care for and store foods to prevent spoilage.

    H. Comprehend the significance of government grading of food.

    I. Know the major regulations of the Pure Food and Drug Act as they apply to household marketing.

  V. Evaluate beliefs about food because they:

    A. Know appeals used in advertising foods .

    B. Are skillful in distinguishing facts from hypotheses.

    C. Use sound criteria for judging sources of nutrition information.

    D. Comprehend how food fads develop.

    E. Are able to identify and appraise values that are involved in food practices.

    F. Apply generalizations of nutrition when evaluating a food practice.

    G. Comprehend factors that influence the health of individuals.

    H. Appreciate the importance of continually checking nutritional states.

    I. Keep up to date with research findings in nutrition.

 VI. Evaluate the worth of programs for the welfare of families, communities, and nations because they:

    A. Know the effects of nutrition upon the mental and physical health of individuals.

    B. Know the effects of nutrition on relationships among people.

    C. Know the relationship of nutrition to world problems and conditions.

Objectives as comprehensive as these cannot be achieved by the efforts of one person alone or by one group of individuals in a com-

Objectives cannot be achieved by efforts of one person alone.

munity. But cooperation among the individuals concerned with nutrition education can be expected to bring best results when they plan programs to reach all family members at approximately the same time. The over-all objectives for all groups may be the same, but the methods will be keyed to the age, responsibilities, and interests of the immediate group.

Nutrition education is likely to be ineffective if an individual is reached during just one period in his lifetime. Information acquired at one period may not be that which is needed for solving problems later on. Furthermore, knowledge of nutrition is constantly increasing. Food technology has changed the availability of some foods, and in some instances nutritive value, also. The readiness of people to learn may change with age and responsibility. Thus there is good reason to plan nutrition education for all groups in a community.

Readiness to learn will be influenced by the ages, responsibilities, and experiences of members of a group. Some experiences need not be repeated when the same individual is taught nutrition at different periods of his life. The factors that influence readiness to learn are discussed in detail in Chapter 7.

When you have selected the objectives that are appropriate for the group you plan to teach, you will wish to assemble the facts that must be understood if the objectives are to be achieved. The facts presented in the following chapter are organized to facilitate such planning.

SELECTING AND USING GENERALIZATIONS

When you have determined the objectives for your teaching, the next step is to decide what knowledge is needed to achieve them. One way to make this decision is to select generalizations that are appropriate for the group to be taught. *Generalizations are statements supported by facts or beliefs that apply in situations beyond those in which the generalization is learned.* A generalization states some relationship between two or more concepts. One generalization in nutrition that you might wish to develop with students is: *Good nutrition* requires that the *nutrients* (or chemical substances) needed by the *body for its functions* be provided in *ample amounts* (p. 132).

Concepts in this generalization have been italicized for emphasis. *Concepts are ideas or notions that one has about something.* In education our concern is that concepts be accurate, clear, and as complete as possible.

You may have called the above generalization a principle and you would be right. Generalization is a generic term which includes principle. There are no generally accepted criteria for differentiating between generalizations, principles, laws, rules, or facts of broad application. In this book, however, the term *generalization* is used to describe a statement of fact or belief that organizes ideas.

Importance of Organized Knowledge

Facts of nutrition are of little use unless they can be applied in situations in which students are likely to find themselves. This calls for organization. Knowledge which is organized is retained better than facts which are specific and isolated. Thus learning is more efficient.

Furthermore, facts learned in isolation can be used again only when like situations are encountered. Only as students form concepts, see relationships among them, and arrive at generalizations can they transfer what they have learned to new situations.

Generalizations can guide you in selecting the facts that you will teach. As knowledge of nutrition increases, there is danger that learning will be superficial. Accurate and complete concepts and generalizations require time for their formation. Thus you are faced with the necessity of selecting what you will teach. This selection can be guided by a set of generalizations that you believe your students should understand and apply because these will indicate the facts to be known, and concepts to be developed. Since the learner develops concepts from his own experience, time is needed to form new concepts or to change those that are undesirable. Many of his concepts of nutrition are false or incomplete but since they are his, he may defend them vehemently. Re-education is the way to change them. Telling him that he is wrong may do little but build resistance to change. What he needs is opportunities to build new, accurate concepts that are his own. These will replace the inaccurate ones if you allow time for him to have the needed experience.

The basic process of acquiring concepts is the differentiation of details and the organization of these details so that similarities and differences are evident. If you wished to develop the concepts in the generalization given above, you might start with the concept, *good nutrition*. As a first step you could ask yourself the question: How can I increase the ability of students to observe details and to identify characteristics that distinguish good nutrition from poor?

Since the most obvious characteristics are physical ones, you might start by showing pictures of the girls, Figures 5.1A, B, C, and D. If you ask students to point out characteristics that are different for the two girls without showing the lists given on the same page, they would be required to think rather than memorize and you would have some evidence of their abilities to observe details and to identify differences and similarities. At the same time misconceptions would be evident. If students seem to need more experience of a similar nature, you could show pictures of different ages, both men and women, with special emphasis on the age and sex of most concern to your students.

CHARACTERISTICS OF GOOD NUTRITION

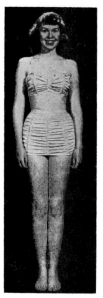

Shiny, luxuriant hair

Sparkling eyes

Well-formed teeth

Square shoulders

Straight spine

Alert posture

High vitality

Firm muscles

Proper weight for height and age

Straight legs

Well-arched feet

FIG. 5.1A

FIG. 5.1B

CHARACTERISTICS OF POOR NUTRITION

Dull hair

Narrow, round shoulders

Curved spine

Sagging, poor posture

Low vitality

Poor muscle tone

Underweight for
height and age

Slightly knock-kneed

Flat feet

FIG. 5.1C

FIG. 5.1D

Since varied experiences are most effective in concept formation, you might plan different experiences that would clarify the concept of *good nutrition.* Animal-feeding experiments or observation of children or of one's age mates could provide opportunities to distinguish the physical characteristics of persons with good nutrition.

By this time students should be ready to organize their learning. If you ask them what they have learned about the physical characteristics of a person with good nutrition, they should be able to make accurate statements. They could make statements about poor nutrition also. As they verbalize the concept of good nutrition, they as well as you will have a basis for knowing what they have learned.

Students can evaluate their own statements by comparing them with those of authorities in reference books or phamphlets. Reference reading will have more meaning for students when they have had some experience related to what they read; they will be motivated to read when a purpose for their reading is evident to them.

If you want to broaden the concept of good nutrition to include how one feels and acts, quite different experiences could be planned. A film such as, *It's All In Knowing How* (1), could be discussed following a plan for discussion such as the one suggested on page 174. Before accepting all of the ideas presented in the film, students could read such references as Leverton, *Food Becomes You* (2), and King and Lam, *Personality "Plus" Through Diet* (3).

Students have been introduced to the other concepts in the generalization being developed — nutrients, body functions, and ample amounts — but such indirect consideration of these is not enough. Probably, you will want to provide opportunities for students to clarify these concepts and make them more specific.

Adaptation of Organized Knowledge

It is difficult to discuss the concept of nutrients without giving consideration to their function in the body. To introduce such a discussion you might want students to comprehend such facts as:

Each day our bodies need to be supplied with many different nutrients:
  Protein for growth and repair of the body
  Minerals and vitamins for growth and to keep the body functioning properly
  Fat and carbohydrate for energy
  Water and oxygen, often not included as nutrients, are necessary before the body can use the food taken in

Most foods contain more than one nutrient, but no single food contains all of them in the amounts needed. Choosing foods wisely means selecting kinds that together supply nutrients in the amounts needed by the body.

*Building and regulative
materials are carried
to areas which
need them.*

Food is first masticated and mixed with saliva in the mouth and is carried to the digestive tract. Here it is digested and absorbed by the blood stream which carries it to the cells in all parts of the body. The red cells in the blood also pick up oxygen from the lungs and take it to the cells. Nutrients and oxygen combine (or "oxidize") and energy, measured in calories, is released for the needs of the body. Building and regulatory materials such as protein, minerals, and vitamins are carried by the blood to the bones, teeth, muscles, and other tissues and organs which need them. Excesses of some nutrients may be stored for later use, while waste products, along with excess water resulting from digestion and oxidation of food nutrients, are eliminated mainly through the kidneys, intestines, and skin.

To give a concept of how to select ample amounts of foods needed daily, the Institute of Home Economics, Agricultural Research Service of the United States Department of Agriculture developed *Food for Fitness, A Daily Food Guide* (4). In this guide, foods are divided into four broad groups on the basis of their similarity in composition and nutritive value. This guide specifies the number of daily servings needed from each food group to supply the Recommended Dietary Allowances (5) for food energy and nine nutrients. When this food plan is followed, as much choice as possible is allowed while the user is given an assurance of an adequate variety and amount of food.

To introduce *Food for Fitness, A Daily Food Guide,* popularly called the "Basic Four," the teacher may wish to use the wall chart which shows the following four food groups and the number of servings needed per day. [3]

---

[3] A large wall chart from *Food for Fitness, A Daily Food Guide,* can be obtained upon request from the National Dairy Council, Chicago 6, Ill.

1. Milk Group
     Children — 3 to 4 cups
     Teen-agers — 4 or more cups
     Adults — 2 or more cups   *milk, cheese, ice cream*
2. Vegetable-Fruit Group
     4 or more servings to include
         a citrus fruit or vegetable important for vitamin C
         a dark-green or deep-yellow vegetable for vitamin A
         other vegetables and fruits including potatoes
3. Meat Group
     2 or more servings
         beef, veal, pork, poultry, fish, eggs
             as alternates
                 dry beans and peas, nuts
4. Bread-Cereal Group
     4 or more servings
         whole grain, enriched, or restored

To round out meals and to satisfy the appetite everyone will use some foods not specified — butter, margarine, other fats and oils, sugar, or unenriched refined grain products. These "other" foods supply calories and can add to total nutrients in meals. However, other foods are to be added only after the variety given in the four groups is satisfied or adequate nutrients may not be obtained.

To emphasize the need for distributing foods in three or more meals and snacks during the day, you may wish to supply food models your students can use to arrange food combinations into meals. [4] This activity permits the development of some ability to select and group, into acceptable meal patterns, the kinds and amounts of food needed for the day. It can also strengthen concepts of kinds and amounts of food to use daily which are important to provide ample nutrients.

If it is desirable to develop the concept of ample amounts of nutrients for a variety of age groups and in conditions of pregnancy and lactation, the teacher is referred to *Food Becomes You* (2). This author uses the *Daily Food Guide* to illustrate how to vary kinds and amounts of food selected from the four food groups while maintaining ample amounts of nutrients for a variety of ages and conditions.

Many food guides have been developed in the past. The teacher may want to mention the "Basic Seven" guide which has been, and still is, in use. In addition there are other daily food intake plans which group foods into nine or eleven different food groups. These plans are more completely subdivided than the Basic Four but can be successfully used as guides. The Basic Four plan, *Food for Fitness* (4),

---

[4] Food models may be purchased from the National Dairy Council, Chicago 6, Ill.

*...the "Basic Seven"
is still in use.*

was developed to simplify as much as possible the daily selection of food intake with the belief that people will use a simplified plan more effectively and willingly than a more complicated one.

When students can make accurate statements about the concepts — *good nutrition, nutrients, body functions,* and *ample amounts of nutrients* — they are ready to organize these into a generalization. This organization must be their own as truly as was the formation of concepts.

You can guide students to form a generalization by asking a question such as: What can you say about the relationship between the amount and kind of food and the functioning of the body of a person with good nutrition?

Students may make statements that are quite different from the generalization with which you started. This is to be expected. Your only concern is that the statements be accurate and as complete as seems reasonable for the group.

When the statements are incorrect or not as complete as you had anticipated, correcting the statements of students does little good because their comprehension is at fault. Reteaching is the only way to improve understanding. You may need to provide opportunities either for students to develop concepts or for relationships among concepts to be clarified. You cannot generalize for your students. A generalization is most useful to the person who formulates it because it then has meaning to him.

Some criteria for stating generalizations may be useful to you.

1. Is the statement a complete sentence?
2. Are the ideas clearly and completely expressed?
3. Does the generalization organize all of the appropriate concepts?
4. Is there a distinction between generalizations based on facts and on beliefs?
5. If the generalization is a simple statement of fact, is the fact so important that it should stand alone?
6. Is the statement free of such undesirable words as "should" or "must"?

7. When statements are of different degrees of breadth, are specific statements grouped to show their relationship to a broad generalization?

Using a concept in a new situation helps to broaden and clarify it. Relationship to new ideas tends to make it clearer, more accurate, and precise. As the concept of *good nutrition* was developed it was contrasted with poor nutrition. The characteristics of one point up the other. The generalization might be stated this way: A continuous check of the diet is needed to maintain good nutrition and to avoid the bad effects of poor nutrition.

The United States Department of Agriculture has compiled many food values in a series of tables which are sold under the title, *Composition of Foods: Raw, Processed, Prepared.*[5] Table III in this compilation gives results of analyses of foods in common household measurements. Students can find answers to many questions concerning the nutrient content of a wide variety of foods listed in these tables. If they wish to locate food rich in vitamins A and C, protein, iron, or niacin they can glance up and down the columns of this table until they spot foods with a high nutrient content of the kind they wish to increase in their diet. It is also helpful to let students make comparisons of the calorie and nutrient content of a variety of snack foods and desserts to help them see which ones have in them good nutrient content as well as calories.

Since it is possible to choose foods from the four groups of the *Food for Fitness Guide* and still make errors which can produce inadequacies in the diet, you will want to point out mistakes commonly made in using this guide. For example, size of servings may vary greatly; breads and cereals may not be enriched or of whole grain; vegetables and fruits may be prepared and cooked by poor methods in which they are exposed to air and warmth for long periods of time; mineral and vitamin content of fruits and vegetables may be lost through pouring off liquid in which they are cooked. Some people make the mistake of counting a single food, such as American cheese, in both the meat and milk groups. Or they may count as a full serving food, such as cheese, used in small amounts for flavor or decoration. Others fail to include a high vitamin C food or a dark-green or deep-yellow fruit or vegetable although they eat four or more servings daily from the fruit and vegetable group.

To expand the concept of ample amounts you may lead your students to use the three meals they have planned and check them for number of servings from each of the four food groups in the day's

---

[5] Bernice K. Watt and Annabel L. Merrill, "Composition of Foods, Raw, Processed, and Prepared," Agr. Handbook No. 8, U.S. Gov't. Print. Off., Washington, D.C., 1950.

*... mineral
and vitamin content
may be lost through
pouring off liquid ...*

food supply. The menu could be placed on the chalk board and evaluated as follows:

Food Group	Number of Servings	Kind of Food	Calories in Average Servings[6]
Breakfast			
Vegetable, Fruit .... 1 good source of vitamin C		Cantaloupe, ½ medium	40
Bread, Cereal .... 2 enriched or whole grain		Oatmeal, ½ cup	75
		Toast, 1 slice enriched	60
Meat .... ½		Egg, 1 medium	80
Milk 1		Whole Milk, 1 cup	165
		Total	420
Lunch or Supper			
Meat 1		Lima Beans with Ham ...... ⅚ c. beans plus 1 oz. ham	332
Vegetable or Fruit 1		Sliced Tomatoes, 1 medium ..	30
Bread, Cereal 1		Cornbread Muffin, enriched ... 2¾ inch diameter	105
Milk 1		Buttermilk, or Skim Milk ..... 1 cup	90
		Total	557
Dinner			
Meat 1		Lean Roast Beef, 3 ounces	255
Vegetable, Fruit .... 2 dark-green or deep-yellow for vitamin A		Baked Potato, 1 medium	90
		Carrots, raw or cooked ½ cup .	28
Bread, Cereal 1		Pan Roll, enriched white .... 1¼ ounces	115
Milk 1		Whole Milk, 1 cup	165
		Total	653
		Total Day's Calories	1630

The total of 1630 Calories furnished by the foods selected to fulfill the requirements of the *Food for Fitness Guide* are too few for the average adolescent girl or boy, or for adults. The best indication of

---

[6] Caloric values of the foods in these menus were adapted from the table of "Nutrients in Common Foods in Terms of Household Measures" in *Food Becomes You,* by Dr. Ruth M. Leverton, Iowa State University Press, Ames, 1960. Pp. 171–91.

whether or not the food energy of the diet is sufficient is the maintenance of a desirable body weight for age, sex, and height of the individual. When the required number of servings of the "Basic Four"
foods have been put in the day's menu, other foods, either in the *Food
for Fitness Guide* or out of it, may be eaten to satisfy the appetite and
maintain the desirable body weight.

Protein and calcium needs are large during periods of rapid growth
so an adolescent boy or girl may wish to increase milk intake for the
day either between meals or as a bedtime snack. Two eggs for breakfast, custard or ice cream for dessert, and sandwiches of peanut butter,
cheese, egg, or meat could be added to increase these nutrients. Use of
additional fruits and vegetables, either during or between meals as
snacks, would increase the supply of minerals and vitamins. See *Food
Becomes You* (2) for further directions for increasing food intake to
meet needs of special age groups, or people under stress such as pregnancy and lactation.

Many tables of height-weight-age averages have been compiled for
boys and girls and men and women. Some tables emphasize the wide
range of normal variation in weights of individuals due to differences
in body structure.

To determine when body weight is at a desirable level, the build
of the individual needs to be considered as well as muscle tone or firmness of flesh, sex, age, and height.

Recent tables for height, weight, and age averages for adults were
published by the Metropolitan Life Insurance Company in 1959 (6).
These weights were for men and women wearing ordinary indoor
clothing, and the heights included shoes. The new findings revealed
that the average weights for men were about five pounds higher than
former studies indicated. This report also gave evidence that weight
reduction to a normal level had a favorable effect on vitality and
length of life. The American Medical Association has accepted the
new findings of the Metropolitan Life Insurance Company as a basis
for an exhibit on weight control which was presented in 1960 at the
Annual Meeting of the American Medical Association. (See Appendix
D.)

For anyone 25 years of age or older it appears to be desirable to
maintain a weight at least five pounds beneath the average weight for
his height and age. During adolescence it may be an advantage to be
five pounds above, rather than below, the average weight for height
and age, because of the stress of this period of rapid growth and development. In *Food Becomes You* (2), Dr. Leverton has presented a
Physical Growth Record[7] to be used in evaluating growth during
adolescence. These records permit the assessment of growth without

---

[7] Individual copies of Physical Growth Record are available at small cost from
the American Medical Association, 535 North Dearborn Street, Chicago 10, Ill.

fitting the individual into any one category as is required when height-weight-age tables are used. Such an evaluation is especially desirable during this period between 11 and 18 years of age when great individual variation in growth and development occurs.

When an average desirable body weight has been decided upon, it is possible to estimate the food energy, in terms of calories, needed for maintenance and, in the case of children, for growth as well. The following is a table of approximate calories per pound of desirable body weight needed daily.

Age	Calories per Pound per Day
Infant: birth to one plus years	45–50
Child: 2–10 years — lower than adult man or woman until adolescent growth begins, approximately	35–48
Adolescence	
Boys 13–15 years	29
16–19 years	26
Girls 13–15 years	24
16–19 years	20
Adults	
Sedentary — man or woman	16
Active — man or woman	20
Very Active — woman	24
Very Active — man	28
Later half of pregnancy	10–20% increase only
Lactation, for milk production ...	800–1000 Calorie increase

If a more complete discussion of energy needs for various ages and conditions is desired, see *Food Becomes You* (2).

A 6-weeks-old baby whose desired weight is 10 pounds would need approximately $10 \times 50 = 500$ Calories per day to maintain his weight and growth. A 14-year-old, moderately active boy whose desired weight is 78 pounds would need approximately $78 \times 29 = 2262$ Calories to maintain his weight. A 25-year-old sedentary woman who, according to tables, should weight 135 pounds will need approximately $135 \times 16 = 2160$ Calories per day to maintain her weight.

It is wise to weigh every week so that changes in body weight become known before they are too great.

The amount of activity one carries out and the rate of growth during childhood and adolescence can increase the caloric need substantially. The rate at which the body uses food energy is high during the first year, slows down some during childhood, increases again during adolescence, and then gradually slows down again as the individual advances in years.

Continuous checks of the diet and of body weight are important in the maintenance of good nutrition. However, if there is presence of frequent colds or digestive upsets, fatigue, constipation, depression, or hyperirritability one needs to see a physician. He can check with you concerning habits of living which influence utilization of food. In

Worry and tension can influence utilization of food.

addition to wise daily selection of kind and amount of food, other factors essential to good nutrition are: Eight or more hours of sleep; daily outdoor exercise; and freedom from undue worry and tension over work or personal problems of living.

Students of all ages have a tendency to form generalizations only partially supported by facts. Their statements may be strong, positive ones needing considerable qualification. This may be due to incomplete information or unquestioning acceptance of material presented either by the teacher or in references. You can teach students to be critical of their conclusions and thus to generalize more accurately.

APPLICATION OF GENERALIZATIONS

Learning to apply generalizations is another aspect of thinking that is not easy. You are teaching nutrition with the hope that food practices of students will improve and so you will want to teach students to use the generalizations they have learned, when deciding what they will eat. Students of all ages often wish to discuss personal problems that might be solved by applying the generalizations they are learning. If you take time in class to encourage application, students may not know as many generalizations but those they do know will be more meaningful.

When helping students to learn facts and ideas and to generalize them, it is helpful to:

1. Present a few important ideas and stress these throughout the class. Relate any details to the main ideas and facts which are to be emphasized.
2. Write important facts on the blackboard and draw attention to them from time to time during the class.
3. Use demonstrations, charts, graphs, films, and other visual aids whenever possible to point out facts, to illustrate how they are related, or to show situations in which they may be applied.
4. Summarize the important ideas. You may do the summarizing, or you may have students state generalizations if time permits.
5. Apply the generalizations to situations with which the student is familiar.
6. Ask questions which require the application of the generalizations in order to answer them.

The use of generalizations does not stand out as a method in itself but should be a part of all classroom experiences. Thus the methods described in a later chapter are not complete unless students learn to draw conclusions from their experiences and to state their conclusions as generalizations.

PLAN ILLUSTRATING DEVELOPMENT OF GENERALIZATIONS

When teaching a class of seventh-grade boys and girls, Helen Barbour (7) used these steps to guide her students in generalizing. Her lesson plan for teaching the effects of food upon growth is reproduced to illustrate one way of teaching generalizations.

Objectives:
When this lesson is completed, students will be better able to:
1. Recognize how food affects growth of the body.
2. Attain good nutrition because they select foods which provide nutrients in amounts needed by their bodies.
3. Distribute foods wisely in meals and snacks.
4. Maintain the body in a condition favorable for utilization of nutrients.

Generalizations for Teacher Reference:
Generalizations 1E (1–20), pages 122–25, and 5A (2–3), page 132, were used when planning.

Class Discussion:
1. What is normal growth?
    a. Inherited qualities — can they be changed? If so, how?
    b. Individuality in rate of growth (rate of growth of girls vs. boys)

Inherited qualities?

Environmental factors?

Height-weight-age tables?

*As you analyze
their suggestions you may
find they need help ....*

    c. Environmental factors affecting growth rate (food, rest, sunshine, exercise, fresh air, worry and unhappiness, etc.)

    d. Illness and infections (bad tonsils, poor teeth, rheumatic fever, etc.)

    e. Height-weight-age tables — how are they used? What does it mean if you are not the weight the tables indicate for your age? (Use weight and height records of pupils.)

2. What influences your height, weight, and body build?

    a. Appetite

      1) Regular meals

      2) Kind of foods in the meals (satiety value)

        a) Protein, fat, and sweets slow down hunger contractions

        b) Fruits, vegetables, and cereals (without fat) leave the stomach quickly

      3) Snacks — if properly selected may not ruin appetite for the the next meal

      4) Exercise, fresh air, rest (enough to allow food eaten to be used well), and sleep help build good appetites

    b. Amount and kinds of food that help you gain weight

    c. Amount and kinds of food that help you lose weight

    d. Need for building materials in a diet either to gain or lose weight (milk, fruit and vegetables, meat, eggs, whole grain or enriched bread and cereals, butter or margarine)

Summary by Students:

You will be given 5 minutes to write sentences that tell what you have learned today. These questions will help you.

1. What influences the way you grow?
2. What affects your appetite, or lack of it?
3. What foods can help you to gain weight?
4. What foods should be reduced in amount to lose weight?
5. What foods do you need whether you are gaining or losing weight?
6. Why is underweight, or overweight, undesirable?

Evaluation:

If students hand in answers to these questions, you will have a basis for determining not only how well they are meeting their objectives, but also how well they are progressing in their ability to write generalizations.

As you analyze their suggestions you may find they will need help in stating generalizations. In the lesson plan, questions that emphasized the ideas presented were suggested to guide students. In an earlier lesson students were encouraged to give reasons why new facts or ideas were important or interesting. Another suggestion was that sentences begin with "if," "because," or "when." Thus, they were encouraged to make complete sentences in their own words to express the ideas that they had gained.

REFERENCES

1. *It's All In Knowing How.* Film available from National Dairy Council, 111 No. Canal St., Chicago 6, Ill.
2. Leverton, Ruth M., *Food Becomes You.* Iowa State University Press, Ames, 1960.
3. King, C. G., and Lam, G., *Personality "Plus" Through Diet — Food Lore for Teenagers.* Public Affairs Pamphlet No. 299, prepared in cooperation with Nutrition Foundation, Inc., 22 E. 38th St., New York City 16. (25 cents.)
4. Institute of Home Economics, *Food for Fitness, A Daily Food Guide.* Leaflet No. 425, USDA.
5. National Research Council, *Recommended Dietary Allowance.* Food and Nutrition Board Publ. 589, 1958.
6. Metropolitan Life Insurance Company, *Statistical Bulletin*, 40:1, Nov.–Dec., 1959.
7. Barbour, Helen, "Relationships of Values and Process Concepts of Selected Students to Generalizations in Nutrition." Unpubl. Ph.D. dissertation, Iowa State University Library, Ames, 1953.

Chapter Six

Generalizations and Facts

ALL PERSONS having responsibility for nutrition education cannot be well grounded in the science of nutrition, and many people who are highly trained in nutrition have given little thought to the way in which their information can best be taught. The nutritionist working with the educator forms an important team in education: the person trained in nutrition to discover and to present the facts, the educator to see that facts are presented to students in the form in which they can be understood and used. In this chapter an effort has been made to organize the practical knowledge in nutrition according to the objectives shown by research in education to be effective in motivating learning. The information is presented in the form of generalizations and statements of supporting facts.

Of the statements in this chapter, those designated by Arabic numerals in bold-faced type and capital letters in light-faced type are primarily generalizations. The subheadings with Arabic numerals furnish supporting evidence or closely related facts. While the information may be useful to people who are not highly trained in nutrition, a sound education in nutrition will enable the educator to make the best use of the material presented. It is to be hoped that as nutrition finds its rightful place in health education, teachers generally will have good training in it.

The difficulty of making general statements in nutrition with a minimum of technical terms is recognized. In this compilation we have assumed that students will learn to call the common nutrients by name. They are briefly defined or described in Appendix E. Because of the widespread use of these terms it is important that people become familiar with them.

*Much information
is yet in a
formative stage . . . .*

A further difficulty is presented by the fact that the field is new and much of the information is yet in a formative state. Practical application can scarcely await the elimination of all the uncertainties. Students should, however, be taught the importance of open-mindedness in nutrition and warned of the need of revising their information in the light of future discoveries.

We have attempted to select and formulate statements which conform to one or more of these tests:

1. Results of reliable experimental evidence, derived under carefully controlled experiments and subsequently reaffirmed by other investigators.
2. Practical working hypotheses advanced by experienced research workers in nutrition.
3. Logical conclusions from knowledge in nutrition and related fields.
4. Critical observations of populations and of species survival.

Information from animal experiments is accepted with qualifications when applied to human beings. But in an effort to bring together the useful and important information, this source cannot be disregarded.

Where results of experiments have not completely established the validity of a finding but at the same time have given a strong, positive indication, the generalizations or facts have been qualified by a term such as "there is some evidence." Such qualifications should not undermine the confidence of the educator in using the statements, but rather serve as a reminder of the need of open-mindedness and the maintenance of the research point of view.

This compilation of generalizations and facts is believed to be unique in several respects.

1. Facts have been brought together from widely scattered reports of nutrition research found in textbooks, bulletins, journal articles, and theses.
2. Facts have been stated with a minimum of technical terms so that they may be readily adapted when they are used by teachers, writ-

ers, dietitians, or others who are concerned with education below the professional level.

3. Facts have been organized to show how nutrition can influence the attainment of important goals, and thus the learning of them will be easy to motivate.
4. Facts have been organized under three broad generalizations that show (*a*) the influence of nutrition upon personal development; (*b*) how to attain good nutrition; and (*c*) how to evaluate the nutritional state of an individual.

Each generalization is followed by statements which support or clarify it. Because a given fact may be necessary for understanding several generalizations, some statements are repeated several times. Thus each generalization and its supporting facts form a complete unit.

The statements are not to be memorized by students, but to be used by the educator as a basis for learning experiences (see Chapter 7). They are planned to lead the student to an understanding of sound nutrition, to awaken him to the significance of nutrition as a force in his life, and to provide a base on which his knowledge can grow. The effectiveness of their application challenges the ingenuity of the educator whether he is a teacher, a public health worker, or a columnist.

1. **Nutrition can affect how you look by its influence on the different parts of your body and the characteristics which relate to your personal appearance.**

   A. Although a majority of common skin disturbances are probably not significantly connected with dietary deficiencies, good nutrition plays a role in producing an attractive skin.
   1. The skin of a poorly nourished person is likely to be dull and lifeless.
   2. When food has contained too little protein, minerals, and vitamins, the red blood cells do not have a normal amount of their red coloring matter, and the skin of the individual may be pale in color.
   3. That the skin is affected, directly or indirectly, by state of nutrition, is shown by the fact that skin disorders appear early and conspicuously in many dietary deficiency syndromes and in some cases of hypervitaminosis.
   4. Overeating, which leads to obesity, may precipitate or aggravate skin eruptions.
   5. For some people common foods, such as milk, eggs, strawberries, or wheat bread, may cause a skin rash known as allergy, which may be detected and treated by a physician.

6. Although the acne of adolescence may be unrelated to nutrition, a good diet, together with cleanliness, may help to combat this disorder.

7. Like all other body tissues, the skin is subject to many influences; good nutrition cannot ensure a beautiful complexion, but without good nutrition one is less likely to have it.

B. The teeth are complex parts of the body, subject to the combined influences of diet, nutrition, and heredity from the time of their formation through the period of maturity.

1. An important measure in controlling tooth decay is to provide the building materials — protein, calcium, and phosphorus — plus vitamins A, C, and D, from the prenatal period until the last permanent teeth are fully developed. The proneness of a tooth to decay depends on its physical form, its cell structure, and its chemical composition — each of which may be profoundly influenced by nutrition.

2. Whatever the cause of poor nutrition — whether poor diet, infection, or disease — nutritional deficiency during the formation of the teeth is a threat to their perfect development and future protection against decay.

3. Strong genetic influences toward caries susceptibility or caries resistance have been demonstrated in rats and probably are present in human beings.

4. The environment of the tooth is an important factor in determining whether it will remain free of decay after it has been formed; the action of bacteria on substances taken into the mouth helps to determine this environment.

5. Since acids formed by bacterial action on carbohydrate foods lodged around the teeth may start decay by dissolving enamel, it is well to cleanse the teeth thoroughly after eating.

6. High carbohydrate foods which tend to stick to the teeth, such as hard caramel candy, are likely to produce tooth decay especially in people who are susceptible to dental caries; the more frequently these are eaten between meals, the greater the tendency toward caries.

7. One part per million of fluorides in drinking water, when used by children whose teeth are in the formative stage, apparently helps to protect the teeth against dental caries.

Foods which stick to the teeth, such as hard caramels . . . .

8. A little more than 1.5 parts per million of fluorides in drinking water, when used by children whose teeth are in the formative stage, may produce defects in the enamel known as "mottled enamel."

9. One may be born with a tendency toward poor teeth but this tendency probably can be checked by good nutrition or further aggravated by poor nutrition.

10. Keeping the teeth clean is essential, but it will not replace the need for good food in the protection of the teeth from decay.

11. Fractures in tooth enamel which may occur when one bites hard objects, or when one injures a tooth in a fall or blow, produce places where food particles and bacteria may lodge and start decay.

12. Good nutrition from one generation to the next offers the hope that people of the United States may eventually increase their resistance to tooth decay.

13. For reasons not understood, some nationalities as well as some families have developed marked susceptibility or marked resistance to tooth decay.

C. The muscles, nerves, and mucous membranes of the eyes, and also the processes by which images are received, are sensitive to the nutrition of the individual.

1. The eyes of the well-nourished, healthy person, with good habits of living, may be expected to be bright and clear.

2. After very long and very severe shortages of vitamin A, the covering of the eyeball and the mucous membrane around the eye may become dry and hard, and sometimes even blindness may result.

3. The ability to see in a dim light or to adapt quickly to marked change in the brightness of light depends in part on a good supply of vitamin A.
4. Itching, burning, and a grating sensation of the eyes when exposed to fairly bright light may be caused by poor nutrition with relation to riboflavin, probably coupled with other nutritional deficiencies.
5. If there is severe lack of riboflavin, the blood vessels of the covering of the eyeball become enlarged or may burst, and the eye may be clouded by thickened tissue or be bloodshot.
6. Because of the sensitivity of the eye to general body conditions, poor nutrition may affect adversely the efficiency of this organ; in fact, vision and the condition of the eyes are often sensitive indicators of the general state of nutrition.

D. Hair and nails are body tissues which reflect the state of nutrition.
1. The universal relationship of excellent nutrition and care of animals to the fine quality of their coats offers convincing evidence of the benefits which people may derive from good dietary practices.
2. When the food supply of proteins, minerals, and vitamins is poor, the hair may become dull, dry, and harsh, and difficult to manage.
3. Though animal experiments have shown relationships between dietary deficiency of specific nutrients and loss of hair and even loss of color in the fur, there is no convincing evidence to support claims of such relationships for human beings.
4. Change in color of hair, black to red, is a frequent observation in the dietary deficiency disease, kwashiorkor.
5. Good protein food, reinforced with minerals and vitamins efficiently used by the body, help to form firm, well-

shaped fingernails which can be groomed to attractiveness, though dietary measures cannot be regarded as insurance against stringy nails.

E. Body size is a result of many factors such as diet, secretions
of glands, inheritance, disease, and activity.

1. Increase in body weight in proportion to height is probably the best over-all index of nutrition during growth,
since body weight represents the composite of all parts
of the body — bones, organs, blood, muscles, and other
tissues.

2. Food deprivation is reflected in change of body weight
much earlier than in retardation of linear growth.

3. The growth spurts during adolescence (about 10 to 12
years for girls and about 12 to 14 years for boys) are
natural and should be supported by a well-balanced,
adequate diet.

4. If the food energy intake exceeds the amount of energy
used by the body mainly for exercise, maintenance, and
growth there will be storage of the surplus and gain in
body weight, due to the accumulation of body fat; conversely, if the food energy intake is less than the body
needs there will be loss of weight.

5. Individuals of the same age, sex, and occupation may
differ widely in their food energy needs for exercise and
maintenance; hence individual differences must be taken
into consideration in the use of general figures on food
energy or calorie allowances.

6. Surplus food fat, protein, and carbohydrate are trans-
formed into body fat, which is then deposited about the
organs, between the muscles, or in a layer of fatty tissue
under the skin.

7. Fat deposits serve as a reserve supply of body fuel to be
drawn upon in case of temporary shortage of, or increased
need for, fuel.

... the hair may become
dry and harsh and
difficult to manage.

8. Fat deposits serve to support and protect the organs and to prevent loss of heat from the body surface.

9. Fat deposits under the skin help to soften the angles produced by the bones, and in proper amounts contribute to the attractiveness of the person.

10. The human body adjusts itself to an inadequate amount of food by a decrease in body weight and perhaps in activity and, ultimately, by changes in the chemical processes of the cells.

11. Children who are considerably below the average weight for their height and age may tire more easily and have less endurance than others, although these conditions are sometimes masked by drives which lead to excessive activity; underweight is a health hazard, especially in childhood.

12. That characteristics of body build are inherited is evident in the similarity of bone structure that is often seen among members of a family.

13. The fact that family members often have similar eating habits may account for the tendency toward fatness or thinness sometimes observed in families.

14. Rest influences body weight through its effect on conservation of energy.

15. A safe program for reduction of relatively large amounts of body weight requires the supervision of a physician.

16. The goal toward which one should strive when reducing body weight is a small, steady loss per week with the

Fat deposits in proper amounts may contribute to the attractiveness of the person.

maintenance of a good state of mental and physical efficiency throughout the reducing period.

17. Because of readjustments of the body to a reducing diet, weight loss may not be immediately apparent; it is therefore important to allow sufficient time before becoming discouraged with the results of a reducing program.

18. Excess weight is often accompanied by development of heart and circulatory diseases and diabetes in middle age; it is generally considered a hazard to safety, health, and physical fitness.

19. Because of the great difficulty of reducing and staying reduced, it is wise never to allow the accumulation of excess weight.

20. Emotional disturbances such as sorrow, nervousness, irritability, anxiety, or lack of acceptance socially may increase or decrease the desire for food and also alter the habits of living, thus these disturbances may be reflected in body weight.

F. Posture is in a large measure dependent on the tone of the muscles and the proper development of the bones, both of which are greatly influenced by nutrition.

1. A well-built and substantial framework together with good muscles provide the basis for a well-shaped body and good carriage.

2. When children, including adolescents, receive too small a supply of protein, calcium, phosphorus, and vitamins C and D, there is danger that the growth of bones will be stunted or that the bones will be improperly shaped.

3. Diets poor in calcium, phosphorus, and vitamin D are liable to cause narrow chests, small pelvic bones, knock-knees, and bowlegs.

4. Malformed bones resulting from poor food supply during childhood remain malformed throughout life.

5. Malformation of the pelvis in childhood may cause difficult delivery for the mother at the time of childbirth and thus the nutrition of one generation affects the welfare of the next.

6. When clothing, smoke, fog, window glass, or geographic location prevent direct rays of the sun from reaching the skin, vitamin D should be supplied to growing children and pregnant and lactating women through supplements such as cod-liver oil and vitamin D concentrates, or through vitamin D enriched milk. Since vitamin D supplements are very potent, and because excess can be harmful, they should be given in doses exactly as directed.

7. Because protein is used for building bone, blood, and body tissues such as muscles, organs, skin, and hair, the protein needs are highest in periods of rapid growth.
8. If children continue to increase in height when they have poor diets, they are likely to develop poor posture and malformations of the body.
9. With well-formed bones, firm muscles, and normal pads of fat and connective tissue, the organs are held in their proper place and the disfiguring effect on posture of a protruding abdomen may be avoided.

G. Nutrition can help to produce the glow of good health which greatly enhances personal appearance.
   1. The glow of good health is often more important to the beauty of an individual than contours of the face or body.
   2. An alert, happy expression and relaxed, erect posture contribute to the sparkling good looks of a healthy, well-nourished person.
   3. Poor nutrition makes people look dull, lifeless, lacking in individuality, and prematurely old.

2. Nutrition can affect your personality, vigor, and ambition.

A. Some personality traits associated with state of nutrition of the individual are cheerfulness and cooperativeness, self-confidence and poise, interest in others, and emotional stability.
   1. Since good nutrition helps the body function properly, it also helps the individual to feel capable of meeting problems, and thus reduces tensions and frustrations.

. . . helps one feel capable of meeting problems and frustrations.

   2. Hungry human beings think of little else than food or subjects closely related to it.

   3. People suffering from chronic dietary deficiencies become morose and unhappy and lose their sense of humor.

   4. When an individual is extremely hungry, he is likely to be irritable, restless, and lacking in self confidence and judgment; prolonged hunger often makes the individual lose his sense of right and wrong, consideration for others, ability to get along with people, and ambition.

   5. Good health helps people to enjoy and take part in activities with their friends; interest in being socially acceptable has been observed to decrease under conditions of poor nutrition.

   6. Thiamine has been called the "morale vitamin," because a body deficiency of this vitamin may cause personality characteristics such as fearfulness, apprehension, timidity, depression, irritability, quarrelsomeness, lack of cooperation, and loss of initiative; this probably is not a specific effect of lack of thiamine but more or less a general characteristic of malnutrition regardless of the cause.

   7. When families fall into the habit of disorganized meals and carelessness in eating, friction and unhappiness often result; at least one good family meal a day will do much to preserve the unity of the family and promote the personality development of its members.

   8. Good nutrition is an important measure in helping to prevent antisocial behavior among teen-agers.

B. Vim and vigor are an outgrowth of the good health which emanates from good nutrition, freedom from disease, and proper habits of living.

   1. There is a distinction between the hyperactivity of a nervous individual and the purposeful action of the normal, healthy person.

   2. Apathy is a general characteristic of poorly nourished people.

   3. There is no reason to believe that any benefits will be derived from excesses of nutrients after the body needs and stores of nutrients have been fully provided.

   4. Vitamins will not contribute to the vim and vigor of an individual unless all of the other nutrients, such as protein, fat, and minerals, are supplied in adequate amounts.

   5. Animal studies have indicated that raising the level of nutrition from "fairly good" to "excellent" increases adult vitality, length of life, and vigor of offspring.

Skipping breakfast results in a decrease in work . . . .

3. Nutrition can affect how you work by its influence on your physical and mental efficiency.

A. Since physical efficiency requires good muscle and nerve co-ordination, it must be affected by the state of nutrition.

1. Skipping breakfast has been shown to result in a decrease in maximum work rate and maximum work output in the late morning hours.

2. Good nutrition contributes to the development of firm muscles and steady nerves; it is basic to athletic prowess.

3. Boys and girls engaging in strenuous exercise need more of the energy-rich foods such as fats, cereals, and breads than do less active people of the same age.

4. Beverages containing caffeine and alcohol may cover up fatigue and give a temporary feeling of well-being; in addition, alcohol has a deleterious effect on coordination.

5. Good nutrition alone will not produce a winning athletic team, but undernutrition and malnutrition, including obesity, impair performance.

6. Members of a winning team need an adequate diet every day, not on days of the game alone.

7. To fulfill its function, a training table encourages its members to maintain weight at the desired level and to eat, every day, a variety of foods which constitute a good diet — meat, milk, eggs, cheese, fruits, vegetables, and enriched or whole-grain cereals and breads.

8. Prior to the training season it is desirable to assess the nutritional status of an athlete to determine specific needs for weight gain or loss so that diet may be planned accordingly.

9. Permission to eat and enjoy foods to which they are accustomed aids in building morale in athletes.

10. Participants in some sports may need as much as 100 per cent more food energy than sedentary persons, depending on the sport and the degree of participation.

11. By checking weight frequently, it is possible to tell if an athlete is getting enough to eat in relation to his energy expenditure.

12. The usual requirement of dietary protein for growth suffices for the young athlete since activity does not affect the amount of this substance needed.

13. With intense exercise, carbohydrate may become a limiting factor in sustaining individuals in prolonged events; in such instances there may be a valid reason for ingestion of some form of carbohydrate that is readily metabolized by the body.

14. It appears that no less than three meals a day represent a desirable pattern of eating for athletes, but where sports are protracted and exhausting, up to five lighter meals a day may be preferable.

B. Good nutrition creates conditions favorable to the maximum mental achievement of which the individual is capable.

1. Good physical growth provides an individual with the physiological bases for mental, emotional, and social development.

2. For individuals with poor nutrition, there is reason to believe that the mental alertness and general progress in studies can be improved by better nutrition.

3. Prolonged hunger and poor nutrition undermine the interest of the individual in mental pursuits such as reading and writing unless highly motivated as by religious zeal or patriotic fervor.

Beverages containing alcohol may impair coordination although they cover up fatigue and give a temporary feeling of well-being.

*Forgetfulness is sometimes
a characteristic of
poorly nourished people.*

4. Forgetfulness and irresponsibility have been observed as characteristics of poorly nourished people.
5. Deterioration of the mind and nervous system characterizes many deficiency states.
6. No specific foods or nutrients can be expected to increase the intellectual capacity.
7. Mental work, unless accompanied by considerable body tenseness, does not increase the energy needs of the body.
8. Drastic malnutrition of a woman during pregnancy can lead to mental inferiority in the infant, for example, lack of iodine may contribute to cretinism.

4. **Nutrition can affect how you grow and develop through its interplay with hereditary influences, environmental conditions, and other factors related to the chemistry of the body.**

A. Hereditary factors may set a limit, but within that limit good nutrition can help the individual to attain his optimum growth and development.
   1. Body size and build are influenced by heredity, but inherited tendencies can be upgraded by good nutrition; good nutrition through several generations has been observed to improve the stock.
   2. Racial and family tendencies in body size may be altered through nutrition; a continued state of poor nutrition is not inherited.
   3. That characteristics of body build are inherited is evident in the similarity of bone structure that is often seen among members of a family.
   4. The fact that family members often have similar eating habits may account for the tendency toward fatness or thinness sometimes observed in several family members.
   5. One may be born with a tendency toward poor teeth, but the tendency sometimes can be checked by good nutrition or further aggravated by poor nutrition.

B. Environmental factors exert a strong influence on health, but nutrition can help in the adjustment to many of the stresses produced by environment.

1. An extremely cold environment or insufficient protection from cold increases the body's need for food energy.

2. The layer of fat deposited under the skin, which helps to protect the body against heat loss when exposed to severe cold, reflects the adequacy of the caloric intake.

3. Under usual conditions of clothing and temperature, heat produced by chemical changes in the food eaten is sufficient to maintain normal body temperature.

4. Inadequate housing or insufficient clothing in severe weather or climates may increase the need for energy to maintain body temperature, and either extra food or stores of body fat will have to be used for this purpose.

5. Underweight, semi-starved, and thin people, who do not have a good layer of fat under the skin, may have difficulty in maintaining body temperature and may need additional amounts of food to keep warm; if it is not provided, body tissue will be burned for this purpose.

6. Cold is an environmental factor which further aggravates the effects of poor nutrition in thin and ill-clothed people, especially children and the aged.

7. An extremely warm environment is likely to decrease the body's need for food energy because of lessened physical activity.

. . . insufficient protection from cold may increase the body's need for food energy.

8. Good nutrition may help to fortify workers in industry against such hazards as exposure to moderate amounts of various chemicals and radiation.

9. Individuals who work at night or are deprived of exposure to sunshine may need to take a supplement containing vitamin D or to use vitamin D enriched milk.

10. When soil and water are known to be deficient in certain minerals, the ill effects may be offset by an automatic source of the substance, as iodides in salt.

11. Excesses of some substances in soil or water, as selenium and fluorides, may bring about nutritional problems.

12. Good nutrition with respect to calcium may help to suppress the deposition in the bones of radioactive Strontium-90.

5. Good nutrition requires that the nutrients, or chemical substances, needed by the body for its functions be provided in ample amounts.

A. The nutrient needs of individuals vary with age, sex, activity, climate, and state of nutrition, and are subject to individual differences due to inherited and acquired conditions and special physiological stress, as pregnancy, lactation, or onset of puberty.

1. The present knowledge concerning the amounts of various nutrients which should be allowed for the maintenance of good nutrition in healthy persons in the United States has been summarized in the Recommended Dietary tary Allowances of the National Research Council;[1] these figures include margins of safety and are selected to cover the expected individual variations (failure of an individual to attain them does not necessarily mean that he is poorly nourished).

2. During the growth period the need for nutrients, such as calcium and protein, is high because the proportion of these nutrients in the body increases during that time.

3. In a specific age group, growing boys usually need more food than growing girls due to their greater activity, muscle mass, and usually larger size.

4. If a child has experienced an extended period of poor nutrition, a liberal amount of nutrients will be necessary over a long period of time to bring the body to good condition.

5. The nutritional requirements during pregnancy, and especially during the latter part, and lactation are generally high and are more likely to be met if good food

---

[1] Recommended Dietary Allowances, Sixth Revised Edition, 1964. A report of the Food and Nutrition Board, National Academy of Sciences, National Research Council, Washington, D.C., Publ. 1146.

habits have been established in the teen ages or in the period before pregnancy.

6. Because of the cumulative demands that may be made on the body stores during repeated pregnancies and because of the difficulty in making quick changes in food habits, a woman should strive to maintain a continuously good diet during the period of reproduction.

7. Requirements for some nutrients are greater for children than for adults, hence children cannot meet their needs simply by eating a fraction of the diets of adults.

8. A well-planned family meal may be adjusted to meet the varying needs of the different family members.

9. Meals which contain as a basis liberal amounts of protein-rich foods and vitamin-rich fruits and vegetables can be adjusted to meet the needs of each family member by varying the amounts of dairy products, other vegetables and fruits, cereals, fats, and sweet foods.

B. Energy from food is used to do muscular work, to produce body heat, to support growth of the body or the production of new tissue, and to maintain the functioning of the vital organs.

1. Calories represent the energy available in food and the energy needs of the body, hence they are a useful guide in determining the amount of food needed by the individual.

2. Physical activity is the outstanding factor causing variability in calorie needs of healthy people of similar size.

Physical activity
causes variability
in calorie needs . . . .

3. The calorie allowances of the Recommended Dietary Al-
    lowances are based on a mean environmental temperature
    of 20° C. (68° F.); when there is exposure to extreme cold
    or heat, calorie allowances may need adjustment.
4. In order to help prevent increased weight in adulthood,
    a step-wise reduction per decade in the Recommended
    Daily Calorie Allowance beginning at age 25 years is sug-
    gested (see footnote p. 297).
5. In adapting allowances for differences in size, weight may
    be used as a basis if the person is not over- or under-
    weight.
6. Weight and weight change are indicators of the relation-
    ship of food energy intake to body needs.
7. Food energy value of the diet depends on fats, carbohy-
    drates, and proteins, since their end products release
    energy as they are broken down in the body cells.
8. Since fats as foodstuffs provide two and one-fourth times
    as many calories as the same weight of carbohydrates or
    proteins, the caloric value of foods increases as the amount
    of fat in the foods increases.
9. The caloric value of foods becomes less as the water and
    fiber content increase, if other components are constant.
10. With low-caloric diets as those of small children, sick
    people, elderly people, or people who are reducing, the
    the foods chosen must be highly nutritious, or essential
    nutrients will not be supplied.

C. Protein contains nitrogen in the form of amino acids which
    are used in growth, functions, and maintenance of the body.
    1. The total protein need of normal adults is influenced pri-
        marily by body size, not by activity.
    2. Because protein is used for building tissues such as muscle
        and bone, and for formation of the constituents of blood,
        protein needs are high in periods of rapid growth, which
        includes production of new tissue.
    3. Per pound of body weight, growing children and adoles-
        cents need from two to three times as much protein as
        do normal adults.
    4. During the second half of pregnancy and all of the lac-
        tation period, women need an estimated increase of 35
        to 65 per cent in protein in the diet.
    5. Liberal amounts of protein in the diet are needed to aid
        in recovery from wounds, burns, and wasting illnesses.
    6. Because there is limited provision for storage of protein
        in the human body, a liberal amount of this substance
        needs to be eaten daily.

7. Lack of protein in the diet will lead to wasting of body tissues, even though plenty of carbohydrate and fat are available for fuel.

8. Proteins in foods are broken down to amino acids in the digestive tract; good nutrition with respect to protein depends on the amino acids available for absorption, not on a particular food source of protein.

9. Some of the amino acids can be produced from others in the body in amounts adequate to meet the body needs; some cannot, and those which cannot be so produced are called "essential"—i.e., they must be provided by the diet.

10. Proteins which contain all of these essential amino acids in adequate amounts are called "complete proteins."

11. Good mixtures of amino acids may be obtained from a variety of foods from vegetable sources, but foods from animal sources are richer in protein and more liberally supplied with the essential amino acids.

12. Because of the superior amino acid content of proteins from animal sources, a diet carries a high safety factor when perhaps half of the protein is from animal sources.

D. Many mineral substances are present in the body and serve important purposes; these minerals include compounds of calcium, phosphorus, chlorine, sulfur, sodium, potassium, magnesium, iron, copper, iodine, fluorine, manganese, zinc, and cobalt.

1. These substances cooperate with protein and the vitamins in such important body functions as building bone and teeth, forming the red blood cells for carrying oxygen to the tissues, producing enzyme systems, and in making gland secretions which control many body activities.

2. When children and adolescents receive too small a supply of calcium and phosphorus, together with shortages in proteins and vitamins, especially C and D, there is danger that the growth of bones will be stunted or that the bones will be improperly shaped.

3. According to present standards, calcium is one of the substances most frequently deficient in the diets of the people in the United States.

4. If growing children and young people are to utilize calcium effectively, it is important that they receive vitamin D in amounts up to 400 International Units per day plus a liberal supply of phosphorus.

5. The amount of calcium needed by the body varies with individuals, depending upon the supply which the body has previously received, upon individual differences in utilization, and upon other constituents of the diet.

6. A child whose diet has been poor in calcium for a long time needs more calcium and substances related to its use in the body than does a child whose diet has been adequate in calcium.

7. Hemoglobin, the iron-containing coloring material in red blood cells, has the ability to carry oxygen from the air to the body tissues where it combines with food nutrients and yields energy.

8. The iron requirement is higher for rapidly growing boys and girls than for adults because red blood cells are required for the increasing volume of blood that is a part of the growth process.

9. Because the normal life of red blood cells is about 100 days, numerous substances including protein, iron, copper, and the vitamins of the B complex are needed continually to rebuild them.

10. A remarkable example of the body's ability to conserve its resources is that a portion of the iron resulting from the normal destruction of red blood cells is stored in the body and utilized in the manufacture of new red blood cells.

11. When there are short-time dietary deficiencies of iron, the body needs will be met so far as possible by supplies which are stored in the liver, spleen, and bone marrow.

12. Anemia may be caused by such conditions as poor diet, profuse menstrual losses, loss of blood through injury and illness, or excessive destruction of red blood cells as from infection.

13. Adolescent girls frequently have diets with too little iron.

14. The thyroid gland attempts to adjust to an insufficient supply of iodides by increasing in size; this condition results in one of various kinds of goiter, namely, simple goiter.

15. Adolescent girls and pregnant women are more subject to simple goiter than are other people.

16. Extensive evidence indicates that during tooth development a controlled intake of fluorides, such as is provided by drinking water containing about 1 part per million, results in substantial protection against dental caries.

E. Vitamins are chemical substances, distinct from the main components of food (fat, protein, carbohydrate, and water) but necessary for the life process.

1. Vitamins aid the body tissues in making use of their building and maintenance materials, hence serious deficiency of vitamins will result in widespread disorders.

2. Vitamins are concerned in the chemical processes involved in growth and thus are needed in liberal amounts by children and youth and by women during reproduction.
3. The amounts of specific vitamins needed vary with body size, food energy value of the diet, state of nutrition of the individual, and conditions that make for excessive losses or destruction as infection or chemotherapy.
4. With the proper selection of natural foods it is unnecessary for the healthy adult to take vitamin supplements.
5. There is no evidence that amounts of vitamins beyond the maximum needed for body functions and stores will result in added vigor and health.
6. Although some vitamins may be stored, many cannot, and therefore should be supplied in the diet every day; excesses are useless, and, if taken over a long period, may endanger health.
7. Statements of dosages of fat-soluble vitamins A and D should be carefully heeded because excesses of these vitamins are not readily removed from the body and may become toxic.
8. Since vitamins are present in foods in very small amounts, they may be lost in processing and preparing for eating unless methods appropriate for their retention are used.
9. Many vitamins dissolve in water and can be destroyed when exposed to light and oxygen, or when heated, especially in the presence of an alkali such as baking soda; these facts should be considered in order to conserve vitamins during food preparation.

6. Good nutrition is promoted by selecting foods which provide the nutrients in amounts needed by the body.

A. Food is one of the most important factors influencing health and well-being of the individual; it is a factor which the invidual can control during most of his life.
   1. The nutritional state of the individual depends largely on the selection of food and the ability of the body to utilize the nutrients contained in the food eaten.
   2. Education and training in the wise selection of food for health are important, since humans are not known to have inherent impulses or drives to select the food they need.
   3. When people refuse to eat many foods, or for some reason cannot have a variety of foods, they are likely to fail to obtain some of the needed nutrients.
   4. Many combinations of foods or patterns of eating may result in a good diet; food guides are helpful in food selection but should not be regarded as inflexible standards against which to assess the adequacy of the diet.

5. A good type of diet for healthy people in the United States consists of meat, milk and other dairy products, fish, poultry, eggs, dark-green, leafy and deep-yellow vegetables, citrus fruits or other vitamin C-rich fruits and vegetables, whole-grain or enriched cereals and breads, and enough fats, sweets, and other fruits and vegetables to meet — but not exceed — the energy needs of the body.

6. There is much evidence that the people of the United States could improve their diets considerably if they replaced some of the calorie-rich, nutrient-poor foods in their diets with milk, dark-green leafy and deep-yellow vegetables and foods rich in vitamin C such as citrus fruits, some melons, and tomatoes and cabbage, when used in liberal amounts.

B. Milk and some products derived from it provide the main source of calcium in the diets of the people of this country, and in addition are an excellent source of protein and riboflavin.

1. The diets of children and growing youth, which include one quart of milk a day, are likely to be adequate in calcium, protein, and riboflavin.

2. One quart of vitamin D milk usually contains enough vitamin D to enable children of all ages and pregnant and lactating women to meet the recommended Dietary Allowance[2] of vitamin D.

3. Two dips, or about one cup, of ice cream provide as much calcium as one-half cup of whole milk.

4. A scant one-fourth cup of nonfat dry milk solids is equivalent to one cup of skim milk.

5. One cup of fresh, whole milk is approximately equivalent in nutrients to one-half cup of undiluted evaporated milk or a one-inch cube of cheddar cheese.

6. Milk is valuable whether used in a beverage or in prepared foods such as creamed or scalloped vegetables and cream soups.

[2] *Ibid.*

7. Such desserts as ice cream, custard, bread pudding, corn-starch pudding, and custard, pumpkin, and cream pie contribute one-third to one-half cup of milk per serving to the diet, while cake and cookies contribute little or none unless highly enriched with milk solids.
8. Unless a conscious effort is made to use cheese and foods which have been prepared with milk, it is difficult to obtain the recommended amount of milk without using some as a beverage.
9. When skim milk is substituted for whole milk in order to reduce the calorie intake, it should be liberally supplemented with foods of high vitamin A value, as dark-green leafy and deep-yellow vegetables, eggs, and liver.
10. Because of the high nutritive value of milk, it is one of the most important foods to include in a reducing diet or most other diets in which the total intake of food is small.
11. Like any other food, milk is not fattening unless taken in excess of the energy needs.
12. For habitual use, plain pasteurized milk is preferable to flavored milk.

C. Whole-grain or enriched breads and cereals are carbohydrate-rich foods which are economical sources of food energy, protein, iron, and vitamins of the B complex — riboflavin, niacin, and thiamine.

1. Cereal foods afford one of the cheapest sources of food energy.
2. Cereals and breads can usually be eaten in liberal amounts without digestive difficulty.
3. Because amino acids are unequally distributed among cereal foods, it is desirable to use a variety of cereals along with some foods from animal sources, as meat, milk, and eggs.
4. When a single cereal food comprises the bulk of the diet, as it does with some nationalities and some economic groups, the nutritive value of the cereal largely determines the adequacy of the diet.
5. Dietary deficiency diseases, as beriberi and pellagra, are most prevalent where people are dependent on a single highly refined cereal.
6. Diets which contain large amounts of cereal foods are liable to be inadequate unless they are supplemented with foods rich in calcium, vitamin A, and vitamin C, and with foods containing animal protein.
7. The nutritive value of a cereal food depends largely on the extent to which it has been milled, subjected to high temperatures, and enriched.

D. Meat, poultry, fish, eggs, and legumes are excellent sources of protein, iron, niacin, riboflavin, and thiamine.
    1. Two to three servings of foods of this group are usually found in the adequate diet.
    2. For adults, a daily diet which includes one pint of milk, one serving of meat, and one egg or a serving of legumes is likely to ensure an adequate supply of protein.
    3. When it is necessary to make a substitution for meat as a source of protein, various combinations of milk, cheese, eggs, dried beans and peas, and peanuts may be used.
    4. Meat substitute dishes should contain liberal amounts of protein-rich foods as milk, eggs, legumes, or cheeses; starchy dishes with a sprinkling of cheese, meat, or eggs are not to be regarded as meat substitutes.
    5. Although meats differ somewhat in their nutritive value, beef, pork, lamb, poultry, and fish are generally interchangeable in the diet.
    6. Although the best proportion is not known, it seems desirable and practical in the United States for some of the protein in one's diet to come from animal sources.
    7. Edible organ meats such as heart, kidney, and liver are valued for their protein, mineral, and vitamin contribution to the diet.
    8. Eggs are a good source of protein, iron, vitamin A and some of the B vitamins; their frequent use as such or in prepared foods contributes to a good diet.

E. Vegetables and fruits add variety and nutritive value to the diet.
    1. The daily use of at least three to five servings of fruits and vegetables comprises a good dietary guide.
    2. The deep-yellow vegetables and fruits usually contain an abundance of yellow pigments, called carotenoids, which are partly converted into vitamin A in the human body; there are other yellow pigments which do not give rise to vitamin A, and some yellow foods, as oranges and rutabagas, are not exceptional sources of this vitamin.
    3. In some foods, as the dark-green leafy vegetables, tomatoes, and prunes, other pigments conceal the yellow pigment, and these foods are valued as a potential source of vitamin A; dark-green leafy vegetables are therefore classed with the deep-yellow in daily food guides.
    4. Citrus fruits, strawberries, cantaloupe, broccoli, sweet peppers, and turnip greens contain large amounts of vitamin C; tomatoes and cabbage are less rich in vitamin C but are practical sources because of economy and availability.

5. The importance of citrus and tomato juices as dietary sources of vitamin C has led the Council of Food and Nutrition to develop the following minimal criteria for the vitamin C content per 100 ml. (Approx. one-half cup) of these foods: orange juice, 40 mg. for single-strength juice at the time of packing; grapefruit juice, 30 mg.; orange-grapefruit juice blend, 35 mg.; tomato juice, 17.5 mg.[3]

6. When potatoes are used frequently, they supply a substantial amount of vitamin C, though the amount actually obtained will vary with the method of preparation.

7. Other vegetables and fruits supplement the food energy, minerals, and vitamins furnished by dark-green leafy and deep-yellow vegetables, the vitamin C-rich fruits, and potatoes.

8. All fruits and vegetables except legumes furnish negligible amounts of protein; most are also poor in calcium.

F. Fat foods may be eaten as needed to complete the requirement for food energy, to provide specific nutrients, and to make one feel satisfied by the food eaten.

1. In the digestive tract, fats are broken down mostly to smaller fragments, glycerol and fatty acids; fatty acids differ in chemical nature and some serve special purposes in the body.

2. Fatty acids differ conspicuously in the length of the carbon chain which comprises them and the completeness with which the remaining combining power of the carbon atoms is used to hold hydrogen atoms; when the carbon atoms are fully linked with hydrogen atoms, the fatty acid is described as saturated; when hydrogen atoms are missing, the fatty acid is unsaturated, or polyunsaturated, depending on the number of carbon atoms incompletely hydrogenated.

3. The character of a fat is largely determined by the chain length and degree of saturation of the fatty acids that comprise it; the process of hydrogenation is used commercially to convert a soft or liquid fat to a varying degree of firmness.

4. High blood plasma concentration of cholesterol, a fatty substance, has been associated with the deposits of this substance in the walls of blood vessels with subsequent impairment of their elasticity, and possible, though as yet not proved, relationship to human atherosclerosis.

[3] Importance of Vitamin C in the Diet: Food Standards. Report of the Council on Foods and Nutrition. *Jour. Amer. Med. Assn.*, 160:1470 (April 28, 1956).

5. Cholesterol is an important substance formed within the body as well as consumed as such in foods; its concentration in blood plasma is determined by chemical processes in the body plus a variety of factors, including diet.

6. Some of the dietary factors that appear to lead to the elevation of plasma cholesterol are: food energy, or calories, in excess of energy needs; high intakes of fat foods, especially if rich in certain saturated fatty acids and cholesterol; high intakes of proteins especially from animal sources; high intakes of rapidly absorbed sugars.[4]

7. High blood plasma concentrations of cholesterol can be lowered by a variety of dietary factors: relatively high dietary intakes of polyunsaturated fatty acids (notably linoleic); high intakes of nicotinic acid; use of starches instead of sugars; diets of strict vegetarian-type; and stepped-up energy metabolism whether induced by exercise or by chemical stimulation.[5]

8. Present evidence of health problems arising from intake of fat is sufficient to warrant a recommendation that fat be eaten in moderation and that a variety of fats be chosen for daily consumption.

9. The fat content of the diet can be controlled roughly by paying attention to the amounts eaten of visible fat of meat, the use of table fat, nuts, and rich sauces, gravy, salad dressing, and rich desserts.

10. Vitamin A — which is carried by fats in butter, cream, and egg yolks, and in very small amounts in meat fats — is lacking in unfortified, refined fats of vegetable origin.

11. When oleomargarine is fortified with vitamin A, its vitamin A value is equal to the average concentration in butter over the seasons.

12. In a low-cost diet, when the expenditure for table fat is disproportionately high, the nutritive value of the diet suffers.

13. Fish-liver oils or concentrates of vitamin D are used to supply this vitamin, since most common foods in their natural state contain it in negligible amounts.

14. Fish-liver oils contain vitamin A and iodine, in addition to vitamin D, whereas many other vitamin D preparations contain vitamin D only.

15. Fat-rich diets are usually high in calories, and the continued use of such diets by relatively inactive people leads to obesity.

---

[4] C. M. Coons, "Fats and Other Fatty Acids." *Food*, USDA Yearbook of Agriculture, 1959, pp. 74–87.
[5] *Ibid.*

16. Fat foods are as completely digested as are carbohydrate- and protein-rich foods.

17. Because fat foods are somewhat more slowly digested than others, they provide a "staying" quality to the diet.

G. Sweets provide a concentrated source of food energy and are useful in adding calories to diets containing enough of the nutrients, in making other foods palatable, and in adding interest and satisfaction to meals.

1. Sucrose, or common table sugar, contributes only calories to the diet and when taken between meals in the form of candy or concentrated sweets, may diminish the appetite for the following meal.

2. Most candy and soft drinks furnish only food energy, while milk, fruit, and fruit juices furnish food energy plus nutrients needed for many body processes.

3. Very active adolescent boys and girls may need the extra food energy furnished by desserts such as pudding, cake, and pie.

4. For children who have an abnormal craving for sweets, special effort should be made to see that they have liberal amounts of milk, meat, fruits, and vegetables.

5. With the correction of faulty diets, by increased use of milk, meat, fruits, and vegetables as needed, children have been observed to lose their abnormal craving for sweets.

6. Good dental hygiene is especially important for children after eating concentrated or sticky sweet foods, since acid substances formed by bacteria on the food residues adhering to the teeth may cause decay.

7. Because sugar can be quicky digested and absorbed, its food energy is quickly released to the body, but foods containing protein and fat provide food energy over a longer span of time.

H. Some substances when eaten or ingested create nutritional problems.

1. Alcoholic beverages yield calories but few nutrients to the body, and if taken in large amounts may increase the needs for several nutrients; for a combination of reasons people addicted to alcohol are often poorly nourished.

2. Mineral oil dissolves the carotene of green and yellow vegetables and fruits, and if used along with these foods may interfere with the absorption of this substance and reduce its value as a source of vitamin A to the body.

3. Some foods, as spinach, contain oxalic acid which interferes with the use of calcium by the body; these foods,

however, often contain several nutrients in large amounts and so should not be excluded from the diet.

4. Since raw egg white contains a substance which interferes with the use of one of the B vitamins by the body, it is best not to use raw egg white frequently.

7. Good nutrition is promoted by handling and using foods so that they will furnish their maximum of the nutrients.

A. Nutrients such as vitamin C, which are soluble in water and changed by exposure to air, are easily lost or destroyed in food preparation.
   1. The liquid in which vegetables are cooked contains valuable minerals and vitamins, and, if not served with the foods, may be conserved by use in soups, sauces, and gravies.
   2. Fruits and vegetables such as apples and potatoes lose much of their vitamin C content when sieved or mashed, as the increased contact with the oxygen of the air decreases their vitamin C content.
   3. Appearance, quality, and nutritive value of vegetables and fruits are conserved by quick cooking in small quantities of water.
   4. If fruits and vegetables are kept at room temperature after slicing or chopping, they may rapidly lose vitamins through exposure to oxygen in air and to light.
   5. Keeping vegetables hot after they are cooked, or reheating cooked vegetables, cause loss of some color, flavor, and vitamins.

B. In cooking foods, the addition of an alkali, such as baking soda, increases the losses of some of the vitamins, especially vitamin C and thiamine.
   1. Addition of soda may preserve color of green vegetables but may cause some loss of vitamin C, thiamine, and, to a lesser degree, riboflavin.
   2. Small excesses of baking soda in quick breads, as biscuits and cornbread, may abolish the benefits of enrichment.

C. Exposure of foods to light has a harmful effect on some nutrients.
   1. Riboflavin, which is liberally supplied by milk, is destroyed when milk is exposed sufficiently to direct sunlight.
   2. Storage in a dark place or opaque containers helps to retain the nutritive value of foods.

Sometimes a villain!

D. Since people eat foods that taste good to them, it is important that foods be prepared so as to be palatable.
   1. When meat is cooked at a low, or moderately low, temperature there is less loss of the juices.
   2. The cooking methods of meat will vary with the kind of meat; dry heat may be used for tender cuts, as steaks or roasts, and moist heat for the less tender cuts.
   3. Tough cuts of meat can be tenderized by long cooking with moist heat at, or just below, boiling temperature; this produces chemical changes in the connective tissue.
   4. When cheese is cooked at high temperature, it becomes tough and stringy; when heated gently, it softens to a creamy consistency and retains its original flavor.
   5. Eggs will be most tender if cooked at relatively low temperatures; sizzling hot fat and boiling water result in poorly cooked eggs.
   6. Overheating fat in frying causes it to decompose and produce irritating substances.
   7. Although the general rule for cooking vegetables is to cook in a covered pan in the smallest amount of water possible and for the shortest time possible, there are exceptions: green vegetables will become dull and brown if cooked in a covered pan, and most strongly flavored vegetables, except cabbage, will be less palatable if not cooked in a fair amount of water.

E. Foods must be made safe for human consumption even though the nutritive value may be slightly impaired.
   1. Pasteurization makes fresh milk safe for human consumption but does not improve its nutritive value or remove the necessity for sanitary practices in later handling.
   2. Milk sold from an open can or container can seldom be considered safe and therefore cannot be considered economical at any price.
   3. After frozen foods are defrosted, they require the same precautions in handling as do fresh foods.
   4. Frozen prepared foods, as creamed chicken, are not sterilized in processing, and hence should not be thawed and allowed to stand but should be cooked from the frozen state.
   5. Mixtures containing milk and eggs are an excellent medium for growth of bacteria and therefore should be cooked immediately or refrigerated.
   6. Because of the danger of ingesting trichinae, small organisms which are sometimes imbedded in the muscle fibers of pork, it is necessary to cook this meat thoroughly, although some of the thiamine may be destroyed.

7. The acidity of foods helps to protect against losses of vitamin C in commercial canning; citrus juice and tomatoes remain an excellent source of vitamin C after canning.

F. Since the nutrients in foods are not usually distributed equally in all parts of the food, discarding portions of food may reduce its nutritive value.
   1. Large amounts of the minerals and vitamins in vegetables often lie directly under the skin, so that vegetables cooked in the skin usually retain more food value than those cooked by other methods.
   2. Through refining grain, the nutritive value of flour and meal is diminished.
   3. By discarding the outer green leaves of a head of lettuce, this food loses much of its value as a source of vitamin A and iron.
   4. Since the juice of acid fruits represents only a portion of the whole fruit, it is probably unwise to replace whole fruit entirely by juices.
   5. Fat from meat which is left as plate waste reduces the calorie value of meat.
   6. Amino acids and fat may be lost if drippings from meat are discarded.

8. Good nutrition may be furthered for low-income families through wise and economical food budgeting and buying.

A. Enough money from the family budget should be allotted to food to ensure an adequate supply of the nutrients needed by all of the family members.
   1. A good plan for budgeting the money to be spent for food will vary with the circumstances of the family, but care should be taken to allow enough money for milk, meat or other protein-rich foods, and the vitamin-rich fruits and vegetables.
   2. Poor nutrition is likely to become prevalent in periods of rising food costs or loss of income unless people see the wisdom of allocating money for food even at the sacrifice of some immediate comforts and items that may reflect the family's standards of living to the public.
   3. Through home food production food costs may be substantially reduced.
   4. Nutrition education makes it possible for many people with low incomes to have diets nutritionally adequate.

B. Wise, economical food buying involves consideration of unit cost, amount of waste, nutrients supplied by the food, and

Home food production substantially reduces food cost.

time, energy, and further expense in preparing the food to serve.

1. Protein-rich foods are often expensive; after the need for them is supplied, economy may be gained by using carbohydrate- and fat-rich foods to meet the energy needs.

2. If a cut of meat contains much bone, connective tissue, or gristle, it may be expensive even though the price per pound is low.

3. Fruits with thick skins or bruised spots, and vegetables with a large proportion of coarse outer leaves or shriveled skins may not be economical purchases because so much of them cannot be used for food.

4. A careful study of the unit cost of fresh, dried, canned, and frozen fruits and vegetables may be necessary to determine the most economical form in which to purchase the food.

5. Milk is an economical source of a number of nutrients; cream is expensive to buy in relation to the nutrients it furnishes.

6. Substitution of dried or evaporated milk for fresh milk is often economical, and is highly desirable if the sanitation of fresh milk is not safeguarded.

7. Good, low-cost diets may be obtained through the liberal use of cereal foods and legumes, supplemented with inexpensive forms of milk and cheap vitamin-rich vegetables such as cabbage, carrots, or tomatoes (home grown or canned).

9. **Good nutrition demands that one be able to discriminate between fact and fallacy in the vast amount of advertising, food misinformation, and popular beliefs about the use of foods.**

A. Sound information about the nutritive value of foods and the nutritional needs of the body provides the best basis for making intelligent choices of foods in the midst of the mass

*No food serves
a special purpose
— such as fish serving
as a brain food.*

of information and misinformation confronting the consumer.

1. There is no reason to believe that any combination of sanitary foods is harmful or poisonous, or that certain foods when used together have some unusual reaction on the body.

2. Foods lose their identity in the digestive tract where the nutrients, regardless of their individual sources, are made available to the entire body; no food serves a special purpose, as for example, fish serving as a brain food.

3. Excesses of vitamins above those needed for the use and stores of the body will not be likely to yield special benefits in the form of extra vim or vigor.

4. Vitamin pills will be beneficial only to the person who has a real deficiency, and many pills contain a number of vitamins which the person does not need in amounts greater than he receives in his usual diet.

5. Special diets, advertised to meet specific conditions, often are seriously deficient in some nutrients and would be harmful if used over a period of time.

6. Claims regarding great nutritional benefits derived from using special types of cooking equipment are often misleading; furthermore, claims regarding "disastrous toxic effects" are unfounded.

7. Acid fruits and vegetables do not produce an acid condition of the blood or of the body.

8. No foods or diets now known can produce any spectacular benefits for arthritis, rheumatism, or cancer.

9. Money spent for "health foods" and "health aids" will usually be better spent for nutritious foods which contribute toward a good diet.

10. Although the individual should always be receptive to new ideas regarding the use of food, food fads and sensational claims should be viewed critically in the light of the best current knowledge in nutrition.

10. Good nutrition is promoted by maintaining the body in a condition favorable for utilizing the nutrients.

A. Since infection may increase the need for certain nutrients, it may be a factor in bringing about a state of poor nutrition on an apparently good diet.

1. Well-nourished children are less likely than poorly nourished children to contract many infections.
2. Growth of children whose diets apparently have been good may be retarded by infection.
3. Nutritional deficiency, whether caused by poor diet, infection, or disease, during the formation of teeth, may result in their improper development and predispose them to decay.
4. Nutrient needs may be increased by illness at the same time that food intake and use are decreased; if the condition is chronic, malnutrition may become a complicating factor.
5. Protein-rich foods furnish materials from which the body can build substances in the blood which help to guard against infection by disease organisms.
6. Large amounts of protein in the diet aid recovery from wounds, burns, broken bones, and wasting illnesses.

B. Emotional stability and relaxation aid in maintaining good nutrition.
1. Emotional disturbances such as worry, sorrow, anger, and anxiety, often increase or decrease the desire for food and thus affect body weight and health.
2. People sometimes try to compensate for lack of social acceptance by overeating and consequently they become overweight.
3. Hyperactivity associated with nervous tension often results in chronic underweight.
4. Adequate rest helps maintain body weight through its effect on conservation of energy.
5. After extreme exercise and tension, a period of rest is needed before a meal is eaten.

C. The nutritional requirements of the undernourished person may be greater than those of a normal person of the same size.

Emotional disturbances often decrease the desire for food . . . .

1. A continued state of malnutrition may reduce the ability of the body to utilize nutrients.
2. The muscles of the digestive tract and the functioning of the digestive organs are impaired by poor nutrition.
3. In certain kinds of nutritional deficiencies the appetite is markedly decreased.

11. Good nutrition is promoted by wise distribution of foods among meals and snacks.

A. The organization of the food of the day into meals and snacks is one of the most important steps in attaining good nutrition.

1. An organized plan of eating makes for convenience and control of food intake, but the physiological benefits of regularity are yet to be shown, as is the optimum frequency of eating.
2. Animal experimentation indicates that frequency of eating may be a factor influencing the utilization of nutrients, but insufficient evidence is available to recommend alterations in current practices of human beings.
3. Breakfasts containing generous amounts of protein of good quality are more likely than others to maintain a feeling of satiety, alertness, and well-being throughout the morning and perhaps even into the afternoon.
4. Skipping breakfast has been shown to result in a decrease in maximum work rate and in maximum work output in the late morning hours.
5. A substantial proportion of some nutrients (especially protein furnished by animal foods) distributed through the meals of the day may be important to the efficient utilization of the nutrients.
6. If one meal is missed during the day, careful planning will be required to furnish the nutrients needed by the body in the other two meals.
7. Excessive hunger, brought about by missing meals, may lead to discomfort and indigestion because of overloading the stomach when meals are eaten.
8. If enough time is allowed for meals, they are more likely to be enjoyed and less likely to be reduced in amount or missed altogether.
9. Informality and freedom from physical discomfort or embarrassment increase pleasure at mealtime.

B. Snacks comprise an appreciable portion of the day's food for many people, and should be highly nutritious.

1. If snacks provide nutrients not liberally supplied in the

three meals of the day, they can help in maintaining a good diet.

2. Food eaten in snacks must be considered in planning or evaluating the day's diet.

3. Snacks tend to be rich in carbohydrate and poor in most nutrients, hence they add little but calories to the diet.

4. If fruit and fruit juices, raw vegetable strips, simple sandwiches, and milk are available as snacks, children may be less tempted to eat rich foods that may spoil their appetite for the next meal.

5. Well-chosen snacks not only give a sense of well-being but they supplement the day's meals so that total food intake fully meets the individual's requirements.

6. Suitable mid-morning and mid-afternoon snacks have been observed to increase the efficiency of many industrial workers.

7. Eating sweet foods not long before meals diminishes the desire to eat at meals.

12. Good nutrition is promoted by supplementing and processing foods as needed.

A. Under normal conditions individuals can obtain the needed nutrients, except vitamin D, through natural foods.

1. Vitamin and mineral supplements are valuable adjuncts for use by physicians in the treatment of many conditions.

2. Fish-liver oils or concentrates of vitamin D are prescribed for children and others known to need this substance since foods in their natural state do not contain vitamin D except in very limited amounts.

3. When clothing, smoke, fog, window glass, or geographic location prevent direct rays of the sun from reaching the skin, vitamin D needs to be supplied to growing children and pregnant and lactating women through supplements like cod-liver oil and vitamin D concentrates, or through vitamin D milk.

4. Natural foods probably have some important, as yet unknown, factors which vitamin preparations may not contain unless they are concentrates of some naturally occurring substances such as liver, yeast, and cod-liver oil.

5. If large amounts of certain minerals or vitamins are taken, they may increase the need for others and so create deficiencies where none existed in the beginning.

6. Some vitamin preparations such as concentrates of vitamins A and D taken in excess of the prescribed dosage may be toxic to the body, and may endanger health.

7. If milk cannot be taken, calcium compounds are often

prescribed by a physician as a supplement to the food intake.

8. If one has been ill or undernourished, vitamin preparations may be needed for a time to furnish the amounts required to hasten recovery.

B. Enrichment and fortification of some foods are good measures when foods have been impoverished in processing and when diets of people are known to be generally lacking in the substances added.

1. Enriched flour is white flour to which three B vitamins — thiamine, riboflavin, and niacin — and iron have been added in amounts approximately equal to those lost in milling.

2. Enriched flours, bread, and cereals improve diets without changing food habits since almost everyone eats these foods in some form every day.

3. Enriched bread is white bread, which contains specified amounts of iron, and the B vitamins — thiamine, riboflavin, and niacin.

4. Enriched flour and bread are especially effective in improving diets of low-income families, since these families usually eat large quantities of such foods.

5. One quart of vitamin D milk usually contains the Recommended Daily Dietary Allowance of vitamin D for children of all ages and for pregnant and lactating women.

6. If iodized salt is used on the table and in food preparation, it will supply enough iodine to prevent simple goiter.

7. When oleomargarine is fortified with vitamin A, its vitamin A value is equal to the average concentration, over the seasons, in butter.

8. Since citrus fruit juices and tomato juice are important sources of vitamin C, standards have been set for the

*Restoring nutrients
lost in processing . . . .*

vitamin C content of these juices; these standards are to be attained by care in selecting and processing the food used rather than by adding synthetic ascorbic acid.

C. Chemicals in food processing serve many useful purposes: as nutrient supplements, anti-spoilants, flavoring agents, moisture-content controls, or means of improving functional properties.
1. Although chemicals have varying degrees of toxicity, many are extremely useful to man when used in recommended amounts and under proper safeguards.
2. Consumer protection against improper use of chemicals in food is afforded by self-regulation of chemical and food industries, and by several branches of government.
3. A 1958 amendment to the food and drug law provides that industry must prove the safety of chemicals used in the processing of foods before the chemicals can be sold for use in foods; this amendment provides for advances in food technology and also safeguards human health.

13. Nutrition plays a special role in the prevention and treatment of some physiological conditions which are prevalent.

A. Weight control requires proper adjustment of food intake to body needs; the many factors involved in this adjustment ment may be difficult to recognize and control.
1. For good nutrition, reducing diets should include the amounts of meats, eggs, vegetables, fruits, and milk needed to supply the nutrient requirements, and should limit fats, breads, and cereals so as not to exceed the food energy requirement for the reducing regime.
2. To avoid feeling hungry when reducing, one may eat liberal amounts of low-calorie fruits and vegetables.
3. If prolonged reducing diets do not furnish protein, minerals, and vitamins needed for growth or maintenance, the body may be permanently damaged.
4. Meals recommended for people who need to gain weight include liberal use of fats, whole-grain or enriched cere-

Underweight people may need more than three meals per day.

als, sugars, meats, eggs, cheese and whole milk, and plenty
of fruits and vegetables.

5. To obtain the amount of food needed to gain in weight,
it may be necessary for underweight people to eat more
than three meals per day and to take much rest.

B. Good intestinal hygiene depends on the maintenance of good
muscle tone, a favorable type of bacteria in the intestinal
tract (intestinal flora), regular time for elimination, and perhaps ability to relax from mental and emotional strain.

1. A generally good diet, possibly with regularity in eating,
contributes to the conditions which promote good elimination.

2. Fruit and vegetables in the daily diet provide nutrients
needed for a healthy digestive tract and, in addition,
roughage which helps in moving the intestinal contents
along the digestive tract.

3. Although it is important that waste materials be regularly removed, the body is protected against toxic products formed by bacterial action on these residues, and
overanxiety about elimination serves only to aggravate
the situation.

C. Although the exact relationship of nutrition to dental caries
is not known, good nutrition may help to prevent dental
caries, to check progressive decay, and to increase the resistance to dental decay in the next generation (see 1B).

D. Liberal amounts of protein, iron, and the B vitamins help
to maintain the hemoglobin and red blood cells of the blood
at a high level, and thus to prevent anemia; it is especially
important that adolescent girls take dietary precautions to
ensure good stores of iron and high levels of hemoglobin in
the blood (see 5C and D).

E. The severe lack of certain nutrients, usually accompanied by
other stresses and strains, will result in dietary deficiency diseases which, though rare in this country, are prevalent
throughout the world; some of these conditions with the nutrient involved are: *scurvy*, vitamin C; *beriberi*, thiamine;
pellagra, niacin; *xerophthalmia*, vitamin A; *endemic goiter*,
iodine; *kwashiorkor*, the nutritional disorder affecting many
children in the world today, complete protein.

14. **Good nutrition is promoted by establishing good food habits and good
attitudes toward food.**

A. Good food habits require that individuals be able to change
the kinds and amounts of food they eat as they change in age,

physical and physiological needs, and social or economic level.

1. As individuals grow older and become more sedentary, they must curtail their calorie intake if they are to avoid overweight and its accompanying ills.
2. If appetite and hunger have become geared to large amounts of food during periods of considerable activity, eating must be controlled when activity has been reduced.
3. With increased incomes and access to good food, a person must be able to control his use of rich foods and social eating and drinking if he is to avoid overweight and possible obesity.
4. When people have learned to like a variety of foods, they can more easily adjust their diet to meet changing conditions.
5. Some knowledge of the nutritive value of foods is important in making dietary adjustments for changing conditions of life.
6. Pregnant and lactating women may need to accustom themselves to larger intakes of some foods than they usually have.

B. The development of food habits is the result of many influences.
1. When parents have some knowledge of nutrition and of the psychology of feeding children, they may do much to help their children form good food habits.
2. The example set by parents and teachers is a powerful force in forming good food habits.
3. The school lunch is one of the best means of showing children the essentials of a good meal.

The development of food habits is the result of many influences.

4. Food habits often reflect the family's customs, nationality, and religious background.
5. Modern advertising influences the food habits of people directly through information about the product and indirectly through associations built up around it.
6. Food habits of people are sometimes revolutionized through new products on the market.
7. Social customs of groups to which one belongs are powerful factors in determining food habits.

C. The development of good attitudes toward food and eating is basic to the development of good food habits.
1. If people can be helped to understand the relationship of nutrition to the values they hold high, they are more likely to become interested in developing good food habits.
2. The primary purpose of eating is to provide for the body needs.
3. Although meals should be pleasant and eating enjoyable, pleasure should never become the primary purpose
, of eating.

D. Continuously good food habits are conducive to the best state of nutrition.
1. The past state of nutrition is an important factor in determining how the present diet is used by the body.
2. If a child is not fully developed or physically fit because of a long period of faulty eating, a liberal amount of nutrients will be necessary over a long period of time to rebuild a good body condition.
3. The best way to ensure good nutrition during pregnancy and lactation, when the needs are extremely high, is to establish good food habits in childhood and to follow them consistently through the teen ages.

15. **Good nutrition requires assuming responsibility for one's own nutrition.**

A. Many of the factors which influence nutrition are under the direct control of the individual.
1. From the variety of foods available the individual has the power to choose or reject, and thus to determine the nutritive value of his diet.
2. Regular hours for eating meals, plenty of outdoor exercise, freedom from hurry and worry, and a nutritious diet help to maintain a good appetite and improve a poor one.
3. By choosing snacks which provide the nutrients not liberally supplied by the meals of the day, many people can improve their nutrition.

*Assuming responsibility
for one's own nutrition! ! !*

4. Eating a wholesome nutritious breakfast helps people to avoid feeling nervous, tired, and irritable before noon.
5. Adequate rest helps maintain body weight by conserving energy.
6. Missing meals has been shown to be highly related to adequacy of the diet.
7. By taking enough exercise, the danger of excessive intake of calories will be reduced.

B. For some factors which influence nutrition, the responsibility of the individual must be exercised through participation in community, state, and national affairs.
1. A sanitary food supply requires proper legislation and public opinion.
2. Fluoridation of a city water supply requires group action and necessitates an informed public.
3. The enforced enrichment of processed foods, when in the interest of public health, requires action at the state and national level.
4. Maintaining a sound economy with a high rate of employment and reasonable prices on basic food commodities is important to good nutrition.
5. Conditions which facilitate distribution from point of production to point of need are essential for obtaining adequate nutrition.
6. Protection of the public against exploitation is a responsibility of the citizens.

16. A continuous check of nutritional state may be made by keeping a record of body measurements, notably height and weight.

A. Height-weight-age tables are helpful in evaluating the growth of children, but comparisons should also be made of the child's present state with his past over a period of time.

1. Ideal reference tables are based on measurements of children known to be in good nutritional state and to represent the population under study in environment and nationality background.

2. Children who deviate markedly from standards of body size may nevertheless be healthy if they are growing and have the other characteristics of good health.

3. Children who are considerably below the average weight for their height and age may tire more easily and have less endurance than others, although these conditions may be hidden by drives which lead the child to excessive activity.

4. One of the easily detectable signs of undernutrition is the failure of children to make expected weight gains; this can be observed by periodic, perhaps monthly or triannual, measurements of height and weight.

5. Growth is manifested in increase in chemical content of the tissues as well as body size, hence, body measurements are not the only means of assessing nutrition.

6. During the adolescent period normal boys and girls of the same age may differ by four or five years in their physical development.

7. Girls begin the adolescent spurt in growth about 2 years earlier than boys, but the growth spurt of boys, when it comes, is greater than that of girls.

8. Rapid growth in weight during adolescence begins in girls at approximately 10 to 12 years, and in boys at approximately 12 to 14 years; this rapid growth usually is greatest in the year before the establishment of the sexual function.

9. Increases in rate of weight gain of adolescent girls should not be ignored; increases that represent a normal spurt in growth should be adequately supported nutritionally.

. . . normal boys and girls of the same age may differ in their physical development.

B. Height-weight tables are useful guides for adults in maintaining proper weight.
   1. The significance of deviations from standards should be interpreted in the light of the health and the body build of the individual.
   2. Generally, deviations from standards of more than plus or minus 10 per cent suggest the need of readjustment of factors related to the energy balance.

C. In order to compare body measurements taken at different times, the procedures used should always be the same.
   1. Heavy clothing and shoes should be removed before weighing.
   2. Comparisons of weights are best if they have been taken at the same time each day.
   3. Accurate measurement of height requires that the subject assume a standard posture and that the reading be made with the eye on the level of the figure indicated by use of a right angle marker placed on subject's head.

17. Since inadequacy of the diet is one of the first steps toward poor nutrition, a continuous check of the diet is an important measure in the maintenance of good nutrition.

A. If the amounts of food eaten during the day are known, the nutrient intake may be computed from tables of food composition.
   1. These figures may be compared with standards to determine the relative adequacy of the diet.
   2. Because of variations in foods and differences in needs of people, the evaluation may be somewhat inaccurate as applied to a single individual.
   3. When records are kept over a suitable period of time or for large numbers of people, a fairly accurate assessment of the adequacy of the diets may be made for an individual or for a population.

B. When a well-kept record of the day's diet is inspected for the kinds and amounts of foods used, a rough estimate of the adequacy of the diet may be made.
   1. Some training in recognizing sizes of servings is important to the accuracy of this method.
   2. In the use of this method it is important to learn the variety of foods included in the different groups and to know which foods are interchangeable.
   3. Various check lists of food plans have been developed for rating diets according to foods used; these are helpful but should be used with caution because there are many ways by which people may obtain good diets, and food plans are not infallible.

C.   Certain blood tests may reveal whether or not the intake of substances, as vitamin C and carotenoids, has been adequate.

D.   When an individual is unduly susceptible to such conditions as infection, fatigue, constipation, depression, and hyperirritability, he should investigate his diet and the habits of living which influence the utilization of food.

E.   The final test of the quality of the diet is in the people themselves, as stated by Leitch, "The diet of the people of most beautiful physique, most abounding energy, and least ill health is, at any given stage in our study of diet, the inspiration of and check on our theories of optimum diet."[6]

18.   **Other criteria for judging the nutrition of the individual are based on the study of body composition, functioning of the various parts of the body, and outward clinical manifestations which can be judged by the physician.**

___

[6] Leitch, I., and Aitken, F. C., "Technique and interpretation of dietary surveys," Nutr. Abs. and Revs. 19, No. 3, pp. 507–25, 1950.

Chapter Seven

Methods of Teaching

DAILY ACTIVITIES become so much a part of an individual that resistance to any change in routine can be expected. This is so with food particularly. Suggest to some people that food practices should be changed and they feel that their personal rights to freedom are being violated. Others will agree that some diets should be better, but they fail to evaluate their own food plan and make changes where needed. A feeling that what one eats is one's own responsibility may be among the reasons why efforts to improve food habits of the American people have been discouraging.

This feeling, however, also can be an asset to nutrition education. If you as a teacher believe this, you will make a more personal approach to your audience than is usually made. People will change food habits when they believe that good nutritional status will help them achieve their own important goals. You will not tell people what they should do. Rather you will teach in such a way that individuals decide to improve their food practices because they recognize the advantages of changing.

The results of educational programs in nutrition have not been proportional to the efforts expended. The field of nutrition has much to offer for the improvement of mankind. There is enough knowledge now available to produce a superior race of people if we will only put it into practice. Application, however, lags far behind the progress of the science.

At this point the evaluation of methods may be as important as accumulating knowledge. We constantly need to "sharpen our tools." Writing on the subject of how to get the most out of health education tools, Stone (1) said, in effect: First, know what you want to teach. Second, whom you wish to reach. Then, "Light a fire . . . build a bridge . . . get down to cases . . . ask for action." In other words, create an interest, and bridge the gap from interest to goal. Illustrate with actual cases. Don't leave your public saying, "So what!" Ask for action in clear, certain, definite terms.

EMPHASIS ON NEGLECTED FOODS

Nutrition education in the past has been too general, according to Pett (2). He stated that it has consisted of a "shotgun" or "blunderbuss" approach; that we have dealt too much in national averages and too little with individual situations. It is wrong to suppose that everyone must drink more milk, just because the national average needs to be increased. We need a new viewpoint, a new method of attack. This new method must be an individual approach based on a definite knowledge of conditions in homes and the community, and carried into effect by individuals in the community.

Ideally the approach described by Pett is based on nutritional appraisal of the specific group involved. This step will take the guesswork out of the problem to be faced. General surveys suggest the scope of the problems with school children and the points of emphasis for the general population. But every teacher should study his or her own group in order to ascertain their particular problems.

Numerous studies have revealed that food groups most likely to be inadequately represented in children's diets are: milk and milk products, green and yellow vegetables, vitamin C-rich foods, and eggs. Since many diets would be satisfactory if these foods were adequately represented, probably the most effective teaching will aim to increase the acceptance and use of these neglected foods.

As new foods are accepted, amounts of food from other food groups should be studied in order to control the total amount eaten.

METHODS TO DETERMINE THE FOOD PRACTICES OF STUDENTS

Several methods may be used to discover and evaluate the food practices of students. The 3- to 7-day record of all foods eaten gives some information. Methods of evaluation will depend on the maturity of the student and the use to be made of the information. Some ways suggested are to:

1. Calculate the nutritive value by a simple short method.
2. Rate the diet as shown in Appendix B, pages 295–96.
3. Examine the record qualitatively for the use of certain food groups in specified units: e.g., 2 to 3 cups milk daily; one serving meat, poultry, fish; one serving green and yellow vegetables. Either the Basic 4 or Basic 7 classification of foods in groups could be used. A comparison of these classifications can be found on pages 106–8. For identification of foods in groups, see Appendix A, pages 291–94.

*Studies of customs
and food habits of any
people should be approached
with the idea of learning.*

Incomplete but valuable information may be secured by observing the selections of food by people in public eating places. School lunchroom selections of food prepared in various ways and plate waste will indicate which foods are well accepted among those served. This information can be particularly valuable if it is compared with data from check sheets that indicate the food likes and dislikes of people. Observations in eating places will give similar information, especially about between-meal snacks.

Parents, too, may provide information regarding foods eaten by their children. But Rodewald (3) found that mothers' reports of foods eaten agreed more closely with dietary records kept by their sons than by their daughters. The girls tended to report better dietaries than their mothers' reports indicated. It helps us to know from the parents what foods are served at home during the same period that the students report their dietaries. A food may be missing on a student's list because of refusal to eat it, or because it was not served to him. The first reason would call for different education than would the second one.

IMPORTANCE OF KNOWING FAMILY FOOD PRACTICES

Efforts to change food habits of people should be accompanied by certain precautions. Due respect must be given habits and customs that do not conform to our standards, if they have resulted in a healthy people. There are many gaps in our present-day knowledge of the constituents of the perfect diet. Studies of the food habits of any group of people should be approached with the idea of learning as well as reforming.

It is also important to remember that food habits are complex. Few foods are consumed as isolated units. Our diets are full of food combinations such as bread and butter; meat, potatoes and gravy; cake and ice cream; sugar and cream with coffee. The intake of any food is likely to influence the intake of other foods.

Dickins (4) has said, ". . . a given diet is an intricate, interrelated combination of foods in which an increase or decrease in the consumption of any one element not only affects the balance of the diet in terms of the contributions made by that particular food, but may also increase or decrease the consumption of related foods." Observations of the effects of a white corn meal shortage in the diets of Mississippi children illustrated her point. With the customary cornbread made of white meal, the children liked greens, buttermilk, beans, and peas.

With biscuits they preferred such foods as sirup and gravy. Interestingly enough, with yellow corn meal, they preferred the foods desired with biscuits, namely, sirup and gravy. The ultimate benefits derived from the substitution of yellow corn meal for white were therefore questionable.

Such dangers would be minimized if emphases of education were on the importance of nutritionally adequate diets rather than on conformity to standard rules for menu planning. If this emphasis were given to teaching, foreign dishes would not be treated as novelties to be featured only at Christmastime or for entertaining. Rather, people would be taught ways of using available foods in preparing such dishes for the enjoyment of family members who like foreign dishes or unusual combinations. Furthermore, national dishes that contain fruits, vegetables, eggs, and milk in abundance, as well as dishes made largely of cereal products and sugar, would be featured in exhibits, demonstrations, or articles.

Most teachers belong to the middle class and believe that they should teach their students the social and food practices which they were taught, even when most of their students come from homes where these practices are strange. Such a belief has led to frustration in many instances because teachers have found that even though students may seem interested in what is being taught, practices at home are not changed.

Results of an exploratory study in a Michigan school are worthy of consideration by teachers. When Hurt (5) studied the attitudes of some ninth-grade girls and their mothers, she found that teaching a unit, "Helping With the Family Meals," was most effective when keyed to customary practices of the families. Girls in three ninth-grade homemaking classes were from families ranked in the lower-middle or lower-class social groups and were taught by the same teacher. In one class the values and practices of middle-class families, usually found in textbooks, were emphasized. In a second class, both lower-and middle-class practices were taught. In a third group, teaching was keyed to lower-class values and practices and included only a few middle-class practices. More students in the second and third groups than in the first group seemed to like what they studied. They said that what they had learned was practical for their homes. The mothers of the students agreed with their daughters.

The results of Hurt's study are not surprising when you consider how much easier it is to understand what is being taught when the teaching agrees with home practices. Likewise, it is easier for the family members to accept the foods that are not completely unfamiliar to them. There is reason enough why many people are confused when they are introduced to unfamiliar foods, cooked in strange equipment, combined in an unfamiliar meal pattern, and served in a manner that seems formal and strange. The family, too, may not appreciate attempts of the teacher to change practices that are as personal as those related to food. This is especially true when the most obvious basis for a proposed change is social custom.

NUTRITION EDUCATION MUST HAVE MEANING FOR STUDENTS

Students can interpret new experiences only in terms of their own past experiences, either actual or vicarious. This is another reason why modification of a family's customary dietary pattern is likely to be more effective than attempts to impose a new one. Communication and understanding are easier when students know the meanings of words used by the teacher. If she believes that meaningful experiences are important, she will be alert to provide experiences that result in common understanding of words.

One basis for misunderstanding may be the different interpretations of nutritional status. Nutrition education may have little meaning to people who are unaware of the characteristics of a well-nourished individual. Words are quite inadequate for describing a boy or girl with good nutritional status. At least a picture of a well-nourished person such as Figure 7.1 must be seen if words describing her are to mean the same to both teacher and student. An impressive collection of pictures of people with either good or poor nutrition may be made from newspapers, magazines, and photographs of friends and their families.

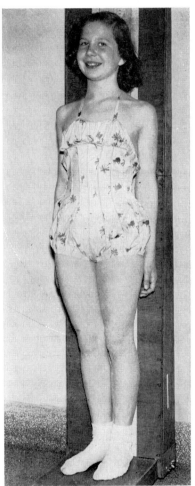

FIG. 7.1 — The marks of physical perfection include beautiful posture, soft glossy hair, radiant skin, and an abundance of energy.

Use available foods for the enjoyment of family members who like foreign dishes or unusual combinations.

YOU CAN MOTIVATE CHANGES IN PRACTICES

Food practices do not change just because people have accurate, meaningful facts. Motivation to use their knowledge in daily living is necessary. The over-all objective of nutrition education is to establish food practices that are nutritionally sound. To accomplish this objective people must desire to make any necessary modification in their meals and snacks.

Learning is likely to be effective when the relationships between the food eaten and the goals important to students are recognized and accepted by them. Most people have as goals: maintaining an attractive personal appearance, making friends, and having enough pep to participate in work or social activities. When nutrition education makes clear the relationship between these goals and the food an individual eats, people are likely to be motivated to learn how to achieve good nutritional status. In Chapter 6 you noticed that facts of nutrition were organized so that they could be used to motivate learning. The usual interests and concerns of people were used as a basis for organizing the subject matter.

Not all people can be motivated to improve nutritional status by appealing to the same interests. Because the interests of boys and men may be different from those of girls and women, you will wish to appeal to each group in different ways. For example, the knowledge that food can help to build big strong bodies, if genetic factors are favorable, may motivate a group of boys to eat enough of the important foods. But as a group, girls are not anxious to have large bodies. Unless the teacher points out that good health contributes to beauty of skin, hair, nails, and so forth, the girls in her group probably will not be interested in changing their food practices.

DESIRE FOR INDEPENDENCE AS MOTIVATION

Eating as one wishes may be a symbol of personal independence even in infancy. Certain tendencies do not change from one generation to the next. Sweeney discussed the importance of capitalizing upon the desire of individuals for independence by helping them make free choices of food in a wise way. She wrote about the importance of setting up situations in which responsible choice can replace either the slavish acceptance of a traditional diet or the equally slavish refusal to accept it in order to appear independent.

At what age should a boy or girl be expected to take responsibility for choice of food? The exact age varies somewhat with individuals but probably adults attempt to use authority long after this method is neither effective nor desirable with children. In fact, failure to teach children how to make decisions about a problem as vital as food may actually delay development of the ability to assume other responsibilities.

Some children prefer the security of doing what a so-called "authority" dictates. The wisdom of such a method of securing adequate food is questionable as preparation for living in a rapidly changing world. Blindly following rules for good nutrition may not provide adequate preparation for adjusting to advances in the science of nutrition and in food technology. The person without ability to make intelligent decisions about food may be helpless when faced with half-truths about new forms of food, sometimes presented in advertisements or in articles by unscrupulous or misinformed persons.

The goals of people change somewhat as they grow from childhood to adulthood; therefore, education that has been effective at one time may not motivate a change in behavior at a later stage of development. As the goals of individuals or groups change, so will the problems they recognize as important to solve. The teacher who can use some of these important problems as a basis for teaching is likely to be most satisfied with the results of her efforts.

When an individual desires to learn how to improve his nutrition, teaching is relatively simple. But he must also be ready for the kind of experiences planned for him.

READINESS TO LEARN

Readiness of a student to learn depends in part upon his past experiences. Words will have the same meaning for a student and his teacher only when they represent similar experiences. For example, a student may be as confused when he tries to visualize the unfamiliar vegetable, broccoli, as he is when he tries to formulate the concept of differences among food groups. The teacher who knows *when* students need experiences that will give meaning to words and *how to* provide these experiences, will increase the readiness of her students to learn about nutrition.

*... if Father ridicules the idea,
he may influence the actions
of his child.*

Although it has not been proved, it seems likely that boys and girls who live in families where they are served nutritious food daily are more ready to learn about nutrition than are children who live in families with poor food practices. When the school reinforces learning at home, children may be expected to have less conflict in accepting teaching at school. There should be no reason for a feeling of disloyalty to the family when evaluation of meals served at home indicates that they are inadequate.

However, there may be the child who is not ready emotionally to accept and use nutrition facts until he has learned that he can appreciate members of his family even though he does not always agree with them. For example, if father ridicules the idea of eating some of the green and yellow vegetables, he may influence the actions of his child. The child's acceptance of these vegetables is difficult even when their nutritive value is known to him. The teacher who helps students resolve conflicts when teachings at home do not agree with those at school, increases readiness of students to learn.

The period when students are ready for any aspect of nutrition teaching depends, also, upon their mental development. During late childhood pupils begin to grasp the notion that changes may be brought about by conditions that cannot be observed directly. But scientific interest can be more fully developed during early adolescence. If students are expected to do a kind of thinking for which they are not ready, thoughts of others may be memorized without understanding. When this happens, it may be difficult to motivate learning at a later, more appropriate time, because the students may think that the material has been learned.

THE USE OF DISCUSSION IN TEACHING

Group discussion is one way to involve individuals in their own learning. A good discussion gives people opportunities to express themselves, to try out new ideas and to think aloud — all of which are ways to participate in the learning process. Unless members of your group participate actively in the opportunities provided for them to learn, they are likely to learn little or none of what you expected them to know.

When your students talk among themselves and to you without fear of criticism, they are likely to share feelings and experiences that may reveal their attitudes, problems, beliefs, and expectations.

It is only when learners describe experiences honestly and without fear that you will know how their experiences differ from yours and be able to plan opportunities for learning that are suitable for your group. Meaning depends upon past experiences — their experiences, not yours.

Discussion in which all or nearly all of the group participates is likely to make clear the complexity of nutrition problems. Students may suggest factors and forces influencing solutions to problems that have never occurred to you. As you guide students through the problem-solving process, they may suggest either alternatives or arguments for or against various alternatives that were not part of your teaching plan. When all ideas are pooled, suggestions are likely to go beyond what any of you had thought. If students participate in identifying nutrition problems and the difficulties to be met in solving them, your teaching is likely to be more effective.

Discussion requires planning on your part because you need to anticipate the suggestions of students and be prepared to use their contributions wherever possible. As you use the suggestion of a student, expand it yourself, or guide his thinking so he can enlarge upon it, or clarify his idea, you increase his confidence in himself and encourage his continued participation. Thus members of your group gradually overcome fear of failure.

Planning also involves anticipation of terms that might not be understood by members of the group. Some of these terms can be defined in words but some need more concrete means of explanation. This is true of many nutrition terms that are in common use. Ideas may be vague or actually inaccurate. When this is true the time needed to develop a new concept is well spent. Unless terms have similar meanings for all members of a group, discussions are likely to be unsatisfactory.

When planning for a meeting, key questions written out will help you structure the discussion enough to keep it moving toward the goal. This does not mean that you dominate the discussion — quite the contrary is true. Often poorly thought-out questions can be answered by "yes" or "no." These result in far too much talking and directing by the leader. Well-phrased questions stimulate discussion and encourage students to think for themselves.

During an actual discussion your questions may be phrased differently from those in your plan, but this is to be expected. You will be able to suggest better questions during discussion because you can adapt your original questions to the thoughts and ideas that have developed during the discussion.

Discussion can be facilitated in ways other than asking questions. For example, you can:

1. Arrange seating so members of the group face each other.
2. Give information yourself or encourage students to read and report to the group.
3. Summarize what has been learned when (*a*) an important point has been made and before going on to the next point, (*b*) the group seems confused because controversial viewpoints have been expressed, or (*c*) the discussion will be continued in another meeting of the group.
4. Restate the question being discussed when the group seems to be "off the track."
5. Arrange for a time to discuss an issue that seems important but does not relate directly to the question.

Group discussion will not be effective unless you believe that members of your group should learn to think for themselves; unless you trust them to interpret their own experiences and to solve their own problems.

PROBLEM SOLVING

Good discussion is essentially problem solving. Members of a group will participate in discussions if they believe that the problems to be considered are important enough to justify seeking solutions to them. As a leader of discussion this is your first concern — that your students are aware of nutrition problems and want to solve them. Problem solving begins with a felt need.

After a problem has been selected for discussion, the next step is to define it clearly. Often nutrition problems are not what they seem to be. For example, when a child does not eat well, parents may not know the possible causes of their child's poor eating habits and thus are not ready to attack the problem intelligently. You may use such means as films, anecdotes, or role playing to encourage students to clarify the problems so that basic causes are evident. Reading also may help students identify the difficulties that must be removed if the problem is to be solved.

When the problem has been clarified, students are ready to set goals for themselves in solving it. This will increase students' feelings of being involved in the process as well as to help you know what they are ready to learn and what goals and values are important to them.

The third step is to propose alternative solutions to the problem, making the list as complete as possible from experiences of the group. If you know alternatives that have not been proposed, you can either suggest them or encourage members of your group to find additional ideas from reading. This is a place where you might use *brainstorming*.

. . . to anticipate consequences

The next step is to anticipate consequences of each proposed solution. Often this is the point where facts are needed, because clear thinking is impossible if opinions are accepted as final when new facts are available. Part of this step is to evaluate each solution in light of the objectives.

The last step is to choose the alternative that seems most likely to meet the objectives. Only when the group plans to act, is it necessary to arrive at a group decision.

Some problems can be solved only by individuals. When this is true, the responsibility for individual decisions can be made clear. When you have helped students analyze a problem to the point of seeing clearly how to make a choice, your responsibility ends unless you find that several members of your group choose the same solution. If this happens you may encourage a decision to try the alternative selected and arrange for a group discussion of results.

Brainstorming

Brainstorming is a technique for getting many ideas before a group for consideration. This technique is unique in discussion because everyone is encouraged to suggest any idea that occurs to him as a possible solution for a problem. Quantity of ideas is important. One purpose is to release the potential of individuals for proposing new ideas.

Judgment is ruled out until the brainstorming session is over. The chairman is responsible for seeing that no contributions are evaluated, either criticized or praised. A group member may expand an idea but he does not judge it. This rule tends to change attitudes toward the ideas of others and of one's self.

THE USE OF DISCUSSION-DECISION METHODS

To break down resistance to change in food habits, Lewin (6) developed a method which lies between an individual and a mass approach. He suggested a group-decision method, which goes beyond group discussion. In group discussion a free interchange of ideas takes place; but no attempt is made to reach a decision. But a discussion-decision method leads to setting up definite goals of action either for the group as a whole or for each individual in the group.

The first experiment by Lewin and Willerman (6, 7) compared the group decision method with a request method, in attempting to increase the consumption of whole-wheat bread as compared with white bread in eight cooperative dormitories for men at the State University of Iowa. Each *request group* was asked to change its consumption of whole-wheat bread to the same amount that had been voluntarily chosen by a *decision group* with which it was paired.

Reaction to the proposal of participating in the experiment, eagerness of the students to reach their goal, and even their relative preference for whole-wheat bread depended upon the degree to which the decision was made by a majority. The *decision groups*, that set their goals at 66 per cent to 90 per cent increase in consumption of whole-wheat bread, reached their goals, whereas the *request groups* paired with them did not.

Radke and Klisurich (8), encouraged by the success of Lewin's studies, carried out two experiments designed to compare effectiveness of lecture versus discussion-decision techniques. The degree of change and the permanence of the new behavior were considered.

Their first experiment dealt with infant feeding. Half of the mothers of newborn babies in the maternity ward of a hospital received individual instruction from the dietitian, and were given a printed schedule to follow in feeding their babies at home. The other half of the mothers met with the dietitian in groups of six. In the meetings, which took as much time as the individual conferences, the dietitian played the role of both expert and leader. The problem of getting mothers to follow instructions given at the hospital was discussed, and the new mothers were asked to suggest better methods of accomplishing this. The discussion gave the mothers a chance to exchange ideas and ask questions.

The leader summarized the discussion, gave her own instructions, and then inquired about their willingness to carry out dietary instructions. The group decided to follow the instructions of the dietitian.

The dietitian made telephone calls 2 and 4 weeks after the group meetings to check the performance of the mothers. How well directions had been followed was estimated by the amount of orange juice and cod-liver oil given the babies, because these amounts had been carefully specified. In the *decision group*, 75 per cent of the mothers were giving orange juice in correct amounts at 2 weeks, and 100 per cent after 4 weeks. After *individual instruction*, 44 per cent were giving orange juice at 2 weeks, and 88 per cent at 4 weeks. In the *decision group*, 44 per cent were giving the correct amount of cod-liver oil after 2 weeks, and 88 per cent after 4 weeks. Among the mothers receiving the *individual instruction*, 18 per cent were giving cod-liver oil after 2 weeks and 53 per cent after 4 weeks. Apparently

Evident need of an educational program.

the 2- and 4-week checkups served as a stimulus for improvement in the following of directions. At both 2 and 4 weeks the decision group had done better than the group receiving individual instruction.

A second experiment conducted by Radke and Klisurich (8) involved a comparison of lecture and discussion-decision methods in increasing milk consumption of homemakers of low-income level. The results of this experiment also showed the success of the discussion-decision method.

Radke and Caso (9) applied the discussion-decision technique in a study undertaken at the request of the Student Council of the Weeks Junior High School, Newton, Massachusetts. The Council asked the Nutrition Center, a community agency supported by the City Health Department, the Community Chest, and the local Red Cross Chapter, to assist in a survey of the lunches selected by the students in the school cafeteria. The desirability of an educational program to follow the survey became evident. As a result, a study was made to test the effectiveness of lecture and discussion-decision methods for influencing the students to improve their school lunch habits.

Approximately 850 sixth-, seventh-, and eighth-grade students participated. Twelve home rooms were assigned to lecture, and twelve to discussion-decision treatment. Eight nutritionists served as group leaders, each having an equal number of lectures and discussion-decision meetings. Each group met for approximately half an hour either before or after lunch.

In the lecture groups, the nutritionist held discussion from the group to a minimum. She presented facts on nutrition and related them to the food habits of the students in the school cafeteria.

Students in the discussion-decision group were encouraged by their leader to contribute ideas. They were led to feel that they were responsible for helping themselves to overcome obstacles in the way of a good diet. Though a goal for personal action was suggested by the leader, the group in each case accepted it and gave some kind of voluntary, unsolicited group expression of commitment. The nutritionist suggested that the commitment be voted upon, with a show of hands. The decision was that each person would include foods from three basic-food groups in his lunch each day. Each person had evidence that the others were "going along" on the decision.

All the students filled out questionnaires about the lunches eaten at school; one questionnaire preceded the meeting and four were given afterward. Through the questionnaires the percentage of students who chose an adequate lunch was determined.

At each testing, the *lecture* and *discussion-decision groups* were compared with a *control group* which had had no nutrition teaching. The three groups did not differ materially on the first questionnaire in the percentage of students reporting adequate lunches. Therefore it was possible to assume the groups to be roughly equivalent. Each later test showed an increase in the number of students in both the *lecture* and *discussion-decision groups* choosing adequate lunches as compared with the *control group*. The improvement was maintained or further increased by the *discussion-decision group* on Questionnaires 4 and 5. However, the *lecture group* fell to the level of the *control group*. These results indicate that motivation for eating a balanced lunch was set up by both the *lecture* and *discussion-decision* methods. The *lecture* had only a temporary effect in improving school lunches. Students in the *discussion-decision group* made a more stable improvement.

The discussion-decision technique may be effective partly because it permits the group member to define his own goals in relation to the question discussed as well as to receive support from the knowledge that fellow group members are faced with problems closely akin to his own.

Discussion is one way to stimulate students' thinking but sometimes it is difficult to guide unless there is a situation on which to focus attention. You and your students can observe and consider a situation together when it is presented in a *film, field trip, role playing,* in a *case study,* or on *radio* or *television*. Each of these methods is discussed in detail.

USING FILMS IN TEACHING NUTRITION

Films can be valuable aids to you in teaching nutrition. They effectively provide students with a common vicarious experience. It is difficult to duplicate the lifelike situations portrayed in a film by any other method. Time and space can be telescoped so that students view either the effects of time or situations that cannot be seen in person. For example, in *Fundamentals of Diet* (10) the growth of plants and animals, that requires months in nature, is shown in a matter of seconds in the film. In another film, *For Health and Happiness* (11), many children of different body types are shown. A comparable group of children would be difficult to observe in most communities because they would not be assembled in one place and might not be dressed so that the characteristics of good nutritional status would be evident.

Movies are most often seen for entertainment, and therefore films are eagerly anticipated by students. In this receptive frame of mind, people can be interested and informed. Films used for education should be informative, but not ponderously dull, lest you spoil anticipation for future ones.

Students may not understand the point even when they are interested by the film. Only when their observation is *directed* can you be sure that students will remember the ideas for which the film was shown.

Because good films are made for more than one educational situation, and would not be as useful if oversimplified, you should guide your particular class to their own understanding of the film. Ask questions to focus attention on the aspects of the situation the students should observe, and thus you will simplify the film for them.

Furthermore, by emphasizing some aspects of a film and ignoring others, you can use the same film for different sequences of learning. The questions that you give to students before they view a film will tend to influence what they see and hear and what they discuss following the film. You may use a certain film differently if your objectives for showing the film are different.

Your Questions Are Important

Questions should reflect your knowledge of what will motivate the students. Students learn what they believe will help them to achieve their goals. Knowing this, you can use questions to point out how the abilities, attitudes, knowledge, or practices presented in the film will influence the attainment of goals important to your students. An illustration of how teachers may use nutrition films can be found in Appendix F, pages 314–19.

In 1949, a workshop group at the University of Tennessee (12) proposed a plan for formulating questions to guide observation and discussion of educational films. This plan was used when the lesson plans in Appendix F were made. It has been useful when planning discussions of different types of films with different age groups. It includes six steps in formulating questions:

1. Question No. 1 calls for information clearly presented in the film.
2. Question No. 2 calls for an examination of ideas in other situations.
3. Question No. 3 encourages drawing inferences, identifying cause and effect relationships, or expressing own ideas.
4. Question No. 4 asks for examination of these ideas as they apply to present-day life or in the light of authority.
5. Question No. 5 asks students to formulate generalizations of their own, based on data from the film, from experience, and from opinions of authorities.
6. Question No. 6 asks students to illustrate the meaning of generalizations; to apply these ideas in everyday practice.

*Field trips
create interest . . . .*

FIELD TRIPS

Much as films may serve to provide students with a common experience about food, field trips may be arranged to increase understanding and knowledge related to processing and distributing food.

You may wish to arrange a visit to a food processing plant or wholesale firm. Call the person in charge and tell him exactly what you want your students to know after they have made their tour. If you will visit the plant first, you will be better able to decide what the trip should include. Avoid unpleasant experiences for your children. Look at the trip through their eyes. For instance, young children from the city may be unfavorably impressed by a visit to a dairy farm and therefore may drink less milk for a while, simply because they do not like the barn odors. Limits in time must also be considered, so talk over with your host the particular places and procedures the students will want to see. It goes without saying that you will arrange in advance a definite time and day for the field trip.

The class should know beforehand what to look for during the trip. You and your class can discuss points of interest together and select the most important highlights of the planned tour. The host will spend more time explaining certain procedures if he knows the students are interested, as evidenced by their questions to him.

It is well to keep groups small enough so that questions and explanations can be understood en route. It is better to ask questions of the teacher or the person acting as a guide than of individual workers at the plant. To interrupt workers may cause accidents or delay in the process being carried out.

Field trips, if properly planned in advance, may create much interest and help the student gain knowledge and understanding which can be obtained in no other way. Real-life situations help to give meaning to words used in the classroom.

Good public relations may be established through contacts with men and women who are active in businesses related to food and nutrition. Invite the host to visit your classroom before or after the tour. This is often appreciated and sometimes accepted. Then you can interpret food and nutrition information and activities at school to these people in the community who might not otherwise learn about them.

Following the field trip it is profitable to have a class discussion of what has been seen and to point out principles and generalizations which are related to the experiences of the field trip.

ROLE PLAYING IN GROUP DISCUSSION

Role playing is another method of getting a situation before a group for discussion. For the actors, role playing may be a moving experience; for the spectators, a concrete situation is portrayed that can be discussed objectively.

Role playing is the spontaneous acting out of a situation by two or more members of a group. The situation portrays an experience of common concern and one that will further group discussion.

Assuming that the majority of boys and girls in a group do not consistently eat breakfast, the leader may use role playing to start discussion, instead of a film as suggested earlier. The method would not be named but could be introduced naturally by suggesting that some members act out an early morning scene in a home.

Group members can set the stage by naming the people in the cast and describing the situation. They can decide what kind of person each actor is to portray but will not tell him how to act. The situation should be described sufficiently to make the problem clear. Spontaneous reactions to the situation as it develops are necessary if roles are to be portrayed realistically.

Role playing is not presenting a skit. The players may be given a short time to decide how the scene will open but they should not plan beyond this point. Underplanning by either the group or players is better than overplanning.

When the roles develop spontaneously, real emotions tend to be expressed and attitudes revealed. When a boy assumes the role of a parent, he is more likely to understand the feelings of his father as he responds to behavior of a boy his own age.

Persons are most likely to be comfortable in roles in which they feel at home. For this reason asking for volunteers is probably the best practice. If individuals do not volunteer, group members can suggest someone for each role. When there is an unfavorable role, the leader may wish to assign it to someone who has enough status in the group to feel secure.

You will be responsible for deciding when the scene should be cut. As soon as the problem is clearly defined, you should stop the acting. There is a tendency to let the scene go on too long. When this happens, the players may have difficulty in carrying on, and the audience may become restless.

While discussing the situation portrayed, suggestions may be made for improving it. When this is done you may wish to have the scene replayed. This may be done by the same players, if they accept suggestions for making a new approach to the problem. If they cannot make changes naturally, new players may be selected to replay the original scene or one that may follow it.

If you use role playing, you will have to "think on your feet" because you will not know exactly what will happen. You cannot formulate your questions as specifically ahead of time as you can with films. But your students may respond better because the situation is real to them.

Preparation of the audience for observation is desirable and can be made when the actors are out of the room. Questions can call attention to the way the situation is handled by each player or to the way the problem is solved. These questions should help to prepare the group for the discussion to follow.

The discussion should lead either to some conclusions or recognition of need for more study of a problem. Your questions will help the group evaluate the situation. You may ask questions that will help the group state generalizations similar to those in Chapter 6. This is most likely to happen if role playing is used near the end of a lesson, when students have had enough experience to draw conclusions. The situation presented in role playing may be used to introduce a lesson, in which case you may ask questions to help students decide what additional experiences they need.

CASE PROBLEMS IN GROUP DISCUSSION

One reason why films are effective in teaching is that situations are presented so that many factors influencing the actions of people are seen. Stories or case problems can serve the same purpose in teaching and they have the advantage of being available when needed.

Because there may be emotional blocks when people try to solve their own problems related to food, case problems can be a means of learning to arrive at decisions objectively. If problems are too personal, prejudices may interfere with thinking so that individuals are either not able or not willing to consider all possibilities when seeking a solution to a problem.

Case Situations in Teaching

Case studies are brief descriptions of specific situations. Many facets of the situation are presented so that problems to be solved and factors to be considered when making decisions are not always evident until the situation has been analyzed.

The situation should be described objectively. This means that what individuals say or do is reported accurately without interpretation. This same objectivity is desirable when describing any other factors in the situation. The factors described will depend upon the purpose for which the case study is to be used. Since one objective of nutrition education is ability to plan for the use of resources to provide food for the family, the situations you use should include: specific information about goals and values of the people involved; amount and sources of income; equipment for storage, preparation, and service of food; demands upon the homemaker's time; financial obligations and money available; and educational background. If, in addition, you hope that students will be better able to extend the variety of foods eaten and enjoyed, the case situation should include: food customs, practices, and preferences; ages and physical state of family members; attitudes toward importance of food and toward change; availability of various foods; and skill in preparation and service of such foods as vegetables, eggs, and milk dishes. Describing some of these factors objectively is very difficult but necessary if discussions are to encourage thinking.

When analyzing case situations, opportunities are provided for identifying not only the factors that may be influencing food practices but also other conditions that may be influencing nutritional state. As part of the analysis you may expect students either to recall knowledge or to recognize when new information is needed before they are ready to propose all possible solutions for the problems involved or to evaluate alternative solutions. The information needed may come from many disciplines: psychology, anthropology, and economics as well as nutrition.

When the case study does not provide all of the information needed for analysis, students should be guided to discover what additional data they need in order to make sound decisions. If the required information is not available, students can recognize how their understanding of the situation is limited.

The case situation may be used throughout a unit of teaching: (a) as an introduction, (b) to focus attention in discussion, and (c) for evaluation. The way in which you wish to use the case and with whom you use it, will influence the questions that you ask to lead discussion. An illustration here might clarify this point. Suppose you were teaching a course in community nutrition to nurses preparing for public health nursing. They have studied normal nutrition and now your objective is: Comprehension of the factors influencing education planned to change food practices of families.

CASE PROBLEM

Jim and Ellie Wills are a young couple who live in a small town where Jim is a carpenter's apprentice. Ellie does not work, but Jim's income allows them to rent a small modern house and maintain a secondhand car on which three payments are still to be made. They have no savings. For food they spend about four dollars a month more than the amount of money recommended by the Extension Nutritionist for families like theirs in similar communities. They have an electric refrigerator, gas range, and utensils for plain cooking. All of their food is bought from the supermarket three blocks from their home.

They have a baby girl, Kay, eighteen months old who has been anemic since birth. At nine months she had diarrhea and was hospitalized. Doctors could find nothing organically wrong with her but recommended that Ellie reduce excessive amounts of vitamins that Kay had been taking. There has been no recurrence of the diarrhea. Kay is fat with pale skin and dull eyes.

Ellie expects her second child in September. She is thin and has been told by her doctor that she should gain weight. When Mrs. Hull, the public health nurse, told her that good nutrition was important during pregnancy Ellie replied, "I don't believe that. Kay has been ill most of her life." Mrs. Hull is not sure what she should do to help in improving the nutrition of this family. Since both Ellie and her husband are high school graduates, she thought that giving Ellie the USDA bulletin: "Food for the Family With Young Children" would help, but it hasn't. Ellie says that the suggestions in this bulletin wouldn't work for her family. Anyway she really hasn't time to study it.

DISCUSSION OF THE CASE

If you used this case to introduce a unit you would probably use it to give experiences in deciding: (*a*) what the problems are for this family, (*b*) what assets they have for solving their problems, and (*c*) what are the problems of nutrition education.

Some of the questions which you might ask are:

1. What facts about this family would justify Mrs. Hull's concern about their nutritional state?
2. How much money is suggested for a minimum food budget in this town (or city)?
3. What is the evidence that changing food practices of the Wills family won't be easy?
4. What additional information would help you understand their problems better?
5. What might be reasons for their problems?
6. What might be done to convince Ellie that the reference given to her by Mrs. Hull is worth studying? (See section on motivation, pages 166–67.)
7. How might the bulletin be made more useful to her? (See section on meaning, page 165.)
8. What are the possibilities for teaching Ellie how to feed her family better?
9. Which of these possibilities might you use when you are a public health nurse?

During discussion of question 4 you might give some additional information about food practices of the Wills family to illustrate how new facts might change plans for trying to improve food practices.

ADDITIONAL FACTS ABOUT CASE PROBLEM

Kay eats with her father and mother and eats what they eat. She has never eaten baby foods and doesn't like whole milk. When she drinks orange or tomato juice, a skin rash develops.

Ellie says that Kay cries for orange juice when it is served for breakfast so they have stopped drinking it. In season, Jim and Ellie have fresh tomatoes often but none of them like tomato juice. They like other fruits and most vegetables except green leafy ones, carrots, and cauliflower.

Continued Discussion of Case Situation

If you wanted to emphasize the importance of knowing the kind and distribution of foods during the day and how to get this information when needed, you might ask such questions as:

1. How would a record of meals and snacks eaten by Jim and Ellie help you understand their nutrition problems better?
2. How might Mrs. Hull get this information?

Additional Information

Mrs. Hull interviewed Ellie and found her willing to report what she and Kay had eaten for two days. She was not sure of sizes of servings but the foods eaten were:

Wed.	*Breakfast*	*Lunch*	*Dinner*
	Oatmeal and milk	Chicken & rice soup	Hamburgers/catsup
	Sweet roll	Ham sandwich	Fried potatoes
	Coffee for Ellie	Bread, butter	Creamed corn
	Skim milk for Kay	Applesauce	Bread, butter
			Chocolate cake
Thurs.	Oatmeal & Milk	Peanut butter	Wieners
	for Kay	sandwich	Cabbage slaw
	Toast, buttered	Creamed corn	Mashed potatoes
	Coffee for Ellie	Chocolate cake	Buttered peas
	Skim milk for Kay	Skim milk	Apple pie

(Kay and Ellie had soft drinks in the middle of the afternoon and before going to bed.)

Continued Discussion

In order to make the nutrition problems more specific you might expect students to discuss questions such as:

1. What nutrients are inadequate in these menus?
2. Should Mrs. Hull suggest that multiple vitamin tablets would help solve their problem?
3. What foods might be added (or substituted) in the menus and snacks to improve the diet?
4. Can Ellie afford to serve all of the foods you suggested?

When discussing the question of how to convince Ellie that changes should be made, you might introduce such additional information as:

Ellie and Jim were married just before graduating from high school. Ellie was proud of her appearance and was often told that she was pretty. She hopes that Kay will be pretty too. When her children are old enough she plans to get a job as a waitress because they hope that some day Jim will have his own business. Jim is on a bowling team but Ellie has no organized recreation of this kind. She is always too tired to bowl and, anyway, they can't afford the fees. When in high school Ellie and Jim liked to roller skate but they haven't done this for a long time.

To apply the principles of motivation your students might discuss such questions as:

1. What seem to be the goals of Ellie and Jim?
2. How might these be used to convince Ellie that what they eat will make a difference in the achievement of their goals?
3. What could Mrs. Hull do to teach Ellie to change food practices of her family?
4. Which of your suggestions would be most appropriate for this situation?

When analyzing this case situation students could identify the factors that might be influencing Ellie's behavior. As part of this analysis, your students would be expected to review nutrition information and to find additional information that helped them clarify problems, discover relationships between factors in the situation, select alternative solutions to problems, and anticipate probable consequences of each solution.

If data about the situation do not include the goals and values of persons involved in the decision this, too, should be recognized. Failure to recognize and consider goals may explain why some solutions to problems are not really accepted by the persons involved. Thus students have opportunities to recognize the role of goals and values in decision making; to appreciate how conflicting values can block selection of satisfactory solutions to problems; and to comprehend why individuals in the same situation may make decisions that are different but appropriate for each of them.

Selection of Case Situations

The selection of case situations appropriate for a specific group is crucial to the success of this method of teaching. The anticipated roles of students, the problems that they recognize as important, and their readiness for the learning needed to satisfactorily solve their problems are important bases for judging the suitability of a case situation. For example, you might use the case of the Wills family with a group of young mothers whose situations were similar to the

Wills' but your discussion would be very different from the one suggested for the nurses. Instead of introducing Mrs. Hull into the case, you would hope that members of your group would identify with Ellie. If this was difficult, the selection of a situation that was more like theirs would make problems seem more real to them.

Unless mothers in the group have some nutrition education on which to build, your introduction of new topics would probably be most effective if you used such experiences as pictures, films, or demonstrations. For example, if you want your students to recognize the characteristics of well and of poorly nourished children you could use pictures of the children shown in this book or you might collect pictures of your own. This knowledge would be needed to recognize that the results of good nutrition are worth the effort needed for Ellie to solve her problems. To learn whether or not their problems are like Ellie's, members of the group might be taught how to assess the nutritional status of their own children.

When discussing difficulties that Ellie is likely to encounter in changing food practices of Kay, you could show and discuss a film such as "And One To Grow On," or "Food as Children See It." After members of your group accept the fact that food practices of children can be changed, you might summarize the principles for changing food practices and then encourage any who have this problem to try these suggestions at home. If you can interest this group of mothers in trying to solve a similar problem at home, your teaching is likely to be more effective. (See Discussion-Decision, pp. 171–74.)

If a problem of your group is dislike of vegetables or milk, you might demonstrate food preparation and serving of important foods. Tasting the final products will be important if you want your students to know what a good product is like and to enjoy the foods themselves.

Use of the same case situation with nurses preparing for public health service and with mothers has illustrated different ways to discuss the case. Experiences with the mothers were discussions of concrete situations such as pictures, films, or demonstrations; with the nurses it was assumed that they were ready for discussion of abstract ideas as presented in the case.

You can use the case situation for evaluation of what has been learned. When this kind of test situation is used, you expect students to analyze the situation to discover problems and to select alternative solutions for a problem and to justify the solution chosen. This is discussed in more detail in Chapter 8.

Writing Case Situations

You may want to write some or all of the case situations used in your classes in order to have some that are appropriate for use with your group or you may believe that when cases seem more real to you, you can make them "come to life" for students. Either of these reasons may justify the time required to collect facts and write a good case situation, but in addition you will have analyzed the situation so you will be better prepared to guide the learning of students. You will be aware of problems and of difficulties in solving them as well as favorable conditions for their solutions.

Do you have adequate data about situations that can be used in nutrition education? Many of you are in positions where you have details about situations that can make people and their relationships with each other seem real. Data should include all available facts that might influence solution of the nutrition problems.

The more that you can learn about members of the group you will be teaching, the more likely you are to write case situations that will have meaning to them. What are their resources, including education? What are their present responsibilities? What do they anticipate as future roles? What are their attitudes that might influence nutrition education? What problems do they recognize? Answers to these questions can guide your selection of situations to write about because your students are most likely to be motivated to study the case if it seems related to their own situations.

The main purpose in using a case situation in teaching is to stimulate students to think for themselves. For this reason the most effective case situations are described objectively with no hint of the "right" decision. When a case situation reports a decision that has been made, thinking of students tends to be blocked unless your purpose is to require either evaluation of the decision or consideration of how a past decision affects present problems.

To be most effective the case should be about people whose identity is concealed but whose problems are real. A situation may be disguised by using past tense and changing location, names, or composition of the family. However, you may want to include facts about the case that give an idea of the atmosphere surrounding the people involved even though they are not directly related to the problem you are discussing. When all of the circumstances that you describe are plausible and contribute to an understanding of a family situation, your students are likely to enjoy learning as the case is studied.

TEACHING THROUGH RADIO AND TELEVISION

Radio and television programs may be sources of case studies that are interesting to students. Family situations are a popular type of program and may provide opportunities for you to capitalize on the current interests of the group.

When programs are given by a competent staff, the information is likely to be both reliable and up to date. For this reason you, as teachers, may find that the effort needed to locate and listen to educational broadcasts is well spent because you will gain knowledge yourselves, or you may be able to arrange for members of a group to get firsthand information that is not available elsewhere.

Undoubtedly, advertisements on radio and television influence the food practices of people. Many commercials are cleverly presented; persons responsible for them know how to appeal to emotions as well as to reason. In fact, some discourage the use of reason!

Older students and adults can be encouraged to evaluate the appeals made to them. Such evaluations require applying facts of motivation as well as recognizing the various ways in which advertisers make their appeal.

When students have opportunities to give a radio or television program, they are likely to be strongly motivated to learn what is needed to do a good job. If you have enough advance notice to allow students to plan and prepare a program, they will be motivated to learn how to organize and present needed facts, to develop needed skills, and to cooperate in a group project. Help from the drama department would be useful when such is available.

Students will probably be interested in making careful preparation when they know that they will reach a large audience and will have no opportunities to correct mistakes or to make additional explanations if ideas are not clear. Time limitations, too, encourage detailed planning.

ANALYSIS OF PROPAGANDA

Means of communication today make it possible for information about food and its uses to confront the public at every turn. Newspapers and magazines make numerous claims for food products and use glamorous colored advertisements to encourage their purchase and use. Television screens are filled with clever quips and gimmicks to draw attention to special qualities of products. Sometimes the first tune a young child learns to sing is a jingle used to advertise a food product. Radio also contributes its share of claims and information about certain items of food.

It becomes urgent that the people receive help in how to evaluate these claims made by the food industry. To do this the following criteria may prove useful to the teacher of food and nutrition.

1. Where was the claim made? Newspaper, radio, television, magazine, billboard, etc.?
2. Was it made by a "self-interested" party?
3. Was any source mentioned for the scientific information?
4. Did the statements seem sensational or extravagant?
5. Are there any experiments, or other type of reliable evidence, to support the claim?
6. Are the statements misleading or in the category of half-truth?
7. What questions do the claims or statements raise in your mind?

Information coming from experiment station bulletins, USDA pamphlets, county home demonstration agents, or from staff members

*Clever advertising
related to foods
may need
evaluating.*

of recognized colleges and universities can be accepted as sound information. Statements which conform to the policies of the Council on Food and Nutrition of the American Medical Association and the Food and Nutrition Board of the National Research Council are considered valid.

A newspaper or magazine article is only as good as the person who wrote the article. If the reputation of the author is not known, information should be checked to verify its accuracy.

Clever advertising sometimes appeals to the public when the principle or generalization involved is not sound. People, both young and old, need help in evaluating the advertising schemes related to food and nutrition.

Frequently a food industry presents an appetite-appealing piece of propaganda in magazines, radio, or television which increases the sale of their product immensely. However, the information given about the product may not be of great importance in regard to nutrient or economic value.

Another way in which food advertising can mislead the consumer is to tell only a part of the function of the food product. No false claims are made, but only a fraction of the possible facts is given.

Teachers can help students and adults evaluate advertising propaganda if they give them reliable sources of information, ways to judge the worth of seals or other evidence of approval, and develop their judgment in the applications of facts and generalizations related to food and nutrition. The development of a critical attitude toward the acceptance of any claims related to food practices is urgent.

ANIMAL FEEDING EXPERIMENTS

Often experiences with concrete things are needed to give meaning to the abstract ideas expressed in nutrition generalizations. Animal feeding experiments and preparation of food at school are two such experiences. When these are student projects, students not only learn about nutrition but also they learn to take responsibility and to work together.

Animal feeding experiments can show living evidence that foods work together to promote growth and health. A daily food guide (see Appendix A, pages 291–94) is considered a practical plan to simplify nutrition and make it feasible in application. Yet many times students do not see the importance of such a guide until they are shown what makes it work and what is behind it.

Those who are trained in nutrition know well that a good basic food guide works because of the supplementation among the essential nutrients in these basic foods. Thus the group of foods containing meat, poultry, and fish provides a good protein base for the daily diet; the milk ensures an adequate supply of calcium; the group of foods containing citrus fruits, melons, and raw green vegetables supplies a large amount of vitamin C; and the green and yellow vegetables afford large amounts of carotene which is at least partially utilized by the body as vitamin A. Properly supplemented with other vegetables and fruits, cereals, fats, and sweets, the resulting diet will likely be adequate in food energy and the needed nutrients.

For a majority of students seeing is believing. It may be possible to work with the science teacher to set up relatively simple feeding experiments with weanling-age rats to demonstrate supplementary relations between two basic foods. Feeding experiments can be arranged in a series which increases in complexity as the interests and abilities of adults and children permit.

Students like projects in which they can participate. When they plan the diets, feed and care for the animals, and keep records of their growth, the results are remembered longer. They also learn as they tell others about the experiments.

Animal feeding experiments may be projects in which several classes participate. Younger pupils may learn only basic health rules or may simply watch animals grow week by week. Older students may make wider applications from their observations. Teamwork and a cooperative spirit are developed through participation of several different classes. The entire project becomes important in the eyes of the children.

You may wish to plan a rat-feeding experiment to demonstrate the need for foods that are missing in the diets of your students.[1] Such an experiment was part of teaching in several schools in Iowa. All rats were fed a basic diet consisting of navy beans, potatoes, rolled oats, white flour, sugar, salt, butter, and lard.

When meat is added to this diet, you will see that a bread, meat, potato, and dessert diet is represented. This is the type of diet eaten most of the time by many students. The second rat was fed the same diet with milk and eggs added.

The diet of the third rat was the same as the second except that green lettuce, spinach leaf, or carrot was added. This third diet contains all of the essential food nutrients except vitamin C. Normally, this nutrient is not essential in the diets of rats because they can make vitamin C in their bodies if their diet is adequate in other respects. When explaining why this nutrient is not needed in the diet by rats, you will have an opportunity to emphasize the fact that nutritional needs of rats are similar to those of human beings in many respects.

---

[1] For directions for preparing the diets and caring for the rats see Appendix G, pages 320–22.

*Exhibit the test animals
in a local window.*

Foods used to supplement the basic diet are served separately. The meat (lean hamburger) may be fed in marble-sized balls once every other day. The milk (dried) should be fed in servings of one tablespoon every day. The egg should be hard cooked and mashed immediately while hot. One egg will make about three feedings. A rat will eat about one-third of a carrot or a 2-inch square of lettuce in two days.

If you guide students' observations, you can help them formulate generalizations such as: Nutrition can affect the way you look and act. You can call attention to the appearance and actions of the rats, and then again point out that nutrients are as important to boys and girls as to rats.

To call attention to the characteristics of each rat you might ask such questions as:

1. Which rat has gained the most?
2. Which rat has the nicest fur?
3. Which rat has the brightest eyes?
4. Which rat is best looking now?
5. Which rat is least irritable?
6. Which rat seems to be the healthiest?
7. Which kind of posture does each rat have? (A healthy rat keeps its body close to the floor when walking; a sick one may be hunched or stiff.)
8. What made one rat healthier than the others?
9. What foods should we eat every day?

You will find that this experiment is interesting to adults as well as to children. Reports of the experiment are a means of reaching parents with nutrition education. Adults may be invited to school, or a parent-teacher program can provide an opportunity to hear students tell about the experiment. The rats will illustrate results, but growth charts help to interpret them. A display of foods eaten by each rat will emphasize the importance of milk, eggs, and green and yellow vegetables.

Another way to reach parents and other adults would be to exhibit animals from an experiment, or pictures of them, in a local store window with the sign "Food Made the Difference." This method will probably not teach as much about the experiment as does the demonstration with reports, but it may reach more people.

Rat-feeding experiments have been found useful in teaching students of various ages. When the same students are taught with rat-feeding experiments in more than one grade, you will wish to vary the experiment. A plan used by Booher (13) is suggested.

Dr. Booher has devised three successive series of experiments with eighteen weanling, male albino rats grouped so that the combined weight of the six animals, composing each of three groups, was comparable. The purposes of these studies and the data for each group are shown in the following experiments:

EXPERIMENT A. To develop the generalization: *Breakfast cereals and milk are supplementary foods.*

Group 1.   Unrestricted amounts of a finely ground mixture of equal weights of 19 breakfast foods (whole grain, enriched, or restored).
Group 2.   Unrestricted amounts of homogenized vitamin D milk.
Group 3.   Unrestricted amounts of both the finely ground cereal mixture and homogenized vitamin D milk.

EXPERIMENT B. To develop the generalization: *Sugar and pure starch are inadequate supplements for milk.*

Group 1.   Unrestricted amounts of a finely ground mixture of equal weights of 20 breakfast cereals combined with milk in the proportion of 1 ounce of mixed cereals to 4 fluid ounces of fresh whole milk.
Group 2.   Unrestricted amounts of cane sugar and milk in the proportions of 1 ounce of sugar to 4 fluid ounces of whole milk.
Group 3.   Unrestricted amounts of cornstarch and powdered whole milk combined in the proportions of 1 ounce of starch to 0.5 ounce of powdered milk mixed with water.
Group 4.   The same diet as Group 3 with cornstarch replaced by the mixture of 20 breakfast cereals.

EXPERIMENT C. To develop generalizations similar to **6 C. 6,** page 139.

Following the same technical details as in Experiments A and B, diets consisting of a mixture of equal weights of 33 breakfast cereals combined with six different proportions of fresh whole milk were fed to six groups of weanling-age rats over a six-weeks period. The objective was to determine, within practical limits, the proportion of average breakfast cereal to milk representing the best nutritive combination of these two foods. The proportions of mixed breakfast cereals to milk ranged from 1 ounce of cereal per fluid ounce of milk to 1 ounce of cereal for approximately 30 fluid ounces of milk.

*It stimulates
interest to have
each rat named.*

Some deductions from an experiment such as the one conducted by Dr. Booher can be drawn by observing:

1. The relative value of a given combination of basic foods in promoting over-all growth and development as compared with any food alone.
2. The effects of replacing one of the two basic foods in the combination selected by food products which contribute only accidental traces of essential food value or none at all.
3. The degree to which nutrients in two basic foods supplement each other when the proportions in which the foods are combined and eaten are changed.

White rats are good experimental animals because they are small, clean, easily handled, and easily cared for. They respond to different foods much as do people. Compared with human beings, white rats have a short life span. Their growth rate is 30 times faster than human growth, which makes the effect of diet quickly apparent. Most children like animals, and the laboratory rat cages soon become a center of interest for children and adults. Ordinarily, rat-feeding experiments require 7 to 8 weeks to be carried to a satisfactory conclusion.

The basic food groups which are least adaptable for demonstrating supplementary relationships by use of the rat are those of citrus fruits and tomatoes and of butter and fortified margarine because the essential nutrients in them are limited to vitamin C and vitamin A. Deficiencies of vitamin A do not develop quickly because this vitamin is stored in the liver and the supply is often not depleted for many weeks. Basic foods most adaptable to showing the supplementary relations are combinations of milk and milk products with breads, flours, and cereals of whole grain, enriched, or restored types.

It is important that students understand the purpose of a rat-feeding experiment. If the initial planning for the project is one in which you and each member of your class assume a share of responsibility, there will be more enjoyment and profit for the group. You should impress on your students that rats are a part of a scientific study and should not be considered pets. If your experiment is to be effective, you will constantly point out the similarity between the needs of the animals and of the students for the foods used in the experiment.

It stimulates interest to have each rat named. The progress of each animal can then be recorded on a large wall chart on which age, sex, diet, and starting weight should be indicated.

As the experiment progresses, students will need guidance in their observations of animal weight and growth, disposition, fur, skin, tail, eyes, ears, nose, breathing, red blood, facial expression, and general appearance of well-being. Encourage students to think of other signs of good or poor nutrition and list them. All details for conducting this experiment can be found in Appendix G, pp. 320–22.

At the end of an allotted time in the experiment, change the menus of the rats. The poorly nourished rats should be fed the diet of the well-nourished animal so that students can see that food makes a difference also in rebuilding bodies. Students usually feel sympathetic toward the poorly nourished rats and will be happy to see them grow bigger and stronger.

It may be desirable to feed the healthiest rat the poor diet, so pupils can recognize the need for a continued good diet. Do not let rats become so undernourished that there is risk of their dying. Probably a class demonstration should always have at least two rats on a given diet. In that way individual differences may be demonstrated. Two rats may be kept in one cage and distinguished from each other by ear marks.

When the rat experiment is completed, it is unwise to give them to children to take home. The janitor may dispose of rats painlessly by placing them in a small can with 1 teaspoon of chloroform or ether on absorbent cotton, then keeping the can tightly covered for 10 or 15 minutes. Other animals, such as the chicken, guinea pig, or hamster may be used for nutrition demonstrations.

PREPARATION OF FOOD AT SCHOOL

Preparation of food is a method of teaching which may help the students to change their attitudes about some foods, and it also provides opportunities to apply generalizations of nutrition. For instance, you can increase the acceptance of vegetables, fruits, eggs, and milk dishes by having the students prepare and eat them.

Rejection of many foods seems to be due to hesitancy to try the new. Studies of the popularity of foods show that often a food is disliked by people even though they have never tasted it. This is more often the case than when people have tasted and disliked the food. We need a spirit of adventure and curiosity in relation to food.

The classroom teacher can encourage this spirit of adventure by guiding the preparation of foods in several different ways and setting

We need a spirit of adventure and curiosity . . . .

the stage so that students will taste each form. If you allow the reactions to each food to be freely expressed, you can show ways to modify flavor or texture so that the food is acceptable. If this approach is made, each individual can feel that he is making an independent choice rather than following rules made by an authority.

The teacher should present a food as being both enjoyable and nutritious. Even though our choices of food are made independently, they are not made wholly on the basis of pleasure in eating. *Every* food has something to offer. When a food is prepared, its role in a well-balanced diet should be presented in a manner the age group will understand.

If Jane says that she will eat but a few foods in each group, you can point out what this means in terms of values which she considers most important. If Jane chooses to continue questionable food practices after you are certain that she understands the facts, the decision is her responsibility, not yours.

PLANNING MENUS FOR THE SCHOOL LUNCH

Have you thought of arranging for students to help plan the menu for the school lunch? Often we talk about food and let the students prepare food in the classroom, but we forget the other real-life situations in which they can help.

Planning menus for the school lunch can be used as a means of changing attitudes of students toward foods. When food preferences are different, students must learn how to make a group decision. This may mean that no one gets his first choice and that some foods on the menu may actually be disliked by a few students. Group pressures may be great enough to result in acceptance of foods by all class members if, at the beginning of the project, everyone agrees to support the decision of the majority.

When students are expected to solve real problems, they are likely to be fair about considering all important factors. In addition to considering differences in food preferences, the person who plans the school lunch menu is faced with the problem of providing at least one-third of the necessary nutrients for a day within limitations of money, time, and equipment. Students who puzzle through the many facts involved in solving these problems are more likely to cooperate by eating the foods actually served to them than are students who are merely told that such planning is difficult.

If this project includes checking plate waste by older students, they may become more aware of dangers to themselves in disliking foods important for good nutrition. Differences in food preferences make group feeding difficult. Limited budgets of both time and money prevent catering to personal tastes, so that meals away from home may be quite inadequate.

Furthermore, the menus planned later by the lunchroom manager may be more acceptable because she, too, can learn more about food preferences from the menus planned by students. The school lunch managers who cooperated in a study in Iowa seemed pleased to be considered a part of the educational team. All of them were willing to describe to the students limitations in each situation and to serve the menus planned by the various classes.

As students plan menus, they learn how to apply the facts and principles of nutrition. Furthermore, facts have more meaning as they are used. Meaningful facts are more easily remembered than abstract ones not related to experience.

MAKING AND USING POSTERS

Making nutrition posters and pictograms for the school lunchroom may be an excellent means for correlating the teaching of nutrition and art. A good poster conveys an important message in an interesting and artistic manner. In the process of selecting ideas for posters, students can be encouraged to study nutrition and to formulate generalizations that can be understood by all of the people they wish to reach.

In the process of organizing ideas so that they can be used for a poster, generalizations must often be simplified and reduced in length. When this is done, one must really know nutrition facts in order to make short, accurate statements. Thus, knowledge may be increased. Furthermore, in an effort to show others *why* good nutrition is important, the student may convince himself.

"Being part of a poster" may create interest too. Have you ever used students as figures in a living poster or graph? One teacher wanted to show her class what proportion of them had good, fair, and poor diets so she asked members of the class to make a poster. First she had 10 girls stand up. Then she divided the girls into three groups to show the per cent of the class whose diets were poor, fair, or good. Four girls in one group represented the 40 per cent of the class whose diets were poor, and four more girls represented the 40 per cent whose diets were fair. The remaining two girls represented the 20 per cent who had good diets. This is a simple dramatic way to make percentages from food surveys meaningful. Of course, you might have to use some imagination if the per cents were different and you needed a fraction of a girl to represent a classification.

A living poster may be more interesting than a traditional one. It can be seen by everyone in an auditorium when many graphic materials cannot. Furthermore you may feel that you haven't time to make illustrative material of desirable standard and so may pass up opportunities to make nutrition education interesting and meaningful. A living poster takes more imagination than time.

Children may have fun with pictograms, flannel graphs, or other visual materials which they may make for themselves if they have the information. The discussion of visual aids in connection with Table 11.1 suggests various ways to present information.

ILLUSTRATED TALKS

Students learn while preparing demonstrations and talks, just as while making posters. If ideas for the talks are selected from many sources, students must learn facts and generalizations and evaluate ways of applying them. The generalizations in Chapter 6 may be very helpful in organizing such presentations either by the students or the teachers. Talks are likely to be satisfactory if such criteria as the following are used to evaluate them.

1. Will the group hearing the talk think the facts selected are important?
2. Will they be able to use these facts as presented?
3. Do the illustrations project the idea clearly to the viewer?
4. Does the summary emphasize a few important generalizations and show ways to apply them?

There are many opportunities for giving such talks or demonstrations to: (*a*) one's own classmates, (*b*) groups of younger children, (*c*) parents, and (*d*) other adult groups. With such audiences, students recognize the importance of organizing their ideas so that each lesson is appropriate for each age group. This will improve their acquaintance with nutrition facts, and strengthen their desire to learn more.

USING LITERATURE EFFECTIVELY

Many interesting bulletins and books are available to the schools and adult groups for nutrition education. They are written for different age groups, with appropriate vocabularies. The concerns of different groups are anticipated. These books cannot replace the teacher, however, no matter how well written they may be. The teacher must guide the use of literature if reading is to be most effective.

Reading as part of nutrition education cannot be routine if it is to be valuable. Reading must be done for a purpose which the students recognize and accept. A reading assignment should be made only after students know why they are to read. During preparation for reading, the teacher can make sure that her objectives and those of her students are consistent, even if they are not identical.

Often students are expected to read for information. Information for what? To repeat facts to the teacher or to help the students think for themselves? If the teacher simply assigns pages in a book to be read, students can do little but guess what the teacher will ask them in recitation. On the other hand, if the students read when they need information, they not only know what to look for, but they have a reason to remember what they read.

Facts acquire meaning with use. If the students can see the usefulness of a fact, they learn it more easily. If no immediate use is evident, the fact is likely to be forgotten soon. For example, foods classified in each of several food groups are difficult to learn when mere memorization is expected. However, when we use the food groupings as a tool for planning menus and evaluating food plans, the facts themselves are more easily learned.

Sometimes students read for the story that is told and not primarily for nutrition facts. The story may describe a situation that is suitable for group discussion because it is similar to one which they might encounter. It may have enough detail to make intelligent discussion possible. When this is true, the story can be used as a case situation.

WAYS TO WORK WITH PARENTS

Because most of our food preferences are formed at home, the influence of our parents and other family members has been greater than that of anyone else in forming our food habits. This means that nutrition education with children may be ineffective unless we work with the parents of those we teach.

Personal contact is probably most effective, because talking over problems can be enlightening to everyone. We may be impatient with failure of parents to apply facts of nutrition until we are aware of the complexity of some of their problems. When two of the authors talked to a group of parents and suggested that children would benefit as much from well-planned menus as did pigs from well-planned rations, one father reminded us that hogs ate what was served to them while children were not so docile.

Establishing desirable food habits or changing undesirable ones is not simple. Many factors may influence a child's acceptance of food. If you recognize the difficulties of parents, they will be more receptive of your teaching for several reasons: (a) You will not put them on the defensive by implying that they could do better if they really cared. (b) You will be sure that ways to increase acceptance of foods are taught along with the importance of the food. (c) You will plan with parents for ways that teaching at school can supplement learning at home.

Meeting parents in a group is usually more feasible than individual conferences and may actually be more effective. In a group you can show how nutrition can affect the way children look, act, and feel, and you can review ways to achieve good nutrition.

From the first meeting with parents, you will be most successful if you can establish rapport. Both you and the parents are interested in the growth of the children. Together you can identify difficulties in establishing good health habits and together you can solve problems.

The steps in problem solving can be used effectively with parents if the problems are real and clearly defined. In the process of solving a problem you will have opportunities to present pertinent facts and to show how alternate solutions will affect the welfare of children.

Parents can be informed by letters or printed material, but some dangers accompany this method of communication. The parents may misunderstand your motives in sending material home or they may not interpret the facts correctly.

Some parents may not be reached in any other way simply because they do not come to meetings or because you haven't time to visit them. If children are old enough to plan ways to get information to their parents, they may also interpret it so that it will be used effectively.

REFERENCES

1. Stone, J. G., "Getting the most out of health education tools." *Jour. Amer. Diet. Assn.,* 16:329, 1940.
2. Pett, L. B., "A new outlook for community nutrition." *Jour. Amer. Diet. Assn.,* 23:13, 1947.
3. Rodewald, Shirley, "Agreement between dietaries reported by Napier school children and their mothers." Unpublished M.S. thesis, Iowa State University Library, Ames, 1950.
4. Dickins, Dorothy, "Some effects of a white corn meal shortage." *Jour. Amer. Diet. Assn.,* 21:287, 1945.
5. Hurt, Mary Lee, "A study of the effect on, attitude toward, and home carry-over of homemaking education while teaching is keyed to lower and middle class values and practices." Doctoral thesis, University of Illinois, 1953.

6. Lewin, Kurt, "Forces behind food habits and methods of change." In *The problem of changing food habits.* Bul., Nat. Res. Council, 108:35, 1943.
7. Willerman, B., "Group decision and request as means of changing food habits." Com. on Food Habits, Nat. Res. Council. Mimeo., 1943.
8. Radke, M., and Klisurich, D., "Experiments in changing food habits." *Jour. Amer. Diet. Assn.*, 23:403, 1947.
9. ———, and Caso, E. K., "Lecture and discussion-decision as methods of influencing food habits." *Jour. Amer. Diet. Assn.*, 24:23, 1948.
10. Encyclopedia Britannica Films, Inc., *Fundamentals of diet.* Educational film. Wilmette, Ill.
11. USDA, Office of Information, *For health and happiness.* Educational film. Washington, D.C., 1942.
12. Tennessee State Dept. of Education, Div. of Vocational Education, Dept. of Home Economics Education. "Teaching materials for use in teaching of child development and related art in homemaking education in Tennessee." Report of a workshop. Mimeo., 1949.
13. Booher, Lela E., "Basic foods work together." *Forecast for Home Economists,* Oct., 1954.

Chapter Eight

Evaluation

EVALUATION IS THE PROCESS of determining where your students are in relation to the objectives for the lesson or course. If you are concerned with growth of students as a result of your teaching, you compare their status before and after teaching. To do this you collect evidence about such behavior as student learning, ability to think, attitudes, interests, or appreciations. Valid comparisons of these data in order to determine growth are dependent upon collecting similar data and interpreting them accurately.

Evaluation is an integral part of any comprehensive plan for teaching. It serves both teacher and student in any learning situation. By means of evaluation the teacher notes the success of the teaching and the learning difficulties of students; the student is motivated by knowledge of his progress toward educational goals. Evaluation is a necessary step in making nutrition work.

Your first two steps in planning for evaluation will have been taken when your objectives have been stated in terms of student behavior and you have selected the generalizations you expect students to understand well enough to use. These two aspects of planning for learning are discussed in Chapters 6 and 7. Objectives for a lesson, a course, or a curriculum are guideposts for teaching. Changes in the behavior of students are the bases for evaluation.

The third step is to identify the situations in which you might find your students and the competences you would expect them to exhibit in each situation. This step would further clarify your objectives. If at the same time you describe ways in which students might meet each situation — from acceptable to unacceptable — your bases for evaluation would be still clearer.

Your evaluation program should be comprehensive enough to indicate growth toward all of your objectives. Meeting this standard is not easy and may not be possible, but another kind of analysis of

[*198*]

your objectives will help. If you think of your objectives as organized in the three categories which follow, you can check to see that none are neglected.

I. Acquisition of important information and appraisal of dependable sources
   A. Recall facts related to the nutrients needed daily.
   B. Recall facts concerning kinds and amounts of foods needed to ensure an adequate supply of these nutrients.
   C. Recognize half-truths, incomplete facts, misinformation, or superstitions concerning a food or foods.
   D. Have some criteria by which to evaluate sources of information.

II. Development of effective methods of thinking
   A. Formulate reasonable generalizations from specific facts as shown by ability to:
      1. Interpret and use data from research related to nutritional needs of persons of different ages, states of health, and activities.
      2. Recognize or formulate sound generalizations related to nutritional needs and ways to satisfy them.
   B. Solve problems as shown by ability to:
      1. Make good decisions when selecting food.
      2. Analyze a problem relative to the choice of foods.
      3. Determine alternate courses of action and the values to be attained through each alternative.
   C. Apply generalizations when making decisions.

Teacher notes the result of the teaching.

III. Development of attitudes and beliefs
   A. Be willing to try new foods.
   B. Accept responsibility for own food practices.
   C. Tend to be critical of information about nutritive value of foods until sources have been evaluated.
   D. Maintain an open-minded attitude toward information about food.
   E. Believe that food selection is essential to good nutrition, and good nutrition to health, and health to happiness.

Only when your evaluation program is comprehensive enough to give an accurate index of status and growth of students, can you be sure that your objectives are realistic and that students are using their opportunities to learn. This ideal is not always achieved, but use of all feasible methods of evaluation will yield more complete evidence than you would hope to get from one type of evaluation.

The fourth step is to select and try the most promising methods for evaluating each of the objectives, paper and pencil tests as well as less formal methods. You may either structure a situation in such a way that choices of students are limited or you may secure data about students in situations when they are unaware of being observed. You may collect all of the data for evaluating progress yourself or you may use the results of self-evaluation by students. Whatever you do, accuracy of your interpretations will be influenced by the objectivity with which you judge the responses of students. Suggestions for making your scores as objective as possible are given with some of the test items which follow in this chapter.

Other ways to facilitate interpretation of student growth are:

I. Be certain that you know what behavior you expect of students. Exactly how competent do you expect them to be? If you have completed the third step you will have descriptions of acceptable responses in the situations you use for evaluation.

II. Collect a sample of each kind of behavior that will give you confidence that students have had opportunities to show you what they know or how they think or feel.

III. Analyze student scores for each kind of behavior separately. This is the only way that you can discover strengths and difficulties. Adding scores for ability to think to those for attitudes is like adding apples and pears. You know how many pieces of fruit you have but you know nothing about how they are distributed.

EVALUATION OF ACQUISITION OF FACTS

The easiest growth to evaluate is whether or not students can recall the facts which you gave them the opportunity to learn. You

*Obtain data when
people are unaware
of being observed.*

can identify the facts that you consider most important, and from among them select those to use in the test. Paper and pencil tests are usually used for this evaluation. Examples are given of matching, completion check sheets, true-false, and problem-type items.

All of these are guided-response types of test items. When you use this type of item rather than an essay type you can obtain responses to more items in a given length of time because students can answer them more quickly. Another advantage is that you can score the items more quickly and more objectively. You can more easily ascertain the relative ratings of the students in a group, or of one group with other groups.

If you wish to know how well students can recall nutritive content of foods, you may use *matching items* in a test such as this:

> Select a food (or foods) in the right-hand column that is (or are) a good source of protein, and place the number of that food in the first blank. Fill each succeeding blank by selecting the food (or foods) that is (or are) a good source of the nutrient, and place the number in the appropriate blank.
>
> | | |
> |---|---|
> | _____ A good source of protein | 1. Beef |
> | _____ A good source of vitamin A | 2. Oranges |
> | _____ A good source of calcium | 3. Cabbage |
> | _____ A good source of iron | 4. Cauliflower |
> | _____ A good source of vitamin C | 5. Bread |
> | | 6. Butter |
> | | 7. Milk |
> | | 8. Eggs |

A check list such as the one illustrated is another means of obtaining evidence of the accuracy of a student's facts. A check list is a device for recording a person's reaction to each idea (word, phrase, sentence, paragraph) that is listed. The reactions to each idea are recorded by a check (x) in columns to the right of the list. Sometimes one column must be selected; at other times all appropriate columns are checked. Following is an illustration of this type of item, taken from materials prepared by Chadderdon (1).

I. In order to plan meals we need to know what foods are especially good sources of the food nutrients. Below is a chart of foods and nutrients. Check (x) in the blank for the nutrients which each of these foods contain in *important amounts* in the quantities used. *

Foods	NUTRIENTS				
	Carbo-hydrates A	Proteins B	Minerals (1 or more) C	Vitamins (1 or more) D	None of These E
Milk		x	x	x	
Butter				x	
Eggs		x	x	x	
Meat		x	x	x	
Citrus fruit				x	
Vegetables, yellow				x	
Candy	x				
Salad oil					x

* The checks, words, and phrases in the blanks indicate the key.

Another type of guided-response item combines checking and completion. An item from evaluation materials prepared by Chadderdon (1) requires students to check correct items and then complete each answer by writing a word or two in spaces to the right.

II. In most families the large meal of the day usually contains meat. For lunch or supper a food other than meat often is used to help supply the protein needed.

Below is a list of prepared dishes. Place a check (x) in front of those letters where the prepared dish has a generous amount of protein. In the space to the right, state the food in the prepared dish which contains the protein.*

Prepared Dishes

x   A.   baked beans   dried beans

____   B.   chicken noodle soup   _____

____   C.   potato salad   _____

x   D.   tuna fish salad   tuna

x   E.   omelet   eggs

_x_	F.	deviled eggs	_eggs_
____	G.	sliced bananas with cream	_____
_x_	H.	cottage cheese and tomato	_cheese_
____	I.	Jello with pineapple and carrots	_____
____	J.	lettuce, bacon, and tomato sandwich	_____
_x_	K.	peanut butter sandwich	_peanuts_

* The checks, words, and phrases in the blanks indicate the key.

As an illustration of the *true-false test,* items are taken from an unpublished test prepared by Barrick (2) as one means of evaluating methods used for teaching freshman college women. Students were instructed to read each statement carefully and then indicate their beliefs as follows:

T = True; you agree with the statement.
D = Doubtful; you doubt the truth of the statement.
F = False; you disagree with the statement.
U = Uncertain; you are very uncertain whether the statement is true or false.

Here are some of the statements:

Vitamin pills should be taken by people who dislike many foods. ____
Products made from milk have the same nutritive value. ____
Canned pineapple is a good source of vitamin C. ____
A reducing diet should consist largely of fruits and vegetables. ____

In the same test are items that express half-truths. This kind of an item is different from one that is completely wrong or right. Examples of these items are:

An easy way to reduce is by taking exercises. ____
Poor nutrition is often one of the underlying causes of juvenile delinquency. ____
Milk is a perfect food. ____
A safe way to reduce is to eat small portions of everything served. ____

If you add a response, **P**, to the four above, you can use the last four items to determine whether or not students detect half-truths. A new response might read **P** = Partly true; you believe that the statement is partly true.

Students who mark the last four items **P** thus will be answering correctly because the statements are neither true nor false. Opportunity to make this response helps the most discerning students because they are most likely to detect half-truths.

Another kind of true-false item identifies the knowledge of students about certain superstitions. An illustration of this kind of item is taken from materials prepared by Chadderdon (1); this illustration shows only four of the more than fifty possibilities suitable for use in a test item.

III. These statements are expressions of opinions which many people have. Read each statement carefully before checking (x) in the column which best indicates your belief. Do *not* sign your name.
Check "True" if you agree with the statement.
  "Doubtful" if you doubt the truth of the statement.
  "False" if you disagree with the statement.
  "I don't know" if you have no idea whether the statement is true or false.

Statements	True	Doubt-ful	False	I don't know
1. Girls of the same age, size, and activity need about the same amount of food.	x*			
2. Vitamin pills should be taken by people who dislike many foods.		x		
3. Protein and starchy foods should not be eaten at the same meal.			x	
4. There are no shortcuts to reducing weight.	x			

* x indicates key.

When scoring a test including these four kinds of true-false statements, you will obtain more specific or exact information about the difficulties of students by three separate scores than a single score. With a score for each type of error, you and the students will be aware of their misconceptions.

The *problem-type question* may be used to check the accuracy of information. It has the advantage of presenting facts about a situation so that there is less likelihood of misunderstanding the statement to which reaction is requested. This type of item was selected from another test used by Barrick (2). The directions for this test were:

On the following pages you will find described a series of situations involving nutrition problems. Read each one carefully and check (x) the answer or answers on the answer sheet. After selecting the best answers, read the entire list of reasons and check on the answer sheet those that explain why your answers are the best ones.

One item in the test reads:

> Marge Macley is allergic to tomatoes in any form. Several fruits are
> served at the dorm for breakfast, so she can avoid tomato juice. Since
> the meals at the dorm are planned to meet daily requirements for good
> nutrition, it is important that she choose the right fruits. If she eats
> plenty of green and yellow vegetables, which of these could she select
> that will be good substitutes for the tomatoes?
>
> a. Grapefruit   c. Oranges
> b. Prunes   d. Pineapple juice
>
> Check the reasons why the fruits you checked above are good substitutes
> for tomatoes.
>
> 1. Grapefruit, like tomatoes, is high in vitamin B.
> 2. Grapefruit contains a large amount of vitamin C.
> 3. Prunes supply roughage.
> 4. Prunes are high in iron.
> 5. Oranges are a citrus fruit and so will substitute for tomatoes.
> 6. Pineapple is a citrus fruit.
> 7. Pineapple is an important source of vitamin C.

Any type of *essay writing* expected of students can be examined
for accuracy of information. The essay type of item for acquisition of
information has advantages and disadvantages. One advantage is that
students may not be aware that the accuracy of their information is
being tested. In other words, in an essay examination the student's
ability to call up spontaneous information has an opportunity for expression. Disadvantages are that (*a*) only a small sample of information is used by the student and (*b*) the time used by the teacher in
discovering and pointing out errors of students may be greater than
that required for constructing and scoring a guided-response type of
test.

The disadvantages of the essay type of item can be partially overcome by some structuring of responses. Another item from Chadderdon's (1) material illustrates how you can obtain free responses and
still increase size of sample of responses from students.

*Essay writing
has disadvantages . . . .*

IV. Phyllis' brother Mark, 13, wants to make the high school basketball team. He is growing very rapidly, so he thinks he will be tall enough. He practices basketball every evening. Mark has asked Phyllis to help him with his diet so he can be active and grow strong. His daily diet meets the basic food requirements.

Check (x) the nutrients which he should be especially careful to include in generous amounts.* Explain your choice in the blanks at the right.

Nutrients				Reasons
x	A.	Carbohydrates	A.	Needs energy-rich foods
x	B.	Fats	B.	Needs energy-rich foods and fats are the highest energy-giving nutrients.
x	C.	Minerals	C.	Needs to develop bones, to form blood, and to build muscles.
x	D.	Proteins	D.	Needs to build tissues during growth and to replace worn tissue.
x	E.	Vitamins	E.	Needs to build tissue.

* The checks, words, or phrases indicate the key.

Knowledge of dependable sources of information is not simply a recall of information. To achieve this objective, students must know sound criteria for judging the source of information and be able to use these criteria when accepting or rejecting information that they read or hear.

The criteria suggested on pages 185–86 can be the basis for tests similar to the ones suggested for recall of facts. Before testing ability to use these criteria, you will wish to know whether or not the criteria are known and accepted by students.

Tests of ability to *use* the criteria may be similar to those on the preceding pages, where ways for evaluating ability to apply generalizations are discussed. Actually, criteria are generalizations that indicate the importance attached to certain characteristics of a product.

Steps to follow in constructing such a test are:

1. Present excerpts from 2 articles to your students, giving complete information of authorship and publication.
2. Have students select the article considered most reliable, with reasons for their selection.
3. Select student statements of reasons which:
   a. Support each article and are good criteria.
   b. Are not sound criteria for determining reliability of the article.
   c. Are not relevant to the problem.

EVALUATION OF DEVELOPMENT OF EFFECTIVE METHODS OF THINKING

Ability To Interpret Data

The ability to interpret data is one aspect of ability to think that is often an objective of nutrition teaching. The effectiveness of many visual materials is limited unless students are able to interpret for themselves what they see. For example, ability to identify similarities and differences in characteristics of well-nourished and poorly nourished individuals requires a level of ability different from that required to memorize these characteristics as they are pointed out by the teacher.

If you have used the pictures of the two teen-age girls on page 104 to teach students to identify important differences in physical characteristics of well-nourished and poorly nourished individuals, you can use the pictures of the two boys on page 208 as a new situation to test the ability of your students to distinguish differences between them. The first time or two the pictures are used as a testing situation you can ask such questions as: Which of the two boys seems to be the more healthy? Give reasons for your answer. The reasons given by each student may be classified in several ways: (*a*) characteristics of good health shown by the boy chosen as the more healthy, (*b*) characteristics of this boy that do not indicate his state of health, (*c*) characteristics of good health that are not evident in the picture of the boy. This procedure will reveal whether or not students can identify accurately the characteristics of good health as shown in the picture.

When constructing a guided-response test item you will wish, among statements of reasons to which students can react, some of each type that apply to each boy. Since statements in the language of students are not likely to be obviously wrong or right, the answers you receive from them can be selected from each of the three classifications suggested in the previous paragraph.

When interpreting data from such a test you will discover students who (*a*) recognize all of the characteristics that apply to the picture of the boy chosen; (*b*) are unable to distinguish between characteristics that apply to the problem and those that do not; or (*c*) know the characteristics of a healthy person but do not restrict their answers to the problem of nutrition.

Tests similar to those using the pictures of the two boys can be based on data such as are found in graphs, tables of food composition, pictograms similar to those in Chapters 2 and 11, or charts such as those which show growth curves of rats on different diets. In each case, a student's responses will indicate whether he (*a*) can accurately show relationships among the data, (*b*) can see all of the relationships in the data, and (*c*) does not go beyond the data presented and thus overgeneralize.

[*207*]

An example of good nutrition.   An example of poor nutrition.

At the end of a lesson, you can test informally the ability of students to interpret data if you ask them to write in complete sentences what they have learned during the lesson. Thus you will know which of your students can state generalizations that are complete and accurate.

Ability To Apply Generalizations

Ability to apply principles or generalizations of nutrition when making decisions is different from the ability to generalize. A guided-response type of item for this evaluation presents a situation in which a person is required to make a decision. Two or more alternatives are offered, from which the student must choose one. After making a choice he checks facts or generalizations that are reasons for his answer. Among the reasons are untrue statements and true statements that do not explain the choice made. If several such items are included in a test, you will have some evidence of a student's ability to apply generalizations accurately.

The two items which follow were selected from the materials prepared by Chadderdon (1).

I

Linda is a little overweight and she thinks it is because she eats too much between meals. Here are the meals she ate yesterday:

Breakfast	Lunch
Egg Toast	Hamburger on Bun
Milk	Buttered Green Beans
	Chocolate Cake
	Milk

Supper

Broiled Ham   Gravy   Mashed Potatoes
Asparagus
Cookies   Milk

Here are some foods that she might eat between meals. Check (x) the ones that will be least likely to cause her to add weight.

x	A.	Apple	___	E.	Malted milk
x	B.	Celery	___	F.	Cookie
___	C.	Candy bar	x	G.	Milk (skim)
___	D.	Lettuce sandwich	___	H.	Ice cream

In this test students are expected to apply a generalization such as: For good nutrition, reducing diets need to include adequate amounts of meat, eggs, vegetables, fresh fruits, and skim or whole milk but the amounts of fats, sugar, bread, and cereals need to be limited.

II

When we go to the grocery we have many choices to make between foods, and most families need to make these choices wisely to keep food costs down. Which one of the following pairs of foods is the better choice from the standpoint of *cost* and *food value?* Check (x) the better one.

Foods

A.	x	1. Broccoli	E.	x	1. Liver
	___	2. Asparagus		___	2. Steak
B.	___	1. Round steak	F.	x	1. Carrots
	x	2. Hamburger		___	2. Canned corn
C.	___	1. Corn flakes	G.	x	1. Cabbage
	x	2. Oatmeal		___	2. Lettuce, head
D.	x	1. Celery	H.	___	1. Canned pears
	___	2. Olives		x	2. Canned peaches

In this test students are expected to apply the following generalizations:

The larger the amount or the more expensive the processing of a food, the higher price as a rule.

Cuts of meat from the loin or steak areas of the animal are more expensive than those from the organs or from less tender cuts of meat, yet they are no more nutritious.

Foods which are more perishable are more expensive than those that can be shipped and held more easily.

Green, leafy, and yellow vegetables and yellow fruits contain more of the protective nutrients than other vegetables and fruits.

A less formal way to evaluate ability to apply generalizations is to judge the work of students when they prepare exhibits and posters. You can observe the importance of the generalizations they select to illustrate the appropriateness of the illustrations and the accuracy of captions. If you do not wish to have students prepare exhibits or posters, they can evaluate those prepared by others. Your questions can direct them to use their knowledge of generailzations as bases for their evaluations. If you require complete sentences when students make these evaluations, you can judge ability to apply generalizations.

The foods that individuals eat are one indication of ability to apply generalizations of nutrition. Food records kept for 3 to 7 days provide more reliable data than do occasional observations of food practices in public places. Seven-day records taken at intervals throughout the year probably give the best over-all picture of food consumption, but such records are not feasible in many situations. Methods of rating and evaluating diets are given in Appendix B, pages 295–96.

Data from food records must be interpreted cautiously because several factors may be influencing the kind and amount of food eaten. Students may know the generalizations and how to apply them, but may not actually practice good nutrition because (a) appropriate food is not available to them; (b) they do not believe that what they eat will make a difference in their health; or (c) satisfactions other than health may be of major importance to them.

EVALUATION OF DEVELOPMENT OF ATTITUDES AND VALUES

Attitudes about food and values of individuals may have greater influence on food consumption than facts they can recall about nutrition.

Identifying attitudes, values, interests, or appreciations is difficult because means for evaluating them have not been refined. Unless you can find a "test" that seems satisfactory, you may wish to use such means as self-evaluation by students, observations, or interviews.

You can study the food likes and dislikes of your students by asking them to check a questionnaire similiar to the one in the materials prepared by Chadderdon (3). The two check sheets that follow are means of self-evaluation by students. Only the first six items in the first check list are given.

How Am I Doing?

Most people could enjoy their food more if they liked a wide variety of foods; then, too, they could be better guests if they ate everything served them. Learning to like many foods is an important part of really growing up, of acting more like an adult.

Below is a list of vegetables to use in checking how well you are progressing toward eating a variety of foods. Check (x) in the column or columns which best describe where you are now. If you prefer some other method of preparing any of the vegetables, add it and check in the columns.

| Food | Eat It When Offered | | Need To Learn To Eat | Have Never Eaten; Need Chance To Taste |
	Enjoy	Do Not Enjoy		
Asparagus, creamed				
Beans, green, buttered				
Beets buttered				
pickled				
Broccoli, buttered				
Brussel sprouts, buttered				
Cabbage salad				
slaw				
buttered				

Learning To Enjoy a Variety of Vegetables

Record of Progress

I agree to try to learn to enjoy three new vegetables.

_____
Name

A. After you have checked the list of vegetables on How Am I Doing?, select three that you checked Do Not Enjoy, Need To Learn To Eat, or Need Chance To Taste. Write the three selected in the following chart.
B. Use every opportunity you have to taste these vegetables, eat them in small quantities, or eat them in combination with foods you like.
C. Record (x) in the blanks of the chart each time you eat some of each vegetable until you can check "Enjoy." If you need more trials, extend the chart in the space below it.

Vegetable	Trials								Enjoy
	1	2	3	4	5	6	7	8	
1.									
2.									
3.									

Systematic observations of individuals in situations where their choices seem to depend upon willingness to try new foods is another way to evaluate this objective. For example, responses of individuals to invitations to eat foods prepared in a demonstration or by class members will reveal attitudes toward food. Another situation for such observations is afforded when a group plans for foods to be prepared. Success of this means of evaluation is dependent upon your ability to observe objectively and record accurately what you have observed; this becomes a basis for later interpretation.

Anecdotal records of your observations will give data for evaluation that are more reliable than casual observations. Often an accumulation of incidents will reveal changes in attitudes that are not evident in one or two observations. Such records require time to keep, and are not necessary for everyone. They are most valuable for the student whose attitude seems to need changing.

Probably the most difficult *attitude* to change is that food does not really make a difference in the way one looks, feels, and acts. Evaluation of students in this respect is difficult too. Barbour (4) interviewed students to discover what they believed were the functions of different foods. One question that she asked illustrates this method of determining their beliefs about food. Reasons given are actual responses made by the students:

Question: Does kind of food eaten affect the way you look?
Answer: Yes.
Reasons given:
1. Eating right foods makes you look better.
2. Have nicer teeth.
3. Sweets make pimples on your face.
4. Kind of food affects complexion.
5. Kind of food affects hands and fingernails.
6. Chocolate and rich foods cause pimples.
7. Not enough food makes you look thin.
8. Some foods give color to your face.
9. Carrots make eyes look well.
10. Make a face when you eat sour or strong foods.
11. Too much fat and starches make you fat.
12. Some foods make hair glossier.
13. Kind of food affects posture.
14. Plenty of proteins fill you out, otherwise you are skinny.
15. Not enough carrots make eyes dull and sore.

Satisfactions from the enjoyment of food or from belonging to a group may be more important to your students than health. To discover the *values* that her students associated with food, Nichol (5) prepared and gave a values test to a group of boys. An item from her test illustrates one type of values test:

Read the following situation carefully and decide how you would act in a similar situation.

Jim is 15 years old and in the 10th grade. His best friends go to a restaurant for lunch where the food is rather carelessly prepared and served but where the boys have a lot of fun. About the only kind of lunch they can get is a sandwich, cake or cookies, and a beverage. Jim doesn't often go with his friends and they cannot understand why he doesn't go with them. Jim enjoys the fun at the restaurant but he doesn't like the food. He thinks he should have more vegetables and fruit and salads to stay healthy. He can get these at the school cafeteria and he likes the food there much better, although the cost is slightly higher. Jim's parents think he is wise to go to the cafeteria.

Check *each* of the following statements to show how each reason would influence your decision in this situation:

    VG if you think it is a very good reason and would greatly influence your decision.

    G if you think it is a good reason and might influence your decision.

    U if you are uncertain whether it would influence your decision.

    P if you think it is a poor reason and would seldom influence you.

    VP if you think it is a very poor reason and would never influence you.

		VG	G	U	P	VP
1.	It is foolish to save money and have a poor lunch.	—	—	—	—	—
2.	Jim should consider whether he enjoys his lunch or not.	—	—	—	—	—
3.	Jim should do what he wants to — it wouldn't make any difference to his being well liked by his friends.	—	—	—	—	—
4.	If Jim is healthy, he doesn't have to worry about what he eats.	—	—	—	—	—
5.	Jim should take the advice of his parents.	—	—	—	—	—
6.	Jim should save as much as he can on his lunch if he needs money for other things.	—	—	—	—	—
7.	Health is one of the most important considerations when choosing food.	—	—	—	—	—
8.	Jim will lose his popularity with the group if he doesn't go with them.	—	—	—	—	—
9.	It is important for Jim to enjoy his lunch.	—	—	—	—	—
10.	Jim is old enough to make up his own mind and his parents should not try to influence him.	—	—	—	—	—

When you are evaluating willingness to try new foods, you may also discover how well students will accept responsibility for their own food practices. Whenever free choices can be made, responsibility must be accepted. Whether or not students recognize this fact

Belonging to a group may be more important than health.

is not easy to determine. Essays which contain free expression of ideas may be most fruitful in revealing attitudes toward personal responsibility. Interviews with students or their parents are helpful, too.

Interest in keeping personal records of growth up to and through adolescence indicates acceptance of responsibility for one's own health. Records of weight kept after growth is completed indicate the same attitude. These records will be especially revealing if growth charts and other records are kept at the same time. One kind of record may be of foods eaten. When the relationship between these two records is recognized, students show satisfactory understanding of this aspect of nutrition.

STUDENT EVALUATION OF TEACHING

Student evaluation of what they have learned from a lesson, unit, or nutrition program may give some data that are not obtained in any other way. If you ask what was the most important thing learned today, you will discover the emphasis which was recognized by students.

To obtain student appraisal of your methods, you can ask such questions as: What is the strongest thing about these lessons? What is the weakest thing about them? What suggestions have you for improvement?

Interpretation is very difficult when opinions of students are used for evaluation. Their opinions must be examined in terms of your objectives, and not always accepted exactly as given. For example, if one of your objectives is to teach students to think, those students who wish you to tell them the answers to their questions may criticize your teaching. When you study their criticisms, you must decide which ones indicate a need to revise your methods and which reflect resistance to your requirement that students think for themselves.

EVALUATION AS A MEANS OF IMPROVING TEACHING

Evaluation cannot be really effective unless it is part of the teaching-learning process. This means that your evaluation program must be "tailor-made" for each of your classes — designed to measure growth toward objectives of a specific class such as comprehension of generalizations or principles, and ability to use learning in situations familiar to students.

This means that you will probably want either to assemble items suitable for your classes or write items of your own. Reasons for describing evaluation items in detail for this chapter were to suggest sources of items for tests and to illustrate types of items that you might use as patterns. If you wish to prepare your own items, two publications may be helpful: Tschudin *et al.* (6) and Wrightstone *et al.* (7).

Evaluation can be a powerful means of motivation. Knowledge of progress encourages students to continue to learn. Thus if you take time to either discuss the results of a test with students, or to guide them in interpreting other data, your evaluation program can be helpful in encouraging members of your groups to use the opportunities that you provide for them to learn.

Students are likely to be impressed by what you include in a test or have evaluated by other means. If your tests emphasize recall of information, students are likely to spend their study time memorizing facts. If your tests require students to solve problems, they are likely to use opportunities provided for them to learn how to solve problems. Evaluation is an important part of the teaching-learning process whether or not you use it consciously for emphasizing important kinds of learning.

If you wish to interpret data from evaluation and use them as a basis for modifying teaching methods, you may find it advisable to note the success of your teaching throughout the nutrition unit. Thus you will know whether or not students are progressing satisfactorily for the time spent and for their maturity. Where progress is not so great as you believe is desirable, you will see that students have different learning opportunities.

When data concerning the growth of students are incomplete, your judgment may not be sound. You cannot know how effective your teaching has been unless you have data about students before and after they have had opportunities to learn under your guidance. This

*Where progress is
not so great as you
believe desirable . . . .*

means that you will need two forms of a test or use the same form with caution. Chances of recalling answers to items can be minimized by spacing tests far enough apart so that students are not likely to remember the items and by omitting discussion of responses to the first test. Type of evaluation depends upon pretests and post tests. It supplements, rather than replaces, evaluation throughout the unit.

The purposes of this chapter have been to illustrate: (*a*) statement of objectives as types of student behavior; (*b*) selection of methods of evaluation that will reveal the kind of behavior indicated as desirable by the objectives; (*c*) devices that have been found useful; and (*d*) some interpretations possible when certain methods are used. There has been no attempt to discuss ways that the validity or reliability of tests can be determined.

REFERENCES

1. Chadderdon, Hester, "Evaluation Materials, Tenth Grade. Food and Nutrition." Iowa State University Book Store, Ames.
2. Barrick, Mary Jean, "Evaluation of three types of audio-visual material for teaching nutrition to freshman college women." Unpublished M.S. thesis, Iowa State University Library, Ames, 1947.
3. Chadderdon, Hester, "Evaluation Materials, Ninth Grade. Food and Nutrition." Iowa State University Book Store, Ames.
4. Barbour, Helen, "Relationships of values and process concepts of selected students to generalizations in nutrition." Unpublished Ph.D. dissertation, Iowa State University Library, Ames, 1953.
5. Nichol, Verna, "Values considered important by eleventh grade boys in selection of food, with implications for nutrition education at the University of Toronto schools." Unpublished M.S. thesis, Iowa State University Library, Ames, 1946.
6. Tschudin, Mary, *et al., Evaluation in Basic Nursing Education.* G. P. Putnam's Sons, New York, 1958.
7. Wrightstone, *et al., Evaluation in Modern Education.* American Book Company, 1956.

Chapter Nine

Concern for Nutrition Education
in the United States

FOUR TIMES in about two decades the government of the United States has demonstrated its continuing interest in nutrition education by sponsoring national conferences in Washington, D. C., to consider the nutrition of the people and methods of improving it. The first of these four conferences, in 1941, pioneered in giving national recognition to the need for nutrition education. Much of what we are doing today is a continuation of recommendations from that conference, modified by progress in research through the years and further influenced by recommendations from the three succeeding conferences.

NATIONAL CONFERENCES — THEIR IMPORT AND CONTRIBUTIONS

Through these conferences we may trace the evolution of our nutrition problems and the efforts to solve them. An appreciation and understanding of the development of nutrition education can be helpful to nutrition educators who need to know the origins of certain efforts that have persisted through the years, and the reasons for the changing emphases.

Attending the four conferences in 1941, 1952, 1957, and 1962 were leading specialists in many fields, including:

home economics
dietetics
public health
education — on all levels of teaching
nutrition research
extension work — with youths and adults
medicine — including many specialties
dentistry
agriculture
trade and industry
consumer groups
The American Red Cross

This partial listing of agencies of the Federal Government which, at one or more of the conferences, shared sponsorship shows the widespread interest of our government in the health of the people as it is affected by the food they eat:

Department of Agriculture (several branches)
Office of Education
Federal Security Agency
Selective Service System
Public Health Service
Department of State
Department of Labor
National Research Council
Department of Health, Education and Welfare
Federal Civil Defense Administration
North American Office of the Food and Agricultural Organization of the
    United Nations

All of the conferences have been so planned that each of the delegates could contribute ideas and observations based on his or her own professional experience; each could have a voice in recommendations; and each could obtain a renewed determination to work toward improving nutrition, plus fresh ideas on how to carry out this improvement.

The recommendations and ideas issuing from each of these meetings were *important milestones in the progress of nutrition education.* Many of the proposals of the first conference (1941) have stood the test of time and have continued to remain as good guides. This first conference originated and developed a national pattern of purpose and direction for nutrition education. Succeeding ones have strengthened and expanded those beginnings.

From the sum total of these four conferences a more or less well-defined *blueprint for nutrition education* has evolved. The broad, national approach has afforded a perspective which is essential to the future of the nutritional status of all Americans. In today's world, this perspective is vital to our nation's future in relation to the other nations of the world.

PURPOSES AND GOALS

Later conferences have tended to deal with more limited areas than did the earliest conference. Both the 1957 and 1962 Conferences were directed mainly toward nutrition education, with the 1962 Conference dealing more specifically with children.

Although each conference had its distinctive objectives, format, and plans for ongoing programs, a certain common core of considerations can be detected. The over-all purposes and goals which guided these conferences were:

1. To appraise current nutrition knowledge, various techniques of adding to it, and ways of disseminating it.

2. To evaluate our food supply and the nutriture of our people.

3. To study the influence of technological improvements in the production, distribution, and processing of food.

4. To measure the impact of changing sociologic, economic, and political conditions upon the diets and food habits of our people.

5. To focus attention on dietary problems which are unique to particular age groups, and to find the best techniques for teaching those groups better food habits.

6. To discuss and assess the role of each specialist in his own field in relation to roles of the other specialists as a means of achieving maximum cooperation toward progress in nutrition education.

We may be tempted to dismiss these conferences simply as history, thereby overlooking their impact on what we are doing today. However, even when viewed only as historical events, the discussions and proposals which occurred on these four different occasions have turned out to have far-reaching consequences. Indeed some of the predictions and estimations made by delegates in 1941 are still remarkably applicable and serve as useful source material for nutrition educators in solving current problems.

The National Nutrition Conference for Defense
May 26 - 28, 1941

Less than seven months before Pearl Harbor, President Franklin D. Roosevelt called the first nationally oriented conference on nutrition, as on outgrowth of preparatory defense measures which had been taken in late 1940 and early 1941. A nutrition policy and planning committee had been formed at the national level and, subsequently, the President appointed Paul V. McNutt, administrator of the Federal Security Agency, as coordinator of health, welfare, medical, recreation, and other activities relating to national defense.

This planning committee then became the Nutrition Advisory Committee to the Federal Security Agency, responsible directly to Paul McNutt.

World developments soon made it evident that food and nutrition would be vital to defense efforts and, potentially, to the survival of the free world. The Nutrition Advisory Committee began to plan a national conference — the first of its kind in history — for the spring of 1941.

Meanwhile, the Land Grant College Executive Committee had urged the formation of state nutrition committees, which were usually led by the president or head of home economics in the land grant colleges. Many of those state committees are still functioning. They are alert to the particular problems of their states, and are vigorous in attacking them. Many sponsor conferences and workshops which are invaluable in helping nutrition workers update this information.

President Roosevelt could not be present at the conference, but emphasized his interest in the sessions in the letter to Paul V. McNutt which was read to the delegates at the opening session (1). The letter summarizes the situation on the national and international scenes at that time:

The White House
May 23, 1941

My Dear Governor:

I am highly gratified to learn that invitations to the National Nutrition Conference for Defense have met with such generous response.
. . . The Conference has significant responsibilities — to explore and define our nutrition problems, and to map out recommendations for an immediate program of action. This is vital. During these days of stress the health problems of the civilian and military population are inseparable. Total defense demands manpower.
. . . Medical authorities recognize completely that efficiency and stamina depend on proper food. Fighting men of our Armed Forces, workers in industry, the families of these workers, every man and woman in America must have nourishing food. If people are undernourished, they cannot be efficient in producing what we need in our unified drive for dynamic strength.
In recent years scientists have made outstanding discoveries as to the amounts and kinds of foods needed for maximum health and vigor. Yet every survey of nutrition, by whatever methods conducted, shows that here in the United States undernourishment is widespread and serious. The Department of Agriculture has estimated that many millions of men, women, and children do not get the foods which science considers essential. We do not lack and we will not lack the means of producing food in abundance and variety. Our task is to translate this abundance into reality for every American family.
I shall follow the work of the Conference with deep interest and expectantly await its recommendations.

Very truly yours,
Franklin D. Roosevelt

THE WORLD SITUATION

The delegates assembled to weigh a new dimension of national concern: the simmering world situation and its possible effect upon our nation. Food was important as a defense measure for us and for the nations which would later become our allies in World War II. The aftermath of the war was to bring widespread devastation, starvation, and misery for the peoples of many lands. Symphathetic volunteers organized the "Bundles for Britain" program in the early 1940's. The scope of this gesture was enlarged to include victims of wars'

tragedies in many countries when the program of CARE packages was developed in the late 1940's.

Another change in emphasis as the conference convened was that the problems of undernutrition and malnutrition in the depression era of the early 1930's had turned into the dilemma of farm surpluses and the urgent necessity to encourage domestic consumption of food. Food stamp plans, combined with free school lunch and milk programs, had been developed on a national basis to provide partial solutions to a paradox: undernutrition in the midst of abundant food supplies. Federal agencies were becoming more involved in the problems of food production, distribution, and consumption.

WARNING SIGNS

Several indications that widespread nutrition problems existed in our nation had become evident before the conference began. They were:

1. A frequently quoted statement, based on studies conducted by the USDA, which asserted: "One-third of the people is well fed; one-third fairly well fed, and one-third poorly fed."
2. Indications that dietary deficiency diseases, particularly pellagra in the South, were sufficiently prevalent to demonstrate the existence of extremely poor nutrition.
3. Rejection of a large number of draftees by selective service as physically unfit (2). Brigadier General Lewis B. Hershey, director of the selective service system, revealed that approximately 400,000 men out of a million (4 out of 10) who had been examined were unfit for general military service. Of the rejected men, he estimated that probably one-third suffered from "disabilities directly or indirectly connected with nutrition" (2). This meant that about 133,000 men could not serve in the armed forces mainly because of their nutritional status, as judged by criteria accepted at that time.

Thus delegates to the conference pondered with urgency the reasons for nutrition problems, the possible solutions for them, and the techniques of presenting those solutions to the public.

HIGHLIGHTS OF THE CONFERENCE
Presentation of the Recommended Daily Allowances

Immediately before the conference opened, the Committee on Food and Nutrition of the National Research Council presented on a network radio broadcast their Recommended Daily Allowances for the various nutritive essentials desirable for everyday diets. The conference approved these Allowances and included their endorsement in 12 recommendations submitted to the President.

Dr. Russell M. Wilder of the Mayo Clinic, who was then chairman of the Committee on Food and Nutrition of the National Research Council, declared (3):

> It is no longer a question of a few experts in our colleges and research centers talking about vitamins and minerals. What we must do now is make people understand that nutrition is not an academic matter but a thoroughly practical consideration concerning every single person in the country — producers, processors, marketers, consumers, nutrition experts — everyone.

> Each meal must be planned with an eye to economy, nutrients, and palatability. For such planning the housewife must have diet instructions expressed in plain, everyday language.

With that in mind, the Committee formulated a table of allowances which was based upon the best available data on nutritive essentials. The values were tentatively set: the Committee chose the word "Recommended" instead of "Standard" for their Allowances to indicate that the values would probably be revised in the future. Actually, few changes have been made through the years.[1] The Committee was careful to explain their purpose and policies in formulating the allowances. They emphasized that the allowances:

— were intended to serve as a guide for planning adequate nutrition for the civilian population,
— gave vitamin figures calculated in terms of food as eaten, not allowing for large losses due to improper cooking,
— listed quantities to provide a good safety margin for nutrients,
— were to be distinguished from the minimum requirements of the Food and Drug Administration regarding the labeling of foods.

Most important of all, the Committee called upon the professional nutrition workers of the United States to transform the allowances into listings of appropriate amounts of food available in various localities. The nutritionists were to serve as "translators" of the data, changing them into equivalents of foods easily understood by the layman. The plan was developed with the thought of safeguarding the adequacy of the diet, but at the same time permitting wide flexibility in the choice of food.

---

[1] The major change in the 1963 revision was a downward adjustment of calorie allowances for the "reference" man and woman, based upon a realistic consideration of the meaning of moderate activity for men and women in the United States.

Launching of the Enrichment Program

Previous to the beginning of the conference, the Federal Food and Drug Administration had conducted hearings to obtain necessary facts for establishing standards of enrichment for flour. These, Paul McNutt announced, had been approved and were to be published in the Federal Register.

This enrichment move was recommended by the Committee on Food and Nutrition of the National Research Council and was begun as a public health measure. Dr. Wilder spoke of the need to improve the nutritional quality of staple foods which were often used in diets of families with low incomes:

It is almost impossible, even for experts, to plan nutritionally good diets for less than 20 cents a day when the sugar, flour, rice and edible fats have had most of their minerals and vitamins removed by methods of refining.

Wilder summed up the need for enrichment of flour (4):

The miller, in time, will be able to present us with a white flour, so made that it retains most of the vitamins and mineral value of wheat. But until he learns to make such a flour — and that will take time — addition to plain white flour of those vitamins which the National Research Council's Committee on Food and Nutrition has prescribed for flour and bread labeled "enriched" will do much to facilitate planning of good diets.

The original program of wheat flour and bread enrichment was compulsory from 1941 to 1946 under War Food Order No. 1. When that order was repealed, it was up to the states to legislate enrichment programs. State nutrition committees became active in requesting this legislation in their states in order to insure that the enrichment program would continue when the national emergency was over. Eventually, 27 states did this, but enrichment was voluntary in the remaining states. Current estimates are that 90 per cent of the bread sold is enriched, indicating widespread voluntary cooperation with the program.

Bringing the enrichment picture up to the 1960's, we find that the Food and Nutrition Board of the National Research Council and the Council on Foods and Nutrition of the American Medical Association have reviewed the policies and principles of enrichment at intervals. The following joint statement was issued in 1961 (5):

The endorsement of the following is affirmed: the enrichment of flour, bread, degerminated corn meal, corn grits, whole grain corn meal, and white rice; the retention or restoration of thiamine, riboflavin, niacin, and iron in processed food cereals; the addition of vitamin D to milk, fluid skim milk, and nonfat dry milk; the addition of vitamin A to margarine, fluid skim milk, and nonfat dry milk; the addition of iodine to table salt. The protective action of fluoride against dental caries is recognized and the standardized addition of fluoride to water is endorsed in areas in which the water supply has a low fluoride content.

The considerations and policies upon which this endorsement is based constitute important material for consumer education and are referred to in Chapter 11.

The Beginning of a National Nutrition Education Program

The recommendations of the Nutrition Conference for Defense were an action program designed to reach every community and, potentially, every citizen. In its recommendations to the President (6), the conference indicated that:

. . . by the use of the modern knowledge of nutrition we can build a better and a stronger race, with greater average resistance to disease, greater average length of life, and greater average mental powers.

This can be done by the conquest of hunger — not only the obvious hunger man has always known, but the hidden hunger revealed by the modern knowledge of nutrition.

The United States is probably the best fed Nation in the world today, but we cannot afford to judge ourselves by external standards. We should judge ourselves by the standard of our own potentialities — our resources in food, in technical developments, in scientific knowledge. By that standard, we fall short of our goal.

The conclusion of the recommendations was indeed prophetic:

No nation, certainly no large nation, has ever truly conquered hunger, the oldest enemy of man. Such an aim is not too high, such a goal is not too difficult, for the people of the United States. It is in line with our tradition of pioneering on new frontiers. It is a particularly fitting task for us in this day when democracy should point the way to a new and better civilization for oppressed peoples all over the earth.

THE 12 RECOMMENDATIONS OF THE CONFERENCE

The conference cited the problem of malnutrition in the United States as:

. . . particularly complex. It has not only medical but social, economic, and psychological aspects. To attack it on a national scale will require peculiarly widespread and wholehearted cooperation on the part of all elements in our population.

The deliberations of the conference led to the formulation of the 12 basic recommendations, referred to as "lines of attack" and transmitted by the chairman, Paul McNutt, directly to President Roosevelt. Here, in brief, are those recommendations, as they were made in 1941 (7):

1. The use of the allowances of calories, protein, and certain important minerals and vitamins, recommended by the Committee on Food and Nutrition of the National Research Council, both as the general goal for good nutrition in the United States and as a yardstick by which to measure progress toward that goal. . . .

2. Translation of these allowances, and other similar technical material, into terms of everyday foods and appetizing meals suitable for families and individuals at different economic levels. . . .

3. Vigorous and continuous research to add to our present knowledge of the nutritional needs of individuals, the nutritional status of groups in the population, the nutritive content of everyday foods, and the effects of various methods of production, processing, storing, and cooking on their nutritive value. . . .

4. More widespread education of doctors, dentists, teachers, social service workers, public health nurses, and other professional workers in the newer knowledge of nutrition. . . .

5. Mobilization of every educational method to spread the newer knowledge of nutrition among laymen. . . .

6. Mobilization of all neighborhood, community, state, and national organizations and services that can contribute in any way to raising the nutritional level of the people of the United States. . . .

7. Vigorous and continued attack on the fundamental problems of unemployment, insecure employment, and incomes inadequate to maintain an American standard of living. . . .

8. Full use of any practical devices, such as the Food Stamp Plan, school lunches, and low-cost milk distribution, which will bring nourishing, adequate meals to those who could not otherwise afford them, and at the same time help to distribute food surpluses at a fair return to the farmer. . . .

9. Efforts to improve food distribution, including processing, marketing, packaging, and labeling, to bring about greater real economies for the consumer. . . .

10. Encouragement, in all practical ways, of greater production of the foods needed in more abundance in the average American diet. . . .

11. Encouragement, in all practical ways, of more production for home use by rural people, especially those at low-income levels. . . .

12. Improving the nutritive value of certain low-cost staple food products, such as flour and bread, by enrichment with nutritive elements that have been removed from them in modern milling and refining processes.

These 12 recommendations have served us well, and most continue to be timely. The food stamp plan of the late 1930's has even reappeared in the 1960's in areas of the United States affected with widespread unemployment; school lunch and low-cost milk distribution programs are continuing to supply nourishment for children while utilizing at least a part of the surplus commodities stored by the federal government. Yet, in some places in 1962, no more than 30 per cent of school children eligible for the lunch and milk program are taking advantage of it.

CONCERN FOR THE HUMAN FACTOR

Many of the ideas and opinions emanating from the first national nutrition conference offer worthwhile suggestions for nutrition educators today. Some particular points discussed in 1941, for example, are strikingly appropriate to nutrition education in 1962.

The Meaning of Food to People

Chairman Paul McNutt spoke effectively and humorously in his opening address (8):

Do not forget that for a very significant part of our population, nutrition is not a nine-letter word emblazoned with men in white, rampant on a field of vitamins. It is a four-letter word spelled F O O D — good food and plenty of it.

Something frequently happens to good food when its selection is distilled through the coils of an expert. Food loses its gastronomic gusto. A fellow gets the uncomfortable feeling that he is eating exactly what he ought to and he develops a sort of technological claustrophobia about it.

Out in Indiana we raise and serve and eat the best food in the world . . . our Indiana porkers veritably fatten with honest pride at the prospect of becoming a part of a Hoosier meal. An Indiana farm dinner, steaming on the kitchen table, constitutes about the best concatenation of vitamins ever strung together. And we have done it for years without ever knowing any of these vitamins by their first name — or even their initials. That kind of dinner contains a vitamin you would not find in a laboratory — the psychological vitamin of human satisfaction. I shall name it vitamin Z, so the doctors can run theirs consecutively.

In more professional terms, Dr. Alice Keliher (9) urged that nutritionists must think a great deal about the emotional factor in food habits:

We can point out to people that they ought to eat vegetables, but they won't eat them if they hate them. In meeting the problem with children in the schools we need to accustom them to certain foods by allowing them to participate in growing, cooking, and working with foods in order to build up a readiness for them.

Thus school gardens became popular and children learned to be handy with the hoe. They also learned how foods grow, and came to appreciate the vital role played by garden stuff in protecting health.

Concern for Caution Versus the Importance of Action

Dr. Wilder (10) commented on the problem of urgency in nutrition education:

But, after all, in a dynamic society we cannot demand complete scientific knowledge before acting. Greater mistakes will be made by waiting for the golden age than by acting on knowledge at hand and changing our course as new knowledge may suggest.

Concern for the "Phases" in Nutrition

Dr. John R. Murlin, professor of physiology at the University of Rochester, traced the development of nutrition education through various phases (11), which he listed as:

1. The *composition* phase — of what do our foods consist?
2. The *digestibility* phase — which foods are most easily digested?
3. The *calorie* phase — how much energy does food contain, and how much does the body require?
4. The *biological* phase — which foods are of greatest biological value?

Then Dr. Murlin added:

Each of these phases has risen to a peak of predominant interest and left a prominent contribution, each now continues to make prominent contributions to knowledge, but has given way to the subsequent phase as the center of interest. It is difficult to fix a time when each of those phases was in the ascendancy. None has completely died out.

We are now (1941) riding the vitamin wave. You know, it is rather precarious sometimes to be on the crest. It all depends on how the wave will behave. If it tips over and breaks, as waves do on the seashore, it may do harm. So I am trustfully living in the belief that we are going to come down off the crest of the vitamins safely.

As Dr. Murlin predicted, we have traveled the vitamin crest with more or less safety. In the sixties we are in the midst of what perhaps is another phase — the "fat phase." We are concerned with the kinds and amounts of fat we eat, and above all about getting fat. From this, our knowledge will undoubtedly increase. In the meantime, the nutrition educator may be comforted by the fact that much will be learned from this concentration of efforts and concern, but at their heights these periods demand discrimination, perspective, and common sense.

CONFERENCE CONCLUSION

In transmitting the recommendations unanimously adopted by the Conference, McNutt (12) said to President Roosevelt:

. . . the National Nutrition Conference was outstanding for its enthusiasm and its whole-hearted devotion to the cause of building a stronger America. Everyone present at this Conference, I am sure, felt that he was participating in an event of great historic importance to the future of his country.

In addition, McNutt told the President:

The recommendations are intended to lay the foundation for a broad national policy on nutrition that will apply both to the present emergency and in the future when this emergency is past.

McNutt's evaluation of the first National Nutrition Conference for Defense has proved accurate with the passage of time.

The National Food and Nutrition Institute
December 8 - 10, 1952

Eleven years after the first national conference on nutrition, 400 delegates assembled to take stock of the peacetime food and nutrition situation, to review existing programs, and to determine how to augment and strengthen them. To do this, it was necessary to examine nutrition education in the past, to evaluate it in relation to what was then the present situation, and to decide where to place the emphasis in the future.

The sense of urgency which had been paramount at the 1941 Conference was not present. Economic conditions were good, many advances had taken place in nutrition science, enrichment programs had been firmly established for more than a decade, and the Recommended Daily Allowances had proved to be of practical value. Food technology had made rapid strides forward: for example, the frozen food industry was satisfying larger public demands for new, convenient foods. Yet, despite these positive aspects, nutrition problems still existed.

The Conference met to redirect or reorient programs of nutrition to fit new dilemmas which had developed in our changing economic and cultural scene:

1. Overweight and obesity — their causes, cures, and prevention.
2. Chronic disease in the aged, particularly as related to long-time food habits.
3. The need to assess regularly the nutritional status of our population on a broad, standardized basis in order to learn more about the possible relationships of diet to health.

Subclinical deficiencies were coming under scrutiny because outright deficiency diseases had largely disappeared. Now the problem was exemplified by the vague, phantom-like symptoms of what the first Conference had termed "hidden hunger": loss of vigor, retarded growth in children, low resistance to infection, increased tooth decay, and abnormal births. All these were viewed as possible indications of poor nutrition. The second Conference recommended that more research was needed on the etiology of diseases to determine more exactly the role played by food habits.

EMPHASIS ON EDUCATION

There was renewed emphasis on education at this conference. Various delegates spoke of improvements in diet, which had resulted in a more productive population, with higher purchasing power and higher consumption. A larger number of our citizens were living longer. Many had benefited from improved food practices because they had been taught the importance of "The Basic Seven" and had consumed enriched staple foods.

CHRONIC DISEASES AND NUTRITION

Nutritionists had become members of the chronic disease team. They clearly were charged with the responsibilities of teaching, persuading, and motivating the layman to improve his food habits in order to improve his health.

Dr. Edward J. Stieglitz (13) cited the "chronic, insidious, and progressive disorders" which in 1952 represented what he termed "the major source of disability and death in the American population." He regarded the degenerative diseases in oldsters as closely related to impaired nutrition.

W. H. Sebrell, Jr., M.D. (14), then director of the National Institutes of Health, Public Health Service, in addressing the opening session of the Conference, told the delegates about world food dilemmas, citing Asia, Central America, and Africa as areas with inadequate protein intake — a serious dietary defect. Dr. Sebrell suggested the planting of high-protein crops, plus fortification of cereal-potato diets with manufactured nutrients. He cited the cultural barriers in foreign populations which often presented perplexing obstacles to nutritionists who saw the need for changes in food habits.

Two new topics for discussion at the Conference were emphasized by Dr. Sebrell: possible changes in federal legislation regarding food additives and supplements; and the necessity of food planning for emergencies.

The latter need was an outgrowth of the frightening possibility of global warfare. Atomic, biological, and chemical weapons were not remote scientific possibilities. They existed, and they could affect our nation's food supply if they accompanied a surprise attack on a scale fantastically larger than had occurred at Pearl Harbor in 1941.

THE NEED FOR NUTRITION SURVEYS

This conference advocated continuous studies of the nutritional status and food habits of the people as a useful tool in determining exactly what nutrition problems were. There were indications of certain trends which needed substantiating: a shift toward a larger share of calories from fat, plus evidence that calcium, ascorbic acid, and vitamin A were in short supply in many diets. Results of the enrichment program begun in 1941 were termed "spectacular" in that they had exerted an extremely favorable effect upon the nutritive value of national food supplies, as indicated by several studies.

CONSUMER FOOD PROTECTION

Under existing laws in 1952, many food fads and supplements in the realm of quackery were escaping federal regulation. There was a need to warn the populace of these worthless and expensive items.

Because loopholes in existing laws prevented legal action, protection of consumers would have to be provided through educational programs. The Conference advocated strengthening federal jurisdiction through improved legislation; meanwhile, the public was encouraged to check the validity of new nutrition theories.

Food Additives

Another problem of food protection for consumers centered upon the absence of federal authority to regulate food additives, although some of them were definitely known to be harmful. There existed a legal gap which needed to be closed: an ingredient of dubious safety could be used until evidence proved it poisonous or harmful — and that could take years. This, of course, was much like calling the fire department after the building has burned down. So the Conference requested legislation which would place strict regulations on emulsifiers, stabilizers, moisteners, preservatives, fumigants, antioxidants, antibiotics, and other ingredients added to food in the production, processing, and packing stages. It is interesting to note that better laws were eventually passed.

The effect of this Conference, directly or indirectly, on the Congress cannot be evaluated, but undoubtedly the purpose of creating a better informed public was realized.

EMERGENCY FOOD PLANNING

The Conference paid considerable attention to the vast changes which had occurred in the realm of destructive weapons. This included not only the obvious threat of nuclear attack, but also chemical and biological destruction which could be delivered by high-altitude aircraft and, eventually, by intercontinental missiles. Because the public attitude toward these potential disasters was "it can't happen here," it was up to federal and state authorities to begin to outline procedures to meet various emergencies. Thus discussions of emergency food supplies, civil defense, and mass feeding were included in these sessions.

Delegates agreed that the best technique of defense was to urge *local* authorities and individual citizens to prepare themselves for emergencies. The philosophy behind this was that in time of widespread devastation in the United States, transportation and communication facilities would undoubtedly be disrupted — citizens would be unable to depend upon outside help. This led to Conference recommendations that families keep several days' food supplies on hand at all times; that local civil defense authorities work closely with commercial

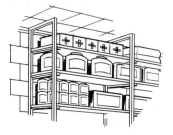

food outlets on emergency food distribution plants, and that the federal government and state governments offer advice and technical help for local civil defense organizations. Much more has been learned since about the effects of radioactive contamination upon food supplies which will be discussed in Chapter 11.

WORLD-WIDE NUTRITION PROBLEMS

Recognizing the importance of world-wide food problems and their effect on our nation's future, Dr. Sebrell (14) in his opening address to the Conference, pointed out that nutrition progress in our nation could well benefit peoples in other lands, emphasizing these nutrition problems:

> A reorientation of our approach to such problems in this country and abroad should be based on intensive, long-range application of the physical and social sciences. In its aspects, this research program should seek additional data on the world food situation. Among the effects of a decade of conflict have been far-reaching changes in population distribution, markets, food production and potential, and other economic and social conditions. A comprehensive national program will recognize international food and nutrition problems and participate in their solution. And this program should be flexible enough to shift not only with new knowledge and national needs, but with the ever-changing world picture.

Sebrell advocated expanded surveys on the nutritional status of foreign populations, as had already been begun by the USDA and the Food and Agriculture Organization of the United States. In Chapter 10, "International Nutrition: A Resource and a Responsibility," the development of our aid and interest in this problem is traced.

The National Nutrition Education Conference
April 1 - 3, 1957

The third national Conference included the word "education" in its title, as did the fourth, thus reasserting and strengthening the importance of education to the problems of nutrition.

The over-all theme of this Conference was presenting nutrition facts to stimulate and motivate people toward improving their food habits. This, of course, could only be done through education. As a background for the Conference, a report was made of findings in a nationwide survey of food consumption, conducted in 1955 by the Agricultural Research Service and Agricultural Marketing Service of the USDA, as an outgrowth, at least in part, of a recommendation from the 1952 Conference for expanded data on food habits.

NATIONAL SURVEY INDICATIONS

The high points of this 1955 Household Food Consumption Survey, as discussed at the Conference, are presented in Chapter 3. Al-

though the Survey showed that sizable segments of the population had
diets poor in certain nutrients — notably calcium, ascorbic acid, vitamin A, thiamine, and riboflavin — it was reassuring to find very few
households with diets extremely low in these nutrients. About 10
per cent had diets that were below two-thirds of the allowance for
ascorbic acid, 8 per cent were similarly low in calcium, and percentages were even less for diets below the two-thirds mark in other nutrients.

Thus there had been considerable improvement since the 1930's,
when one-third of diets were classed as "poor." Now the "poor" classification included only about one-tenth of the households. Undoubtedly the enrichment program had accounted for much of the
improvement, but other factors were: improved economic conditions,
new developments in food technology and marketing, and the effect
of nutrition education. One indication of the 1955 survey was that
most of the dietary improvements apparently occurred before 1948,
when another extensive food consumption survey had been conducted.
The 1955 data showed few significant improvements in nutrient levels
over those of 1948. This observation was considered to convey an important warning against complacency.

Fat Consumption

A trend was definitely showing in 1957 regarding the amount of
fats in diets. In the spring of 1955 an average of 155 grams of fat per
person per day was available for consumption; the percentage of
calories from fat in the diet apparently showed a noticeable increase
between the years of 1935 – 36 and 1955: from 38 per cent to 44 per
cent. More data are needed to translate these figures into actual consumption, since little is known about the percentage of disappearance
of fat through plate waste and perhaps other disposals of fats purchased but not consumed. In other words, the per capita figures may
not represent accurately the fat that has gone into the stomachs of
people.

Analysis of the Survey

In analyzing diets on the basis of regions or groups, the USDA
survey revealed that, in general, the population studied in the South
was less well fed than those in the Northeast, North Central, and
West — the four regions used for the survey. The findings also indicated that farm diets generally were furnishing larger amounts of all
nutrients than were city diets, except for vitamins A and C.

In evaluating the needs of nutrition education, the third Conference concluded that (15):

1. High-income families need education for nutrition as well as do
   middle- and low-income families. Although diets tend to improve
   with increased income, there often is a corresponding shift away
   from low-cost grain and pork products which are rich in thiamine.
   Thus, when working with higher income groups, nutritionists per-

haps do not need to emphasize protein and niacin — nutrients found in higher cost foods — but do need to emphasize thiamine as a nutrient needed in these diets.

2. Nutrition problems continued to exist, despite economic well-being and availability of nutritious foods. There were new problems emerging which affected particular groups: old people, teen-agers, pregnant women, and preadolescents. These people need to be reached and motivated appropriately in order to improve their food habits; each group requires special answers for its problems. More research was needed in nutrition education for varying age groups and socioeconomic groups.

3. The 1955 survey indicated it was possible to obtain a nutritionally adequate diet for even less money than families were already spending. The problem was in knowing how to spend food dollars advantageously to obtain the necessary dietary improvements.

4. It was more feasible to begin by modifying existing food habits in order to achieve better diets than to attempt major overhauls of dietary patterns. "Put people before food" was the admonition.

5. A new influence upon nutrition education was a consideration of the cultural aspects of eating patterns. The anthropologist entered the nutrition scene officially, along with the education specialist, Dr. Robert Fleming, who outlined principles of learning and the importance of human factors and values involved in teaching and learning; Dr. John Cassell, an anthropologist, stressed that food habits are "among the oldest and most deeply entrenched aspects of many cultures." Changes require time and study of the roots of the habits.

The Nutrition Education Conference January 29 - 31, 1962

Nutritional needs of children was the theme of the fourth nation-wide Conference, which considered the evaluation of children's diets, problems related to obesity, dental health, and the social and emotional aspects of their food habits.

Dr. Ruth Leverton, assistant administrator of the Agricultural Research Service of the United States Department of Agriculture, said that the nutritional status of children was probably the best it had ever been in our nation. However, she pointed out the growing concern about overweight children and about certain imbalances (16):

1. Imbalance between the amount of food energy needed and the amount supplied by the diet, especially in teen-age girls.
2. Imbalance between the need for food and the many opportunities to consume food; imbalance between the energy yield of many foods in relation to their nutritive value.
3. Imbalance between opportunities to make choices of food and the training and experience with which children have been equipped to make wise choices.

Dr. Leverton advised that young people need to be taught how to balance their food intake with energy needs; they need purposeful physical activity, and they need to be taught the importance of the kinds of carbohydrate in the diet. She cited studies with laboratory animals showing that diets with a high sugar content stimulate animals to eat more and that more fat is deposited on their bodies than when the carbohydrate in their diet is mainly starch. She also suggested at least a partial replacement of sugar- and fat-rich desserts in teen-ager's diets with whole wheat and enriched breads and cereals, and that these foods be used with vegetables such as potatoes as sources for additional calories to meet the high energy demands of that age group.

Dr. Leverton mentioned the importance of linoleic acid as a nutrient, suggesting to the Conference that some attention be given to the use of corn, cottonseed, or soybean oils in salad dressings or in cooking.

Finally, the importance of milk intake to children's diets was stressed by Dr. Leverton, who said that the milk intake should not be limited as long as the children are eating a well-balanced diet and not overeating, calling attention to the following situation:

> About 65 per cent of the schools in the United States are now participating in the school lunch and special milk programs, but in some schools only 10 to 30 per cent of the children are availing themselves of the service.

She summarized her remarks as follows:

> We can feel a sense of accomplishment in the fact that the diets and nutritional status of our children have never been as good as they are today. To maintain the progress which has been made, however, requires watchfulness, encouragement, and reinforcement by parents, teachers, nutrition educators, and everyone who is concerned with nutrition and health.

CULTURAL FACTORS INFLUENCING CHILDREN'S FOOD HABITS

Dr. Margaret Lantis, anthropologist, directed the attention of Conference delegates to some of the cultural influences on children's food habits (17). She noted the popularity of the vending machine and its effect of "encouraging piecemeal eating" among children and adults. Further, Dr. Lantis remarked:

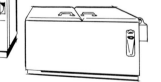

> Recently . . . snacks and coffee breaks have become part of our life so that, aided by the refrigerator, the vending machine, and others of the newest gadgets, we are becoming paradoxically like the simpler, less organized, less routinized societies in this custom of frequent, unplanned eating.

Citing as examples that eating becomes closely integrated with certain entirely unrelated activities:

> Our children, outside institutional life in which eating is more controlled, are growing up with the expectation that the family doesn't just stop for gas — it stops for gas and pop. . . . A person doesn't just bowl or skate — he bowls and has a cup of coffee or eats a hot dog. An adolescent doesn't just wait for a bus — he waits and eats a candy bar, or if a girl, she stops in the drug store to have a soft drink.

In discussing automation as a factor that may determine the appetites of the future, she traced the development of "mass feeding machines" which offer only "bland versions of chicken and noodles, Spanish rice, beef stew . . . and such."

Dr. Lantis stressed another important influence that looms large for children as well as adults — that of decision making:

> Another effect of our self-service merchandising is an emphasis on individual choice, not, however, large choices between basically different types of food but small choices. The cellophane-wrapped assortment of small boxes of dry cereal and the machine that vends small packages of cookies and crackers or an assortment of four soft drinks provide good examples. The child at the breakfast table with the array of cereals in front of him is not choosing between bacon and corn flakes, for example, but merely between one kind of flakes and another kind of flakes.

And, finally, Dr. Lantis pointed out:

> It is more important for a child to choose between a candy bar and an apple . . . than for him to choose among 12 chocolate bars. . . .

How can this multitude of decisions within a truly small range of choices be solved? Dr. Lantis acknowledged that nutritionists have been attempting to help the child. However, many others are trying to influence the youthful consumer's choices, too: parents, teachers, pediatricians, advertisers, retailers, and producers of foods. So it is vital to teach the child practical knowledge which, Dr. Lantis said, will prevent him from being misled by "gimmicks" and fancy packaging.

Dr. Lantis concluded:

> They can be taught to figure things out for themselves regarding food purchases, and to be proud of their technical knowledge."

THE FOOD INDUSTRY

Horace L. Sipple, executive secretary of the Nutrition Foundation, discussed the activities of trade associations and individual food companies in nutrition education (18). The Nutrition Foundation, supported by food and related industries, has financed basic nutrition research through grants-in-aid to universities and medical schools, attempting to reach the public with sound nutrition information. Sipple cited the value — and pitfalls — of advertising, pointing out:

. . . the tendency, which has not been resisted by some companies, to over-emphasize the favorable characteristics of their own product, thereby creating the impression that this product is superior to others of its type.

Sipple also stressed the use of sound nutrition principles in food advertising, warning that it was wise to avoid the "more than," "better than," "no other is as good" types of sales messages.

Concluding, Sipple appealed to the food industries to increase the dissemination of good nutrition facts by extending their present programs of publications, films, and support of nutrition research.

He asserted:

The extra educational effort required would not only aid greatly in combatting food faddism and nutrition quackery by replacing fantasy with fact but would also help meet the need for a practical guide to good nutrition in everyday life.

WHAT WE HAVE LEARNED

Looking back over the 21-year period covered by these four conferences, we can check their recommendations in the light of what we now know. In the main, the 12 recommendations from the first conference are as pertinent in the 1960's as they were in the 40's. They constituted a rational guide for a national nutrition program which still can give purpose and direction to present and future efforts to improve food habits.

Education is a theme which has been the foundation of all four conferences. But it is important to note that emphasis has been on education for *change* — not education in terms of set formulas and patterns to meet specific situations. No list of dietary rules can be tailored perfectly to fit a given individual on a permanent basis, because he is constantly changing. His environment is changing, too. Therefore, it is necessary to equip him with knowledge adequate to meet the changes within himself and his environment.

The value of research was demonstrated repeatedly at these conferences. Many projects were begun largely through the impetus of the demand by nutrition educators for better data on dietary and nutrition problems. The 1955 food survey by the USDA served a need which had been indicated at the 1952 Conference. The importance of periodic surveys nationally and internationally has been stressed in 1957 and again in 1962. Plans are under way for another survey in the mid-sixties.

Another important long-range effect of these conferences has been the expression of interest in nutrition among professional workers in a variety of specialties. For example, clinical nutrition is now a well-established medical specialty. Nutrition as a science has widened and expanded through the years to include more extensive application of the sciences of physics, chemistry, and biochemistry; the social scientists are now interested in what the nutritionists are doing, and nutrition workers in turn are paying close attention to the efforts of their colleagues in the social sciences.

A glance back to the beginnings of our national concern for nutrition education demonstrates the pioneering role of home economists and dietitians, and their increasing responsibility for nutrition education through the years. The primary teaching load still is placed upon these specialists, along with the public health nutritionists, but nutrition educators generally have the advantage of expanded research and information accumulated by many specialists in other fields. The effectiveness of their work depends greatly on their ability to make use of their great resources in many areas of knowledge.

Perhaps the sharpest contrast of all, as shown in a review of these conferences, is the emphasis in 1941 upon the problems of undernutrition versus the 1960 dilemma of overweight and overeating. The "affluent society" in which we live stresses the amazing fact that our land of plenty does not automatically guarantee good nutrition. One of the goals of nutrition education is to enable the individual to take intelligent advantage of his ever-expanding opportunities for choice in the realm of food, and to help create conditions where people everywhere will have enough of the essentials of an adequate diet for their health and well-being.

These national conferences have led the way for nutrition educators who are endeavoring to accomplish that goal.

REFERENCES

1. National Nutrition Conference for Defense, FSA, *Federation Proceedings*, pp. 1–2. U.S. Govt. Print. Off., 1941.
2. *Ibid.*, p. 64.
3. *Ibid.*, p. VIII (Foreword).
4. *Ibid.*, p. 14.
5. *Jour. A.M.A.*, 178:1024–25, 1961.
6. *Proceedings*, Natl. Conf., *op. cit.*, pp. 232–33.
7. *Ibid.*, pp. 230–32.
8. *Ibid.*, p. 4.
9. *Ibid.*, p. 138.
10. *Ibid.*, p. 12.
11. *Ibid.*, p. 23.
12. *Ibid.*, p. 229.
13. Stieglitz, Edward J., National Food and Nutrition Institute, Washington, Dec. 8–10, 1952, *Proceedings*. USDA Agr. Handbook No. 56, p. 67.
14. *Ibid.*, p. 6.
15. National Nutrition Education Conference, April 1–3, 1957, *Proceedings*. USDA Misc. Publ. No. 745.
16. Leverton, R., Nutrition Education Conference, Washington, Jan. 29–31, 1962, *Proceedings*. USDA Misc. Publ. No. 913:8–11.
17. Lantis, M., *ibid.*, pp. 24–30.
18. Sipple, H., *ibid.*, pp. 47–49.

Chapter Ten

International Nutrition:
A Resource and a Responsibility

Efforts to apply the science of nutrition to human welfare on an international scale have become spectacular. The universal concern for food supplies around the world is perhaps one of the major expressions of the humanitarian spirit of this age. A brief chronology of the milestones in world nutrition, along with a statement of the purposes of the Food and Agriculture Organization and the World Health Organization, is given in Appendix.

The need for continued concern about world food supplies is apparent in extensive analyses made by both the USDA and the FAO. Nutrition educators bear considerable responsibility in making known to the public the extent of world food needs and their significance to all human beings.

For detailed studies of the world food situation the reader is referred to "Food and People," by the subcommittee on foreign economic policy of the joint economic committee, Congress of the United States, for sale by the Superintendent of Documents, U.S. Government Printing Office, Washington 25, D.C. Also available from the Superintendent of Documents is "The World Food Budget, 1962 and 1966," Foreign Agricultural Economic Report No. 4, by the Economic Research Service in cooperation with Foreign Agricultural Service, USDA.

The reader is referred also to "The World Must Eat," a booklet prepared by FAO and UNESCO's Gauting Institute, published in 1962 by Oceana Publications, Inc., Dobbs Ferry, N.Y. One of a study guide series, it includes much factual information about world nutrition. At the conclusion of each chapter appears a section titled "Things To Do," which offers suggestions to teachers for planning meaningful activities in international nutrition.

[*238*]

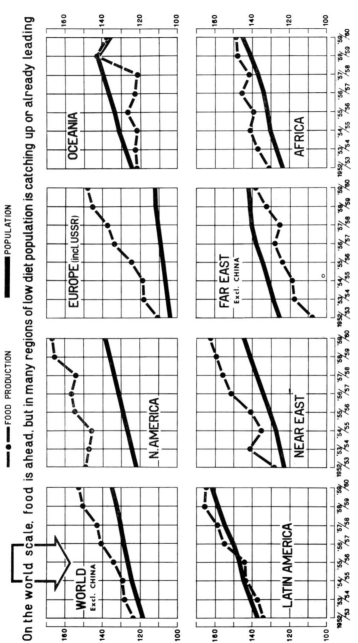

Fig. 10.1 — The race between food and population, with indices of prewar = 100. On the world scale, food is ahead; but in many regions of low diet, population is catching up or has taken the lead. (Source: "The Basic Freedom — Freedom From Hunger," FAO Bul., 1960.)

A most basic consideration in the world food situation — as in a family — is the number of mouths to be fed. Is there enough food to go around, and will there be enough in the face of the growing population explosion? On a world-wide basis, food production is keeping ahead of the population. In some of the most populous areas, however, the relationship between population and the food supply is not good (see Fig. 10.1).

The future depends upon how well we can keep up food production in relation to the growing population, and whether we can successfully distribute foods from lands of abundance to places of scarcity and from seasons of abundance to times of scarcity. Although the problem appears to be simple, the solutions for it are highly complex. Science must play a major role in increasing the productivity of lands and developing new ways to meet nutrient needs.

From available evidence, the world food situation presents these two basic aspects:

1. Diets are nutritionally adequate in the 30 industrialized nations of the temperate Northern Area, accounting for a third of mankind — more than 900 million people. Conditions are such as to assure the food supply in this region for the foreseeable future.

2. For most of the 70 less-developed countries in the semitropical Southern Area, diets are nutritionally inadequate because of shortages in proteins, fats, and total calories. The following are listed as exceptions to the general situation in the Southern Area: Taiwan, Turkey, Lebanon, Israel, Republic of South Africa, Federation of Rhodesia and Nyasaland; and in Latin America, Argentina, Uruguay, Chile, Brazil (in sections), Costa Rica, Cuba, and Mexico.

An impressive overview of the world's nutrition problems is afforded by three of the "diet deficit" maps prepared by the USDA from data available in 1958, Figures 10.2A, B, and C.

CLOSING NUTRITIONAL GAPS

Existing nutritional gaps can be closed only by increased food production or by the production of goods that can be traded for food. Major problems affecting food production are:

1. Low income per capita
2. High ratio of population to land
3. Lack of chemical fertilizers

Fig. 10.2A, B, C — Countries showing calorie deficits are generally those with high concentrations of population and low development of industry and agriculture. Protein deficits are less widespread than calorie deficits, and they occur in some countries where calorie deficits are not prevalent. A large number of countries have a short supply of fats. (Source: "The World Food Budget, 1962 and 1966," ERS, USDA.)

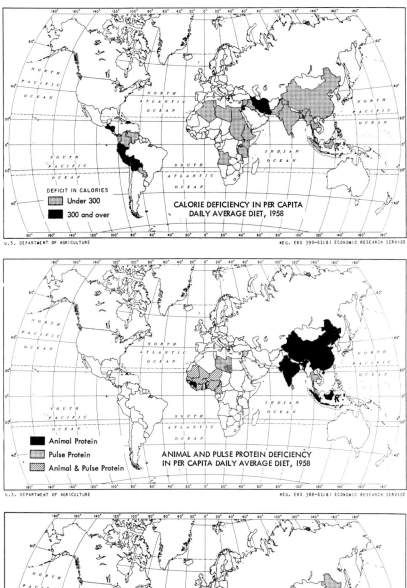

DEFICIT IN CALORIES

Under 300

300 and over

CALORIE DEFICIENCY IN PER CAPITA
DAILY AVERAGE DIET, 1958

Animal Protein

Pulse Protein

Animal & Pulse Protein

ANIMAL AND PULSE PROTEIN DEFICIENCY
IN PER CAPITA DAILY AVERAGE DIET, 1958

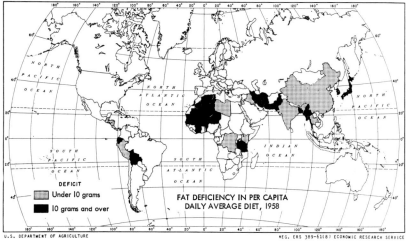

DEFICIT

Under 10 grams

10 grams and over

FAT DEFICIENCY IN PER CAPITA
DAILY AVERAGE DIET, 1958

The "Food for Peace" program represents a major effort by the United States to work toward decreasing the food gap. It has received strong bipartisan support in the legislative and executive branches of our government. President John F. Kennedy stated on January 24, 1961: "We must narrow the gap between abundance here at home and near starvation abroad. Humanity and prudence alike counsel a major effort on our part."

Again in his State of the Union message on January 30, 1961, he said, "The product of our abundance must be used more effectively to relieve hunger and help economic growth in all corners of the globe."

The American people must be made aware of the fact that improvement of the world food situation will require much more than gifts of food in time of need. Only when food is given in a way which will not dislocate the economy of the recipient country can we dispose of agricultural surpluses to mutual advantage.

Public Law 480 represents an ingenious effort on the part of our country to divert some of our surplus foods to other countries. Commodities sent abroad are not paid for in American dollars, but the equivalent sums in the currency of the recipient countries are allocated to economic and social development of the country itself. Thus in India, where some of the largest transactions have been made, rupees generated by the program have been used for economic development, loans to private United States and Indian firms, and various agency programs. So-called "wheat" money has been important to India's developmental efforts.

Short-term food programs are only a stopgap measure. Long-range efforts to improve the total economy of a nation, together with education of the people, must be primary goals for aid programs.

An increasing force in international nutrition is the expansion of food industries around the world. According to a special report in *Food Engineering,* July, 1962, page 49, "A world boom in food manufacturing is in the making." This special report further states that North America and Western Europe are setting the pace, but other countries are making rapid gains in manufacturing output, as 80 per cent in Algeria, 67 per cent in Russia, and 40 per cent in Japan. The trend is not limited to the "developed" countries. United Nations economists predict a 154 per cent increase for underdeveloped nations in the value added by food manufacturing between 1958 and 1975. The Middle East is expected to gain 319 per cent; Africa, 224 per cent; Asia, 209 per cent; Latin America, 102 per cent; and four countries in Europe, 162 per cent.

American food industries now extend around the world. One well-known firm of the United States has plants in Canada, Argentina, Brazil, Colombia, Ecuador, England, Mexico, Panama, Paraguay, Peru, the Philippines, Southern Rhodesia, Trinidad, South Africa, Uruguay, and Venezuela. It has manufacturing agreements in several other countries.

These enterprises will have a far-reaching effect on the nutrition of the people both through economic development, dietary improvements, and perhaps nutrition education. In the United States, food industries have performed a major service in supporting nutrition research and in developing and disseminating nutrition education materials. We would expect food industries to continue these interests in their world as well as their national enterprises.

THE MEANING OF MALNUTRITION

Along with the world's food needs, the nutrition educator has a responsibility to interpret to the public the meaning of malnutrition as it affects people in nations with wide food gaps. Malnutrition in poorly fed areas of the world is a complex situation in which adverse effects of nutrient shortages are compounded by many other conditions. The most prevalent form of malnutrition has been frequently described as simply the lack of enough food, although in many areas the primary problem is shortage of good quality protein, while in other countries vitamin deficiencies are paramount (1).

Results of malnutrition are evident in high rates of infant and maternal mortality. However, there is some evidence that the mortality rate of children age 1 to 4 years is more indicative of the nutritional level of the country than is the infant mortality rate, because these older children do not have the protection of mothers' milk and are generally exposed to the family's food — or lack of it.

Moreover, the mortality of infants from poor nutrition is greatly complicated by deaths due to poor sanitation. When the mortality rate of older children (age 1 to 4) exceeds 10 per thousand, a serious nutrition problem is said to exist in a country. In some nations this rate is as high as 30 per thousand; in the United States it is 1 or 2 per thousand. The infant and child mortality rates, as multiples of the corresponding rates in the United States in 1955, have been compiled by Scrimshaw (2), and given in Table 10.1.

TABLE 10.1

INFANT AND CHILD MORTALITY IN UNDERDEVELOPED AREAS*
(Multiples of 1955 U.S. rates)

Africa and Asia			Latin America		
Country	Infant mortality	Mortality 1–4 years	Country	Infant mortality	Mortality 1–4 years
Egypt, 1947	8	45	Ecuador, 1955	4	26
Algeria (Moslems), 1948....	6	35	Colombia, 1956	4	18
Federation of Malaya, 1947	7	22	Guatemala, 1955 ...	4	39
Singapore, 1947	5	14	Brazil, 1956	4	11
Ceylon, 1952	3	21	Mexico, 1955	3	22
Thailand, 1947	2	16	El Salvador, 1956 ...	3	21

* Source: See Ref. 2 at end of this chapter.

It is difficult for well-nourished and overfed people to understand the meaning of starvation. Actually to see it is a shocking experience (see Fig. 10.3). Characteristics of the starved person have been described in a joint report of the Food and Agriculture Organization and the World Health Organization in grim terms which people can readily visualize and understand. The following paragraphs are excerpted from World Health Organization Technical Report Series No. 45, Nov., 1951, pages 22–27:

The typical starved person, without other complications, is emaciated, pallid, grey, apathetic, and depressed in appearance. Neglect of personal appearance, indifference to the impression made on others, and slow movements and speech give an impression of stupidity. The skin is dry and cold, and the hair is lifeless. In proportion to the degree of starvation, the individual will experience weakness, hunger, fatigue, and a sense of being old.

In starving children, characteristic findings include a facial expression resembling old age, loose folds of hanging skin, protruding abdomen, feeble crying, and, if unrelieved, sudden death with "acute laryngeal weakness and respiratory failure."

Early in starvation, the patient's world of concern shrinks and becomes limited to fewer persons and events. In severe to extreme starvation, almost the only interest is the patient himself and the question of food.

The starved person is accident prone. He moves away too late from the path of an oncoming vehicle and may trip and stumble because he pays too little attention to obstacles and drags his feet.

Social niceties quickly disappear and these are followed by progressive abandonment of moral niceties. Theft, especially of food and clothing, becomes common. Social and political organization are difficult to maintain. Basic intellective capacity, surprisingly, is not altered except at the extreme level, but intellective activity is reduced much as is physical activity. The extremely starved person is incapable of useful work. The moderately starved person has little endurance in heavy manual labor.

The report states that interesting age and sex differences in mortality have been observed in famine. Among adults, females almost everywhere seem to withstand starvation conditions better than males and this holds for all ages. Among both males and females, the older persons, especially those beyond middle age, usually show a much greater increase in mortality than any other segment of the population, with the possible exception of infants under one year. Children survive fairly well, but this may be due to conscious efforts to protect them. The highest mortality is observed among elderly urban recluses. It seems probable, according to the FAO and WHO analysis, that in famine conditions the greatest threat is to the males, the elderly, and to the youngest infants.

Only the most severe starvation suppresses entirely the linear growth of children, but the weight growth is very sensitive to the nutrient supply. Hence, periodic measurements of height and weight are a practical index of the nutritional status of the entire population. Normally a large part of the energy expenditure of children is devoted to voluntary activity which promptly diminishes when they are undernourished. *A simple observation at play,* according to this report, *can often allow a shrewd estimate of the level of prevailing undernutrition.*

Fig. 10.3 — A quarter of a million copies of this poster blanketed France during the French National Week for the Freedom From Hunger Campaign. (Source: FAO **News:** II, 6, p. 2.)

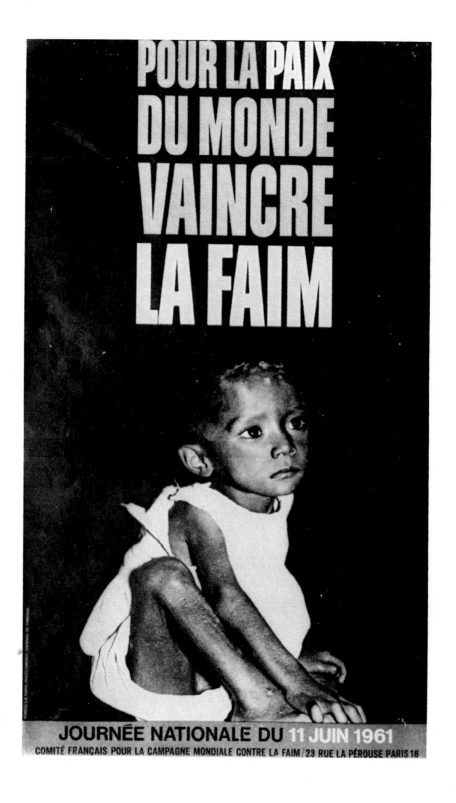

POUR LA PAIX
DU MONDE
VAINCRE
LA FAIM

JOURNÉE NATIONALE DU 11 JUIN 1961
COMITÉ FRANÇAIS POUR LA CAMPAGNE MONDIALE CONTRE LA FAIM / 23 RUE LA PÉROUSE PARIS 16

The response of the severely undernourished to good food and care is little short of magic. (See Figs. 10.4 A and B.) But rehabilitation takes time, skill, and understanding as well as the provision of food and medical care.

Dietary Excesses and Imbalances

By no means are nutrition problems in the underdeveloped countries limited to dietary deficiencies. Excesses or imbalances of nutrients may also cause major health problems. For example, in some countries there are mainly two economic groups: the "haves" and the "have-nots." The wealthy merchants who sit in their shops are obese; the burden bearers are thin but sinewy. Wives of the rich men are also fat because most of the housework is done by women who work hard and characteristically are thin.

In Somaliland, some nomadic tribesmen daily use 2.5 to 4 and even up to 9 liters of milk per day, thus acquiring an excessively high intake of protein, fat, and calcium. Such intakes apparently do not cause health problems.

The Bantu typically have an iron overload, consuming from 100 to 200 milligrams per day. Many suffer toxic effects and siderosis. Some consume large amounts of salt, but it is not known whether this contributes to hypertension or high mortality from cerebral-vascular diseases.

The Bantu are also heavy consumers of alcohol, most of which originates in a fermented porridge or a beverage similar to beer.

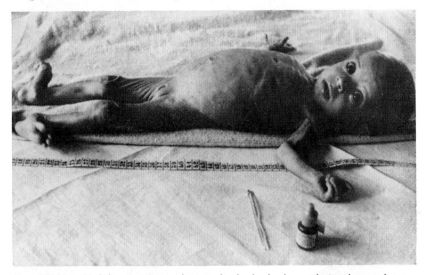

Fig. 10.4A — Molok, age 4 months, as she looked when admitted to a demonstration foundling home in Teheran, Iran, which operated on funds and aid furnished by UNICEF and WHO, with additional support from Government and municipal authorities. Molok's measurements were: weight, 3,100 kgs.; height, 60 cms.; chest, 36 cms.; and head, 38 cms. (Source: Iran Public Health Dept., issued by FAO, 1959.)

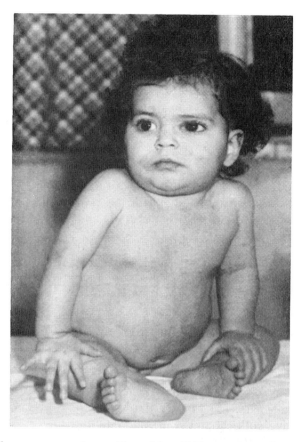

Fig.10.4B — Molok after 10 months in the demonstration foundling home. Her measurements: weight, 7,400 kgs.; height, 74 cms.; chest, 48½ cms.; and head, 45½ cms. (Source: same as Fig. 10.4A.)

Estimates are that they consume from 45 to 55 milliliters of alcohol per day, compared to an average in the United States of 30 milliliters.

FOOD AND POLITICS

If the public could acquire a clear concept of the meaning of starvation, semistarvation, and the ravages of dietary deficiency diseases, national and international programs for improving world nutrition hopefully would be expedited. Perhaps then we would find more national public support of world food plans.

"Food for Peace" is a slogan critically challenged by some economists. Millikan and Rostow (3) have stated that it is likely a misconception that revolt and political instability within less developed countries result largely or directly from hunger; or that alleviation *per se* of hunger will reduce revolutionary tendencies among people; or that if people are only better fed, they are less likely to shift from one to another political extreme.

Dr. Earl Heady (4) has added the comment that major war does not typically come from the chronically destitute and illiterate strata of populations who, on the contrary, accept their status as their lot in life, after being ingrained in it for generations and even centuries. Further, Heady says that food alone will not build up deep-seated political and economic convictions for people who cannot read. He continues:

> Peace or not depends more on sustained general economic development, with opportunities in other vectors of consumption space, than on food alone. Hence, we direct our efforts to the extent to which food from the United States can serve either positively or optimally in promotion of sustained economic development of less advanced countries.

It is not the purpose of this book to argue the many viewpoints about the political role of food in today's world. However, those who teach nutrition should be aware of the broad interrelationships between the world food supply and international affairs. Regarding the slogan "Food for Peace," for example, Dr. Heady has said that the slogan itself combines two powerful ideas that are rapidly becoming deep-seated international values; they are serving as magnets to draw the international activities of East and West more nearly into the same orbit and away from conflict.

The essential point to be made here is that improving the health and productivity of people in underdeveloped countries through better food is probably one of the first steps toward improving their economy. Adequate food will not ensure peace, nor will peace necessarily result in enough food. But the political and economic problems of a nation are somehow related to food, and they can be alleviated to a degree by adequate food supplies. From a practical standpoint, adequacy of food probably cannot be isolated as a main factor bringing political and economic stability.

It is extremely difficult to assess the socioeconomic effects of nutritional levels. Therefore, we must concern ourselves first with nutrition as it relates to the health and productivity of the *individual and the family,* but we cannot overlook its effect on larger groups, as the community and the nation, compounded as they are with other factors. The interdependence of the peoples of the world in the maintenance of an adequate food supply makes of it a public issue which can best be met by an informed populace.

INTERNATIONAL NUTRITION AS A SOURCE OF NEW KNOWLEDGE

The body of knowledge in nutrition science has been greatly expanded because of world-wide interest in it. Its very roots have international moorings: nineteenth century chemists, physiologists, and physicists of Germany and France laid the foundation for an understanding of energy metabolism, the nature of foodstuffs, fats, proteins, and carbohydrates, and the composition of foods.

Recognition of dietary deficiency diseases in the British navy, the Japanese navy, and in prisoners of the Dutch East Indies led to the discovery of some of the vitamins. The entire problem of protein malnutrition and how best to cope with it is now being explored on a world-wide basis, because it is one of the most frequent and most serious forms of malnutrition in the world.

The Effects of Protein Malnutrition

Protein malnutrition is evidenced by a variety of conditions. As in other dietary deficiencies, syndromes may occur in many degrees of severity, some barely recognizable, and some in the form of a now well-known disease, kwashiorkor, as it is named in Central Africa. In other regions, and in other languages, it has different names. South Africans call it "infantile pellagra"; the Jamaicans term it "fatty liver disease" or "sugar baby"; the French, Germans, and Latin Americans each give it labels which translate similarly into "nutritional edema syndrome" or "nutrition dystrophy." These names — and many others — all mean protein malnutrition, which is caused by diets high in carbohydrates and poor in quality and amount of protein. Protruding abdomens and skin lesions, characteristics of this disease, are apparent in Figures 10.5A and 10.5B.

Fig. 10.5A — Child eating a paw-paw in Tanganyika village shows symptoms of kwashiorkor complicated with parasitism. (Source: FAO photo.)

Kwashiorkor strikes hard at children when they are changed from a diet of mother's milk to the family food, which is usually a starchy gruel made from such regional staple foods as cassava or manioc. The disease has been described as that of the "displaced child" (i.e., displaced from mother's milk) or "red boy," the latter indicating the dispigmentation of the black hair which is characteristic of a large segment of people in the countries where kwashiorkor occurs. Other effects of the disease are much more severe: the abdomen enlarges and the liver becomes infiltrated with fat.

For a dramatic account of the ravages of this disease, the reader is referred to an article entitled, "The Red-headed Negro," by J. F. Brock (5), one of the early observers of the disease.

Some of the most significant work on kwashiorkor in children has taken place in nearby Guatemala, where the incidence of kwashiorkor is high and where pre-kwashiorkor, an underlying protein malnutrition that has not reached the stage of diagnosis, is very great. Dr. N. S. Scrimshaw (2) described these latter children as being retarded nearly four years in bone formation when they reached school age. Furthermore, he stated that the highest mortality in preschool children was among those with pre-kwashiorkor, who later developed kwashiorkor when the added stress of infection was superimposed, or who died when the infection itself proved overwhelming because of lowered resistance.

Retardation in physical growth and maturation, according to Scrimshaw, is associated with retarded intellectual performance. He described the research of Gomez at the Hospital Infantil in Mexico. Gomez found a direct correlation between low scores on the Gesell and Goodenough tests and the degree of deficiency in weight below standard values. Scrimshaw concluded:

> The evidence that performance on intelligence tests is also affected by malnutrition is a further indication of the urgency and purpose of efforts to improve the nutritional status of children in technically underdeveloped areas.

For the graphic effects which can be produced by improving the nutrition of children suffering from kwashiorkor, the reader is referred to the film, "Hungry Angels," (6) which also shows the tragic results of nutrient deprivation.

Alleviation of dietary deficiency diseases throughout the world bears a rich harvest in the cultural and socioeconomic realms but, in addition, it can bring spectacular expansion of knowledege. Kwashiorkor furnishes a good example of a world-wide condition that has precipitated a tremendous amount of research. The results of investigative efforts will lead to much more than just the prevention and treatment of kwashiorkor throughout the world.

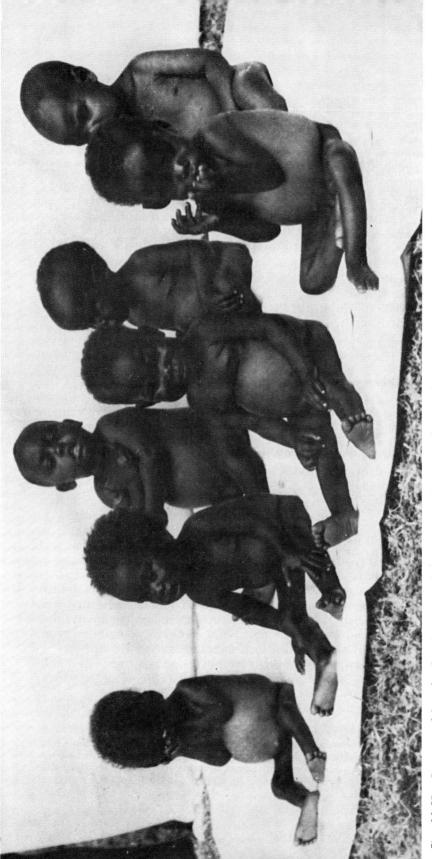

Fig. 10.5B — Ravages of kwashiorkor (protein malnutrition) are clearly visible as potbelly, edema, altered hair texture, and expressions of misery. (Source: Regional Information Office, FAO, and courtesy of the Government of Kenya.)

Questions growing out of the world-wide problem of protein malnutrition for which answers are now being sought are:

1. What is the minimum protein requirement of individuals under different physiological and environmental conditions?
2. What proportion, if any, must be furnished by proteins from animal sources?
3. Can vegetable mixtures be developed that will meet the protein needs for growth, reproduction, and maintenance?
4. What are the irreversible effects of protein malnutrition and the delayed effects of early protein malnutrition in the re-alimented individual?

Kwashiorkor as an international public health problem thus has stimulated much basic laboratory research. One phase deals with the interrelationships of dietary nutrients and the integrity of the liver. The effects on the liver of low-protein diets and the relation of specific amino acids to utilization of dietary fat and carbohydrate at different levels are also being extensively studied. This has much bearing on the mysteries of the nutritive process, and it is of practical interest in developing a better understanding of the specific condition of liver cirrhosis, which affects a considerable number of our own adult population. Thus international nutrition has become an important resource for the expansion and application of nutrition research.

Hypertension and Coronary Heart Disease

In a sense, the world is one large nutrition laboratory. Every country, with its particular set of food habits, offers an opportunity to study the results of eating regimes as they have affected generations of people. Unfortunately, there are many complicating factors so that population studies can seldom be used to establish cause and effect relationships. They do, however, show associations which may yield important hypotheses to be later tested in controlled situations.

From such observations an almost overwhelming amount of evidence has accumulated to show an association of diet with coronary heart disease — a health problem of immediate interest in the United States (7). Diets rich in total protein and in protein from animal sources are often high in cholesterol and fats containing mainly saturated fatty acids. When such diets are low in carbohydrates and fiber, they may result in a high level of blood cholesterol in middle-aged people — an age group with high incidence of atherosclerotic (coronary) heart disease.

According to J. C. Groen, *et al.* (8), such people may also be characterized as:

. . . living in a rapidly changing society, with progressive industrialization, rapid communication, high levels of prosperity, low total and infant mortality, everybody's possibility and almost necessity to ascend the social ladder, emancipation of women, loosening of family bonds, disappearing illiteracy and great moral and social value attached to responsibility for and achievement in the work.

On the other hand, in population groups which consume a diet which is poor in total and animal protein and in total fat, especially in saturated fatty acids (but with a relative preponderance of polyunsaturated fatty acids), with a high content of carbohydrates and fiber, the blood cholesterol level has been found low even in middle and older age groups, and the frequency of atherosclerotic (coronary) heart disease is much less.

These populations offer a contrasting picture in most of the "interhuman psychosocial relationships" described. They emphasize the complexity of analysis of nutrition findings in population studies and the necessity of further study with definitive segments and controlled conditions.

Lactation

Lactation is another condition for which international studies offer promise of new understandings. Breast feeding of infants in the United States appears to be declining in frequency, whereas in many other countries it is the main way to nourish babies over a long period of time. W. O. Robertson (9) has presented data to show the incidence of breast feeding in the United States. Of the total sample, 24 per cent indicated that their infants were completely breast fed at one week of age. Another 6 per cent reported that their infants were breast fed, but received supplemental or complemental feedings. Thus 30 per cent of the infants were either completely or partially breast fed at 1 week of age, but by 8 weeks only 15 per cent of the infants continued to receive any breast feeding. At 14 weeks of age, the percentage had fallen to 10, and at 18 weeks, to 7.

In contrast, these reports have come from various parts of the world: Jelliffe (10) indicated in a large-scale investigation in Southern India that permissive breast feeding was usually carried on uneventfully and was continued for two to three years. There was a tendency to stop breast feeding earlier in urban regions. Gopalan (11) in India also found that lactation up to 2 years to be usual in lower socioeconomic groups, while among well-to-do mothers 80 per cent were unable to breast feed for six months.

In Afghanistan, breast feeding is universal and prolonged. In the city of Singapore, Malayan mothers may breast feed for two or three years, while Chinese women, especially the well-to-do, tend to follow the Caucasian pattern. Ninety-three per cent of rural Malayan women were able to breast feed their babies, but the observer commented on the increasingly fashionable use of the bottle for feeding babies, which is equated with modern progress of mothers.

A study in rural Haiti showed 90 per cent of mothers to be successful for the first six months, and 81 per cent for the second. In the wealthier and more sophisticated island of Trinidad, there was much less success in both Negro and East Indian mothers.

In many countries, employment of women was cited as an interfering factor. Jelliffe (10) has stated that the common factor to all tropical peasant groups is irregularity of feeding, usually termed "demand" or "opportunity" feeding. He has noted a wide variety of practices with reference to posture and positioning during feeding, breast preparation during the antenatal state, and the absence of what may be a "bottle-induced Western cultural concept, 'wind', with the associated alleged need for 'burping.' "

Gopalan's studies on lactation among Indian women have led him to certain conclusions and caused him to raise certain questions (11):

1. Surveys indicate that there is almost an inverse relationship between the position of the mother on the socioeconomic scale and her lactation. The situation cannot be ascribed entirely to emotional and psychological factors.

2. While a great deal of attention has been focused on the possible effects of undernutrition on lactation, not much thought has been given to the possible role of overnutrition in inhibiting lactation.

3. Field studies suggest that the resumption of menstruation after delivery, takes place after a much longer interval in poor mothers than well-to-do mothers. The implications of this finding merit investigation.

4. The action of substances used by Indian women as galactogogues (stimulants for milk production), such as garlic, cotton seed, and tamarind, were studied. Although under the conditions of high milk production observed, they seemed to have no influence, the further study of their use in cases of lactation failure was thought possibly worthwhile, and the role of hormonal factors in lactation needs further study.

These international studies have focused attention on the fact that much further research is needed to elucidate the maternal nutritional requirements during lactation. Controlled experiments to discover the factors related to successful lactation are needed.

Dental Caries

A fourth public health nutrition problem for which understanding has been greatly increased through international study is dental caries and other forms of dental disease. In some parts of the world, dental caries is almost unknown. In other parts — again these seem to be in the more highly developed countries — they are rampant. Studies have been made of the Alaskan Eskimos who, in the more remote settlements, had unusually good teeth. Even though filed close to the gums, their teeth were free from cavities (12).

But in the less remote areas becoming touched by civilization, dental disease is increasing. The increase appears to be related to the cultural transition and to be more serious in the more acculturated groups.

Again the observations suggest new opportunities to extend our knowledge (a) about the pathogenesis of dental disease, and (b) about "the ravages of a diet perhaps damaged by some dietary change."

Variations in the rate of dental decay were observed throughout Europe with changes in diet incidental to the privations of World

War II. In war-torn countries with restrictions on food consumption, decreases in caries rates were observed generally during the war. Extensive studies were made by Toverud (13) in Norway, where reduction in caries rates for children 3 to 6 years was very great from 1939 to 1947. During subsequent years the rates increased.

Children up to age 5 and pregnant and lactating women had priority for foods essential for mineralization. Except for preschool children the diet was very low in fat and probably somewhat low in carbohydrates, particularly for older children. Total calories also were insufficient for older children.

For all persons the sugar supply was less than one-half of previous consumption; all candy was practically eliminated. Bread was made of a 95 per cent extraction flour. Consumption of fish, potatoes, and root vegetables increased.

The change in mouth environment brought about by the drastic reduction in consumption of sugar and sugar products during the war years was considered by the investigators to be the main cause of the reduced caries rate. Cleansing effects of the coarser diet were thought to be beneficial, also. Furthermore, an increased tooth resistance due to favorable conditions in the earliest posteruptive maturation of the enamel surface may have been a factor.

Later in Vipeholm, Sweden, several researchers (14) investigated the effect of sucrose supplements in varying forms on the teeth of inmates of a state hospital. The conclusion was reached that sucrose did foster the development of caries, but that the form in which it was taken was a factor to be considered. Caries rates were highest with sticky sweets that adhered to the teeth. A small percentage of the subjects was remarkably resistant to caries, regardless of treatment.

In 1958, a study of Lin and Smith (15) of diet and dental health in Newfoundland children was reported. In a statistical comparison of the average caries figures and average nutrition scores, there was a reduction in dental caries with improved nutrition, significant at somewhat in excess of the 2 per cent level.

NEW WAYS TO MEET DIETARY NEEDS

International nutrition gives rise to the development of new ways to meet dietary needs. The problem of meeting the need for an adequate supply of amino acids using little or no animal products and at a minimum cost has led to an intensive study of a number of foods and combinations of foods, as well as the use of supplementary amino acids.

Additional sources of high-protein foods for supplementing both the low-protein content in cereal foods and the limited supply of dry skim milk are now available. Outstanding sources of high-protein foods are flours derived from cotton seed, peanuts, sorghums, and soybeans.

One of the highly successful mixtures developed is called Incaparina. As indicated by the name, this originated at INCAP (Institute of Nutrition of Central America and Panama) in Guatemala to help combat the protein malnutrition of the children of that country. The mixture consists of:

Whole ground corn	29 per cent
Whole ground sorghum	29 per cent
Cottonseed flour	38 per cent
Torula yeast	3 per cent
Calcium carbonate	1 per cent
Vitamin A	4500 IU per 100 grams

Feeding tests with both animals and children have demonstrated the high nutritional value of this mixture. With suitable flavoring and when mixed with water, it is well accepted.

In India a multipurpose food (MPF) has been developed and is being distributed as indicated in the following news release, excerpted from Weekly India News, Vol. 1, No. 45 Phalguna 10, 1884 (Saka) March 1, 1963.

A Union Food Ministry mobile kitchen van will begin rounds of residential areas in the Capitol from the middle of next month to popularize the use of multi-purpose food in the family diet.

The three home science experts will go in the van to impress on housewives the desirability of departing from traditional food habits and using dietary supplements.

A high-protein multi-purpose food, made from groundnut flour and Bengal gram and fortified with vitamins, has been evolved by the Central Food Technology Institute.

The food has found favor with schools and hospital administrations, but housewives have still to be won over to its use in the home.

Nutro-biscuits and Chikki, made from the multi-purpose food, are being widely used in school lunch in many States.

Multi-purpose food is being produced in the country at the rate of four tons per day. Two ten-ton-capacity plants for processing groundnut flour will shortly be set up in Bombay and Coimbatore.

One-thousand kilograms of Nutro-biscuits and 16,000 pieces of Chikki in ready-food packets were presented by the Association to jawans (soldiers) in forward areas.

In Indonesia a product called Saridele has been developed from a dried extract of soybean, supplemented with minerals, vitamins, and sugar (16).

Considerable attention has been directed to the potential of fish flour as a source of concentrated protein of good quality. This presents technical problems in production, however, and will require special planning to teach people to use it or producers to incorporate it into other foods. The Central Regional Food Technological Institute of Mysore, India, has produced an odorless sardine fish flour. How useful this will be to the people of this country may depend upon its continued identification with a food of animal origin.

The nutritive value of cereals supplemented with essential amino acids, such as lysine added to wheat flour, is another possibility for improving the quality of diets. Other cereal products would require the addition of two or more different amino acids, not now readily available at low cost. Much research is needed on the feasibility of this method of dietary improvement.

The general advantages of mixed diets in normal nutrition argue for solution of protein and other nutrition problems by recourse to combinations of foods. The more limited the mixture, the greater is the care needed to assess its adequacy and to prepare and package it carefully for distribution.

Dr. Esther Phipard (16) has quoted Dr. Scrimshaw as follows:

> There are obviously a great many different useful sources of protein for the prevention of protein malnutrition in technically underdeveloped areas. Milk must still be considered of first importance, and, of course, increased production of cheese, eggs, and meat should be encouraged. For some regions, fish flour or meat meals may be practical new sources of animal protein. Oilseed meals such as those from sesame, peanut, sunflower; legumes such as soy, cow pea and chick pea, and concentrates of leaf protein may be of major value in one area or another.

PRACTICAL PROGRAMS FOR IMPROVING NUTRITION

One of the most significant efforts in world nutrition has been the expansion of the school lunch program on a world-wide basis. On August 21, 1962, the White House reported that the number of children overseas receiving school lunches under the "Food for Peace" program had increased by 10 million over the previous year, reaching a new total of 35 million. In interpreting our foreign aid program to the public, diplomats on several occasions have cited the school lunch program as an example of positive and concrete benefits.

"India News," in September, 1962, included this following item:

> The Education Minister, Dr. Shrimali, told the Lok Sabha that ten million children are likely to be covered by the Mid-Day Meals Program by the end of the current plan. The scheme now benefits 700,000 children. He said that the Government was anxious to speed up the program.

School lunches around the world present widely different pictures; in no two places will the menus be the same. In Japan a full meal of bread, milk, and a side dish of meat, soyabeans, potatoes, fat, and oil, thickened with wheat flour or starch, has been described by the Ministry of Education (17). In the quantity served, it provides a total of 647 calories and 27.7 grams of protein. In 1958 almost 10 million children participated in the school lunch program. Effects on the children are shown in Figures 10.6A and 10.6B.

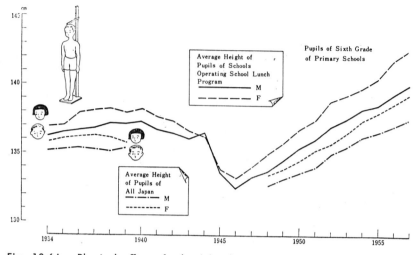

Fig. 10.6A — Physical effect of school lunch program in changes of average height of pupils in sixth grade of Sendai City, Japan, public schools. Measurements were begun in 1934 with approximately 4,000 pupils, and by 1955 the number of pupils had increased to 6,000. Effects of the war years are clearly shown, as is the tendency of the girls to respond more rapidly than the boys to improved nutrition. (Source: Statistics compiled by Tohoku University as published by the Ministry of Education, Government of Japan, MEJ6218, "School Lunch Program in Japan, With Statistics.")

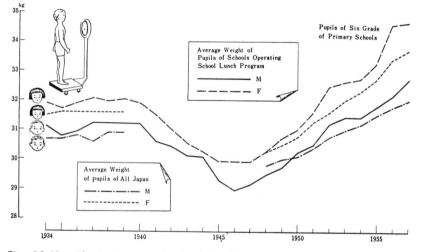

Fig. 10.6B — Physical effect of school lunch program in changes of average weight of the same Japanese pupils. (Source: same as Fig. 10.6A.)

In Iraq the school lunch scene differs greatly from the U. S. A. (see Fig. 10.7). In Figure 10.8, children are helping prepare the school lunch. The menu might include a hard-cooked egg, samoon (a native bread), an orange, okra, an onion or a cucumber, plus reconstituted milk furnished by UNICEF.

Figure 10.9 shows boys in Morocco consuming a nutritious meal served in a school lunch as part of an educational program emphasizing use of fish as a means of improving protein consumption. Concurrently, children in classrooms are learning about the production and use of this commodity (see Fig. 10.10). Note that this lecture is being recorded on tape for use in an expanded teaching program. Lessons also include trips to the fish market where pupils learn about different fish available (see Fig. 10.11).

Thus the school feeding programs around the world are serving the nutritional needs of children while exploring new ways of meeting those needs. Other programs in practical nutrition are helping to raise the standards of living, to reduce suffering and misery, and to improve the productivity of the population.

Milk distribution schemes throughout the world are helping to improve the health of mothers and babies. Figure 10.12 shows such a station in Iraq.

In many nations, children and adults are thus being helped toward better diets while they are learning the importance of nutrition. Pro-

Fig. 10.7 — Boys eating good school lunches in a village school in Iraq — minus the comforts American children have come to expect. (Source: AID photo.)

Fig. 10.8 — School children in Iraq help prepare and serve a good lunch. (Source: AID photo.)

grams in some countries, notably India, are including efforts to make sure that good meals are served in the canteens in the rapidly growing industries.

In Iraq there is much too little milk to go around. Facilities for sanitary handling and easy distribution are lacking (see Fig. 10.13).

TEAMWORK IN IMPROVING NUTRITION

International nutrition efforts have demonstrated the importance of teamwork in improving the nutrition of the people. Thus, as a Home Economist with a mission of the FAO in Iraq, one of the authors of this book found herself working with a specialist in well digging from England, a dairy expert from Sweden, a poultry specialist from Germany, a rice agriculturalist from China, an extension worker from Greece, a dietitian from France, and a soil scientist from the United States. Under working conditions of this sort, one becomes acutely aware of the breadth of nutrition problems.

The value of teamwork in ascertaining an over-all view of the nutrition problems of a country is well illustrated by the program of investigation followed by the Interdepartmental Committee on Nutrition for National Defense (ICNND). The purpose of this group has been described as "to assess, to assist, and to learn" about the food and nutrition in countries in which we are giving military support. (See Appendix H, p. 325.)

FIG. 10.9 — Moroccan children enjoying school lunch planned to promote greater use of fish, a food in abundance, to improve protein consumption. (Source: Public Information Service, United Nations, **FAO Bulletin**, 9/60, p. 4.)

Originally the primary subjects of investigation were people in the armed forces, but it is pointed out that these people come from the civilian homes of the country. The studies when possible are also extended to include civilian groups; in fact some of the studies now are focused on the civilian population.

A team of workers such as those engaged in the nutrition survey may include clinicians, dentists, nutritionists and dietitians, food technologists, biochemists, statisticians, and nurses. By 1962 teams of this type had visited the following countries: Korea, Formosa, Iran, Turkey, Libya, the Philippines, Pakistan, Spain, Peru, and Viet Nam.

The ICNND team working in Viet Nam, a country of high current interest, made a film showing their activities. The following excerpts from their report (18) show clearly how the cooperative efforts of the

Fig. 10.10 — Biology class in Morocco studying the anatomy of a fish — a "work project" of the Government to stimulate interest in improving the national diet. (Source: same as Fig. 10.9.)

team can assess the nutritional status and needs of a population with varying local situations:

The results of this survey reveal that a number of specific nutritional deficiency states exist in the Republic of Viet Nam. Within the limits of the current state of knowledge, one must say that by far the most important of these is the deficiency of thiamine in the diet — a problem which exists among all groups surveyed, the differences being ones of degree only. Despite the absence of beriberi among the selected population groups examined, the disease was observed among patients in several hospitals in Viet Nam and deficits of thiamine are clear from the dietary and excretion data. The military implications of chronic deficits of thiamine intake are obvious.

By available standards, riboflavin deficiencies of approximately the same order of magnitude as those of thiamine also exist throughout the population groups examined. Although the clinical manifestations of riboflavin de-

"If you give a man a fish you feed him for one day. If you teach him to fish you feed him for many days."

An old Chinese proverb

Source: FAO *News*,
August 1962, p. 5.

Fig. 10.11 — Elementary Moroccan school children visit a fish market where they learn about different kinds of fish available. (Source: same as Fig. 10.9.)

Fig. 10.12 — In a village school in Iraq a home economist distributes dried milk to mothers of small children while giving them information on improving nutrition. (Source: AID photo.)

ficiency when present are by no means as clear as those for thiamine, riboflavin is an essential nutrient necessary in adequate amounts. Fortunately,
means of combating these two deficiencies are available. The means, which
are relatively inexpensive although admittedly not easily initiated, are discussed in detail.

Endemic goiter is common in at least two areas — Kontum Province in the
Highlands and the Central Delta around Can Tho.

Vitamin A malnutrition is moderately prevalent in many areas as measured by dietary intake and determinations of serum levels. No clinical evidence of vitamin A deficiency was seen.

Borderline intakes and serum levels of vitamin C were encountered in
many regions.

On the other hand, there are few if any indications of problems relating
to total calories, protein, calcium, or niacin. The people of Viet Nam are
small. However, the results of the survey provide little insight into the presence or absence of growth retardation. In the general sense, the nutritional
status of the military is superior to that of the civilian population, without
appreciable differences between the Army, Navy, and Air Force. Among the

Fig. 10.13 — The limited
amount of native milk in Iraq
is distributed in the form of
leban (soured milk) carried in
wooden containers. (Source:
AID photo.)

civilians, the Highlanders of Kontum Province present the most serious problems, and the urban children in schools the least.

The survey opens up many areas requiring further work both fundamental and applied in nature. Among the specific applied areas, degrees of urgency exist for several, particularly initiation of thiamine and riboflavin supplementation programs and investigation into the susceptibility of the military man to precipitation of clinical beriberi under conditions of stress. The etiology of goiter in Viet Nam required further study, primarily to rule in or out the possible role of goitrogens. The anemia problem is complex, with a need for determining the role of intestinal parasitic infestation, malaria and iron deficiency (relative or absolute), as well as the interrelationships of the intakes of the water-soluble vitamins.

INTERNATIONAL NUTRITION EDUCATION CONFERENCE

Among the many efforts to help peoples around the world improve their nutrition was an International Seminar on Education in Health and Nutrition held in Baguio, the Philippines, October 13 to November 3, 1955. Sponsored jointly by the FAO and WHO (19), the conference included 48 participants from 22 countries and territories. The 24 main points emerging from the seminar are worthy of study by nutrition educators. Of special importance are the sections dealing with objectives and evaluation.

Cultural Factors

The significance to nutrition education of observations on many cultural groups has been previously mentioned. Burgess (20) has outlined conditions which seem to militate against the success of health or nutrition improvement programs as follows:

1. Lack of appreciation at the outset of the full implications of certain educational procedures.
2. Lack of knowledge of the economic and practical limitations of the village household — coupled with too rigid adherence to and insistence on textbook practices.
3. Lack of sympathy with the beliefs, practices, and people on which the villager had hitherto relied for guidance in health matters.
4. Lack of knowledge of the resistances inevitably aroused by advice and instructions that appeared contrary to the local beliefs about child rearing and the causes of ill health.
5. Lack of adequate explanation of the purpose and methods of functioning of the available health and nutrition services.
6. Lack of cooperation, at administrative and community levels, among the personnel of the various services.
7. Lack of scrutiny and testing of educational materials to make sure they conveyed the message intended and were easily understood by those to whom they were addressed.
8. Lack of appreciation of the relative uselessness of a scheme imposed from above as compared with the effectiveness of beginning with something in which the villager was interested and prepared to cooperate — even if it was not directly connected with nutrition.

Fig. 10.14 — Daily food plans of five areas — Japan, Peru, South Pacific, the Philippines, and Iraq — offer interesting contrasts in detail and give valuable insight into different ways people can meet their nutritional needs.

SUMMARY

Every individual has a responsibility to work toward better conditions for mankind. Nutrition educators have additional responsibilities unique to the knowledge and skills they possess. For some, there are opportunities to aid in educating peoples throughout the world to make the best possible use of their food supplies. For all, there is the opportunity to create a better understanding on the part of the citizenry of the scope and meaning of malnutrition on an international scale (see Fig. 10.14).

The nutrition educators have an obligation of providing people with the information they need to adapt a rational attitude toward our foreign aid policies as they involve food. Lastly, nutrition educators can greatly enrich their teaching by expanding their knowledge with the ever increasing flow of information that is coming from international study and experience.

REFERENCES

1. Scrimshaw, N. S., "Progress in Solving World Nutrition Problems." *Jour. Amer. Diet. Assn.,* 35:441–48, 1959.
2. ———, "What Modern Food Science and Its Application Mean to Developing Countries," *Science and Food, Today and Tomorrow.* Natl. Acad. of Sciences–Natl. Res. Council Publ. 877, pp. 29–41, Washington, 1961.
3. Millikan, M. F., and Rostow, W. W., *A Proposal: Key to an Effective Foreign Policy,* pp. 19–22. Harpers, 1957.

4. Heady, E. O., "Food for Peace — Bane or Boon to the Economy of the United States." Presented at the Ohio State University Land-Grant Centennial: International Symposium on the Role of Food in World Peace.

5. Brock, J. F., "The Red-headed Africans," *Atlantic Monthly,* 192 (No. 6) :68–71, Dec. 1953.

6. *Hungry Angels.* Association Films, Inc., 1108 Jackson St., Dallas, Texas.

7. Pollack, H., and Krueger, D. E. (eds.), "Epidemiology of Cardiovascular Diseases." *Amer. Jour. Publ. Health,* (Suppl.) 50:1, 1960.

8. Groen, J. C., *et al.,* "Incidence of Nutrition and Ways of Life on Blood Cholesterol and Prevalence of Hypertension and Coronary Heart Disease Among Trappist and Benedictine Monks." *Amer. Jour. Clin. Nutr.,* 10:456–70, June 1962.

9. Robertson, W. O., "Breast Feeding Practices: Some Implications of Regional Variations." *Amer. Jour. Publ. Health,* 51:1035–42, July 1961.

10. Jelliffe, D. B., "Culture, Social Change and Infant Feeding." *Amer. Jour. Clin. Nutr.,* 10:19–45, Jan. 1962.

11. Gopalan, C., "Nutrition and Lactation." Fifth International Congress on Nutrition, *Federation Proceedings,* 20 (No. 1) Part III:171–84, Mar. 1961.

12. "Alaska: An Appraisal of the Health and Nutritional Status of the Eskimo." A report by the Interdepartmental Committee on Nutrition for National Defense, Aug. 1959.

13. Toverud, G., "The Influence of War and Postwar Conditions on the Teeth of Norwegian Children." *Milbank Memorial Fund Quart.,* 35:371–469, 1957.

14. Johansen, E., "Nutrition, Diet, and Calcium Metabolism in Dental Health." *Amer. Jour. Publ. Health,* 50:1089–96, 1960.

15. Lin, T. Y., and Smith, M. D., "Diet and Dental Health in Newfoundland Children." *Canad. Jour. Publ. Health,* 49:516–19, 1958.

16. Phipard, E., and Shepherd, G., "Nutritional Needs by World Regions." Chap. 3, in *Food — One Tool in International Economic Development,* pp. 60–71. Iowa State University Press, Ames, 1962.

17. "School Lunch Program in Japan, With Statistics." Ministry of Education, Govt. of Japan, MEJ-6218, Nov. 1958.

18. "Republic of Viet Nam: Nutrition Survey, October–December 1959." A report by the Interdepartmental Committee on Nutrition for National Defense, July 1960.

19. Food and Agriculture Organization and World Health Organization of the United Nations, Report of an International Seminar on Education in Health and Nutrition, Baguio, the Philippines, Oct. 13–Nov. 3, 1955.

20. Burgess, A., "Nutrition Education in Public Health Programs — What Have We Learned?" *Jour. Amer. Publ. Health,* 51:1715–26, 1961.

Chapter Eleven

The Challenge of Change

If NUTRITION EDUCATION is to be effective in motivating people to make better food choices, it must be in tune with a variety of constantly occurring changes and trends. The individual himself is a changing organism, and his environment is constantly undergoing transformations that profoundly affect his food supply and perhaps his eating practices.

Nutrition education which ignores the impact of change is purely academic. This approach cannot be functional for the masses of people, because it is unrealistic and unrelated to their needs.

In this chapter nutrition educators will be alerted to some of the aspects of change involved in the dynamics of nutrition education.

PROGRESSIVE CHANGES WITHIN THE INDIVIDUAL

One of the most basic principles of nutrition — often reiterated in this book for the sake of emphasis — is that food intake must be related to the varying physiological and psychological needs of the individual. We do not automatically make adjustments in food intake, however, following changed physiological needs. One responsibility of the nutrition educator is to help people recognize the *need* for adjusting their food consumption in accord with changing body requirements, then to help them find *ways* of doing so.

The fact that most physiological change is gradual creates difficult problems in teaching nutrition. If the points of transition in the food needs of the individual were more easily detected, we could deal much more realistically with them. But unfortunately such transitional stages are not well marked — they almost creep up on people unnoticed.

[*268*]

Accomplishing the goal of continually adjusting food intake to meet body needs through the life cycle would do much to improve the quality of the health of all our population, but particularly of our older people, because preparation for a happy, productive old age is a continuous process which begins in childhood.

We have been inclined to teach nutrition more on a horizontal than on a vertical basis. In the table of the Recommended Dietary Allowances, for example, we are more likely to look at the figures across the pages than those which are vertically arranged. We have therefore tended to focus attention on problems of a specific age rather than on varying body needs from one age period to the next. Thus we tend to isolate the need of the preschool child, the teen-ager, the pregnant woman, and the adult — with little concern for the transitions which occur between such stages in life. This traditional approach is termed "realistic," because education must begin with people as they happen to be. But it is an incomplete approach, because it tends to ignore what people have been or are later to be.

In general, long-range planning is a difficult procedure. How it can be successfully applied to such personal factors as health or specifically to nutrition has not been clarified, but the long-range approach is one of the most challenging aspects of nutrition education.

We must teach people where they *are*, but we must also devise ways to help them see *where they are going*. The school child is taught his nutritional needs, but could we not go a step farther and help him to see the needs of older brothers and sisters, mothers and fathers, and even grandparents — and how those needs differ from his own? Perhaps, too, we could begin early to help children acquire a sharp image of what healthy people are like at all ages, not just at the child's own age, emphasizing the role nutrition plays in achieving good health throughout life.

It is sometimes asserted that the best way to ensure good nutrition in the succeeding stages of the life cycle is to establish good food habits

. . . transitional stages of life creep up on us unnoticed.

in the current period of life. The validity of that statement depends upon the concept of "good food habits." If the idea is focused only on kinds and amounts of food, it may not even serve the needs of a specific age group, since these needs themselves are not static or homogeneous. It certainly will not solve the problems of future needs.

For example: the perfect diet for one teen-age boy may not be suitable for another. It certainly must be modified considerably for him as a young businessman; an excellent diet for the latter could be disastrous for a middle-aged executive.

Education for the development of good food habits, therefore, should involve some effort to alert people of all ages to the importance of their changing food needs. Not only are the facts of nutrition needed in such education, but the attitudes and philosophies of individuals toward eating are also of vital concern.

Nutrition need never be regarded as a dull subject for there are many concrete and interesting ways to teach even the most abstract facts. Perhaps the most effective teaching devices are those which the educator has had the pleasure of developing to suit the needs of the particular group to be taught. The opportunities for creativity in nutrition education are infinite.

Certain teaching devices may be used to help people visualize the nature of needed modifications in food energy and nutrient intake throughout the life span. Figure 11.1, based on Table 11.1, may be developed as a flannel graph to show the changes in food intake. In this example, a girl 7 to 9 years of age is used as the starting point for what might be termed a "Calorie Count-down," or, more accurately, a "Calorie Count-up-and-down." The chart shows first as a "starter" the foods which might be used by the girl to meet her food energy needs, distributed among three meals.

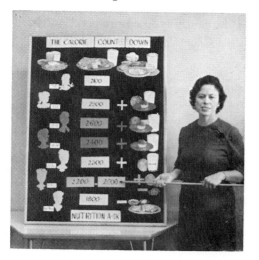

FIG. 11.1 — Colored illustrations of foods, cut from magazines or advertising, can be developed into a flannel graph to help students visualize needed adjustments in diets to meet calorie allowances for various ages.

TABLE 11.1

THE CALORIE COUNT-DOWN*

The "Starter" — 2100 Calories		
Girl 7–9 yrs.	Luncheon	Dinner

Breakfast	*Luncheon*	*Dinner*
Orange juice	Cheese	Roast
Egg Bacon	Bread Butter	Potato Broccoli
Toast	Lettuce Tomatoes	Slaw
Butter Jelly	Cookie Apricots	Roll Butter
Milk	Milk	Ice Cream

Adjustments From the "Starter" as Needed by Advancing Age Groups

Age	Allowance	Additions or subtractions from the "Starter"		
		Food	Unit	Calories
(years)	*(calories)*			
10–12	2500	Milk	1 cup	+166
(girl)		Cake	1 (cupcake)	+161
		Apple	1	+ 76
				+403
13–15	2600	Milk	1 cup	+166
(girl)		Cake	1 (cupcake)	+161
		Apple	1	+ 76
		Banana	1	+116
				+519
16–19	2400	Milk	1 cup	+166
(girl)		Cake	1 (cupcake)	+161
				+327
25	2300	Milk	1 cup	+ 86
(woman)		(nonfat)		
		Apple	1	+ 76
				+162
25	2600	Milk	1¾ cup	+289
(pregnant, 2nd half)		Meat	2 oz.	+177
				+466
25	3300	Milk	2 cups	+332
(lactating)		Meat	3 oz.	+266
		Orange	1	+ 70
		Butter	1 T.	+100
		Cake	1 (cupcake)	+161
		Custard	1 cup	+283
				+1212
45	2200	Apple	+1	+ 76
(woman)	to	or		+ 76
	2000	Cookie	−1	−109
				−109
65	1800	Jelly	−1 T.	− 33
(woman)		Bread	−1 slice	− 61
		Cookie	−1	−109
		Fat	−1 T.	−100
				−306

NUTRITION: A—OK !

* Estimations based on servings of "average" size and figures used in "Composition of Foods," USDA Handbook No. 8.

Additions and subtractions from the "starter," appropriate for advancing years are shown in terms of common foods. In the adjustments, considerable emphasis should be given to the types of foods which lend themselves to adjustment of food energy with little adverse effect upon the nutrient intake.

It is interesting to note that the chart shows the food energy needs of the woman 45 years of age to be almost like the needs of the girl 7 to 9 years. Women of such age, therefore, might do well to compare their food consumption with that of their very young granddaughters, for — depending upon their activity — they may need even less food energy than do small children.

Another teaching device is a simple bar graph, as in Figure 11.2, which shows how nutrient needs of boys and men may change with age and activity. Such changes may be made more meaningful by showing, in conjunction with the bar graph, the amounts and kinds of foods involved in the differences between needs for boys and men and in effecting the desirable changes.

Other types of bar graphs may be built upon flannel or sketched on a blackboard concurrently with a discussion. They may also be constructed from blocks or painted tin cans. One visual aid expert uses rectangular colored sponges to show such units as 10 per cent of the day's needs, for example. Even students in the class may be lined up to represent units in a bar graph — a technique which might emphasize even more clearly that nutrition education is concerned directly with people and their food needs. (For other ideas see Chapter 7.)

Failure to adjust intake to meet the needs of certain *nutrients* perhaps produces less dramatic and obvious results than excessive or deficient total *energy* intakes, which result in overweight or underweight. People should be made aware that even subtle dietary problems may be equally serious in terms of health. Calcium and iron are two nutrients for which the variable needs during life are sometimes disregarded because deficiencies in both may be undetected for long periods of time.

Again using the example of a child aged 7 to 9 years, Figure 11.3, based on Table 11.2, shows the progressive dietary changes needed in terms of milk, which in some form is the principal source of calcium in our diets. Nearly two-thirds of the calcium in household food supplies comes from milk, ice cream, and cheese. Assuming that the usual basic diet (without milk or its nonfat products) supplies 300 milligrams of calcium, Table 11.2 shows how much milk or its equivalent is needed to supply the total calcium needs. Here the change in amounts needed from one age to another is impressive.

Changing calcium requirements can be satisfied in various other ways besides drinking fluid milk. For the weight-conscious individual,

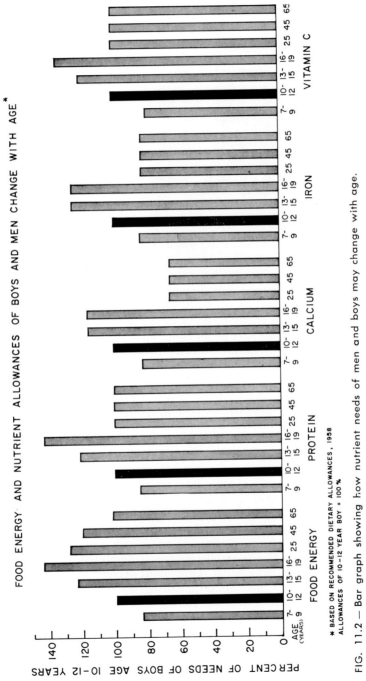

FIG. 11.2 — Bar graph showing how nutrient needs of men and boys may change with age.

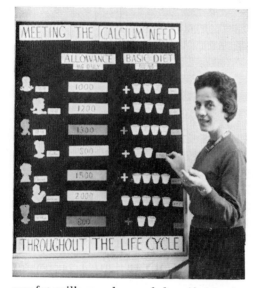

FIG. 11.3—This flannel graph, using colors and illustrative materials similar to those in Figure 11.1, will help students visualize changing needs for calcium throughout the average life span.

nonfat milk may be used, but if this alternative is chosen, some attention must be directed toward foods of high vitamin A value.

Self-direction in changing food intake to meet changing nutrient needs should become part of an individual's health consciousness, so that he reviews and readjusts dietary habits much as he periodically checks up on his physical or dental health status. Perhaps one of the best ways to keep people aware of the need for revising food habits is to encourage them to watch the scales. Overweight and obesity are the harsh penalties paid by our middle-aged population for disregarding their weight status and failing to adjust food intake appropriately in their earlier years.

Periodic medical examinations may also serve as useful guideposts to nutritional status. In the course of time, increasing use undoubtedly will be made of laboratory tests to help people keep a closer tab on how their health is being affected by what they eat.

Nutritionists have accepted the responsibility of showing people the many advantages of variety in the diet, particularly through the use of daily food plans. Perhaps another such equally effective tool is needed to teach the essential concept of flexibility and adjustment in diet to meet changing needs. One might devise a chart consisting of concentric rings or "wheels" representing different stages in the life cycle and on which could be shown appropriate changes in diet throughout the life span, in each of the four basic food groups.

CHANGES IN FAMILY LIVING

For a broad review of over-all trends in our society which affect family living and, in turn, influence the eating practices of families, the reader is referred to the paper, "Reviewing Our Orbit" by

TABLE 11.2
MEETING THE CHANGING NEEDS FOR CALCIUM IN DIETS OF WOMEN AND GIRLS

Age	NRC* RA	Furnished by Basic Diet		Milk To Be Added†
(years)	*(mg. Ca)*	*(mg. Ca)*		*(cups)*
7–9	1000	300	+	2.4
10–12	1200	300	+	3.1
13–19	1300	300	+	3.5
25 normal	800	300	+	1.7
pregnant (2nd half)	1500	300	+	4.1
lactating	2000	300	+	5.9
45 plus	800	300	+	1.7

* Allowances recommended by the Food and Nutrition Board of the National Academy of Sciences—National Research Council, 1958.
† To meet the recommended allowances (1958).

Beatrice Paolucci (1). In this paper each of the broadly described changes holds implications for adjusting emphasis in nutrition education. These include changes in the family's social setting; the family function and roles of responsibility of its members; income level and sources of family income; earner's occupations; the manner of living, including increased leisure time; and the retail food markets. All these factors have found expression in a number of easily recognized trends in family living, many of which are of direct concern to nutrition education. Here is a brief interpretation of some of the outgrowths of these trends as reflected in eating practices.

Meals Taken Away From Home

This trend, previously mentioned in Chapter 4, calls for greater responsibility by the individual in selecting food to meet his total daily needs. Safeguarding the quality of meals served in homes is not enough. The practice of eating away from home affects both children and adults in the family, all of whom need some guidance in their independent selection of foods. The homemaker has the added consideration of planning daily meals to supplement those which members have eaten away from home.

. . . including increased leisure time . . . .

Similarly, in the interest of improved nutrition for the people of our nation, educators must be concerned with those having management responsibilities in the food service industry, who must be encouraged to offer nutritious food to the public and to aid people in selecting good meals from the menus. Thus nutrition education cannot be focused entirely upon the homemaker, because food service is increasingly in the hands of the managers of large food service units.

Automation is entering more and more into the picture of away-from-home food consumption: for example, vending machines in offices, factories, and even schools are encouraging the use of bland and liquid foods. A further increase in this highly impersonal manner of procuring food must be studied for its potential effect upon family meals and the appetite of the individual.

We must also consider the increasing potential of public eating places and food-selling devices to reduce the gap between the cost of meals they offer and of meals which are prepared and served in the home. One must examine carefully the psychological as well as the physiological effects of these changes in ways of eating upon the total food habits and nutrition of the individual.

Casual Eating

Between-meal eating was once considered one of the greatest dietary sins. Now we have come to regard snacks as a part of the regular eating pattern for many people. It is important that snacks be included in assessing the total food intake. Intermittent eating, if not considered, will obscure the entire dietary picture for the individual. The more casual their eating, the more difficult it may be for people to evaluate total intake, and thus the more important it is for them to know food values.

We can only surmise the extent to which families have departed from the traditional practice of eating three regular meals a day. It

. . . the relaxation and enjoyment of outdoor eating help achieve close mealtime companionship.

has not been established how eating an adequate diet irregularly and at more frequent intervals affects the health of human beings. Effects of regularly spaced, full meals as opposed to frequent small feedings of the same nutrients have been noted in studies with small animals. Results in the experimental animals suggest possible metabolic advantages of the latter scheme.

Evidence is as yet too slender to warrant a drastic departure from the traditional three-meal pattern, which provides many advantages in convenience, custom, and, above all, an opportunity for strengthening family relationships.

Another type of irregular eating is the outright missing of meals, which has often been associated with poor nutrient intakes. Only a small percentage of Iowa school children who missed breakfasts had an adequate nutrient intake for the entire day (2), while the number of meals missed correlated highly with the inadequacy of diets for 140 town school girls studied in 1960 (3). Similar observations have been made in other sections of the country.

The family dining table has been replaced to some extent by cookout meals on patios or camp-out sites. Food served on such occasions can be as nutritious as more formal meals; perhaps it usually is. The relaxation and enjoyment of outdoor eating can go far to help families achieve closer mealtime companionship. Probably outdoor cooking and eating should receive a greater share of attention from nutrition educators, with emphasis on convenient and inexpensive ways of achieving good nutritious meals. The significance of this aspect of family life was thus emphasized by President Eisenhower as he opened the 1960 White House Conference on Children and Youth (4).

We strive to make certain that the number of failures (with youth) is held to a minimum. And in this effort we have developed appropriate programs — physical, recreational, educational, moral, psychological, occupational. Underlying all these as both preventive and cure is a happy family; one that finds its greatest enjoyment as a group in such things as the family picnic, family games, the "cookout," or home movies.

Increased Amount of Leisure Time

While laborsaving devices have lightened the work load of the homemaker, automation has shortened the working week of the wage earner. The effect of increased amounts of leisure time on the nutrition of individuals depends upon how such time is spent.

If the individual is inclined toward spectator sports, reading, watching television, or listening to the radio — all passive types of leisure activity — either he will have to adjust his food energy intake downward from the previous level (assuming it was suitable) or he will augment the statistics on overweight and obesity. Reduced energy output requires reduced food intake; low-calorie diets must be carefully planned in order to be nutritionally adequate.

*Spectator sports
usually require food
energy intake adjustment.*

On the other hand, it is conceivable that physical fitness programs may become increasingly popular in our nation. This would, of course, be a healthy development for millions of people who need more physical activity and wholesome recreation. As food intake is increased to meet the higher energy needs of a more active person, it becomes easier for him to obtain nutrients in the amounts needed for good health.

Employment of Homemakers

Research on this subject has been reviewed elsewhere in this book. Indications are that employed homemakers are doing as well as other homemakers in the job of feeding their families. The number of employed homemakers is growing; an increasing number of them are mothers of young children. Perhaps nutrition educators should exert a more concentrated effort to help employed women acquire the knowledge needed to simplify the shopping, planning, and preparation of nutritious meals. Moreover, nutrition education in the secondary and college levels should be fully geared to the possibility that tomorrow's woman may not be a full-time homemaker. Management, therefore, is becoming even a more important component in the nutrition education of the future than it has been in the past.

Increased Tensions and Stresses

The study of school girls in Iowa, mentioned in Chapter 4, showed the adequacy of their diets was positively related to the family relationships (3). California workers have called attention to the need for pleasant, unhurried meals for teen-age girls (5). They very aptly concluded from their study of 25 girls that not only did the girls themselves need further information in the selection of nutritionally adequate diets, but also some way should be devised to reach parents of these teen-agers, persuading them to work toward providing a cheerful, relaxed atmosphere for mealtimes at home.

Because the interaction between the family meal and the emotional climate of the family is strong, the net result may be keenly felt in the nutritional status of each member of the family, especially during childhood.

Mobility of Families

This is a very important factor in today's society, affecting people of all economic levels in both rural and urban areas. It seems reasonable to expect that changes from one locality to another might to some extent affect eating patterns. USDA studies, however, have shown regional differences in food consumption to be relatively minor. Effects of mobility on nutrition may be due mostly to disruption of family routines, emotional disturbances, or changes in socioeconomic status which may occur when moving to a new community.

NUTRITION AND THE FAMILY CYCLE

Home economists are especially concerned with the family as a unit in society. In each phase of the family cycle new problems are presented. The nutrition educator, especially in home economics, may increase her effectiveness by an analysis of the particular problems involved in the eating situation at different stages of the so-called family cycle. The following outline represents an approach to nutrition education from this standpoint.

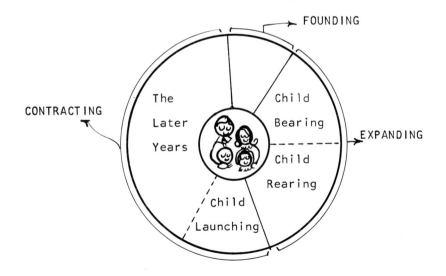

DEVELOPMENTAL TASKS

For the Founding Family

1. Adopting good health as an important goal in life.
2. Synchronizing food likes and dislikes of two people.
3. Acquiring the knowledge needed to make wise decisions regarding choice of food for self and others.
4. Planning meals to meet the needs of two young adults.
5. Developing ability to prepare appetizing food.
6. Establishing meal-time practices basic to the cultural patterns desired for the new family.
7. Establishing traditions that foster family unity and good family relationships.
8. Laying the foundation for health throughout the family cycle.

For the Expanding Family

CHILD BEARING

1. Understanding the relation of nutrition to success in reproduction and health throughout the life cycle.
2. Correcting possible dietary indiscretions in the previous diet of the mother-to-be.
3. Adjusting the diet to the special nutritional demands of the last half of pregnancy.
4. Planning for period of breast feeding of the infant.
5. Knowing the nutritional needs of the infant and the economics of infant feeding.
6. Understanding the psychological aspects of infant feeding and methods of introducing new foods.
7. Recognizing the evidences of good and poor nutrition in the infant and young child.
8. Managing time, energy, money, and other resources so that tensions may be reduced and the care of the infant can be approached with feelings of security and relaxation.
9. Understanding the influence of the food habits of the parents—especially of the father—upon the nutrition of the family and the developing food habits of children.

CHILD REARING

1. Planning nutritious and appetizing meals that can be adapted to individuals with a wide range of social, psychological, and physiological needs.
2. Adjusting home meals so that they effectively supplement food eaten elsewhere.
3. Maintaining an environment conducive to good eating behavior and the development of good food habits.
4. Managing expenditures for food so that they will yield maximum returns in health and satisfaction to all members of the family.
5. Utilizing the eating situation as an opportunity to fulfill the psychological as well as the biological needs of the family.
6. Coordinating eating practices in the home with nutrition education that family members receive elsewhere.
7. Keeping a log of the physical growth and maturation of the children and the major episodes in health.
8. Encouraging all members of the family to participate in the task of feeding the family.
9. Assuming responsibility for helping children develop good food habits.
10. Helping children to adopt good health as an important goal for their lives.

For the Contracting Family

CHILD LAUNCHING: the Children

1. Assuming full independence in the selection of an adequate diet in a wide variety of situations.
2. Learning to discriminate between real and apparent variety of food offered.
3. Learning to judge the nutrient returns for money spent at such places as lunch counters and vending machines.
4. Cultivating the habit of mental assessment of the adequacy of the day's food supply in terms of a daily food guide.
5. Developing a sensitivity to standards of sanitation and cleanliness in public eating places.
6. Evaluating performance in terms of how it may or may not have been affected by eating practices.

CHILD LAUNCHING: the Parents

7. Adjusting meal patterns to changing family membership and food intake to diminishing food energy needs.
8. Adapting to a changed tempo of living from that which characterizes a family with growing children to one of greater security, relaxation, and monotony.
9. Facing the need of dietary modifications necessitated by the threat of chronic disorders.

THE LATER YEARS

1. Maintaining a high level of nutrient intake so as to offset factors that may interfere with utilization; e.g. incomplete absorption, emotional stress.
2. Adjusting to physical difficulties in handling food and in eating.
3. Modifying diet in accordance with changing metabolic processes.
4. Solving the mechanical problems of food buying, storage, and preparation.
5. Adjusting diet to income limitations and possibly to living alone.
6. Understanding the role of nutrition in delaying and preventing the symptoms of senility.
7. Maintaining a strong interest in life and a sense of usefulness.

CHANGES IN THE FOOD SUPPLY

The dual responsibility of the nutrition educator is first, to help people recognize their individual nutritional needs; and second, to teach them how to meet those needs. Although a substantial proportion of food eaten in our nation is consumed ready prepared in public eating places, the quality of the diet of the family still depends largely upon the "market basket" which conveys food to the home.

Shopping for food is a major household task. The retail food market is a rapidly changing scene, where more and more services are offered. More and more people, including farmers, obtain their total food supply at retail outlets. Most household tasks have been greatly mechanized, but laying in the family food supply appears to be an exception because this requires increasingly more mental and physical work. Perhaps it may be reasonably assumed that the time and energy the homemaker has gained in "convenience" foods have been balanced at least in part by the additional effort she expends for more frequent trips to the market and the huge bags of groceries she must carry home. Rapidly vanishing are the days of the telephoned market order which was brought to the home by a cheerful delivery boy.

In education, we have been inclined toward working from the menu to the market basket. Perhaps a more realistic approach is from the market basket to the menu. Ways to undergird the adequacy of diets of families at the market basket stage are badly needed. Most valuable educational tools in this respect are the food plans at different costs developed by the USDA.[1, 2] The market basket should be a focal point in nutrition education for homemakers.

Making wise decisions in the food market requires alertness, knowledge, and skill. Not even a nutrition educator can be expected to know the merits of each of the 6,000 or so different items crowding the supermarket shelves. But she can be most helpful to the consumer who needs some intelligent criteria for selecting foods from this vast array.

We can expect that pressures to capture the food dollars of the public will increase. Therefore, educating people to choose foods wisely in the market place, to elect responsible people to public office, to expand nutrition services, and to encourage talented young people of integrity to enter the food-oriented professions are increasingly imperative.

CHANGES IN FOOD BUYING

Some criteria which may help consumers in purchasing food for their families are:

1. The contribution of the item to the over-all food needs of the family.
2. The return in actual food value for the money spent.
3. The price of the item in relation to alternate choices of similar food value.
4. The importance of the built-in services in the item as weighed against the probable cost of those services when obtained in other ways.
5. The necessity and economy of such additives as vitamins and minerals.

---

[1] See *Food,* the USDA Yearbook of Agriculture, 1959, pp. 576–88 for such plans.

[2] See also, E. Cofer, E. Grossman, and F. Clark, "Family Food Plans and Food Costs." Home Econ. Res. Rept. No. 20, Supt. of Documents, Washington, 1962. (35 cents.)

***It is unrealistic
to believe she
will read every
label . . . .***

Intelligent food buying requires reading the labels. It is unrealistic to believe that the homemaker will stop to read the label on every package she drops into her market basket. But she can learn by occasional study what is on the labels of the foods she most frequently buys. The information thus gained could be significant to the health of her family and the conservation of food money. Indeed, a study of labels on common food products can be the point of departure for many interesting and timely nutrition lessons.

The Food and Drug Administration is diligently and effectively using existing federal laws to protect consumers from the presence of hazardous ingredients. A weakness in the situation, however, is that many states do not have laws incorporating important sections of the federal regulations. Federal agencies do not have jurisdiction over foods produced and sold locally within states. Moreover, many states do not have adequate laboratories for testing and sufficient services for inspection of food products. Consumers should be aware of this situation, for it is up to individuals and professional organizations to work toward improvement of state laws and programs for their enforcement.

The Council on Foods and Nutrition of the American Medical Association and the Food and Nutrition Board of the National Research Council, through their statement of policies on the addition of nutrients to foods, are helpful in forming judgments about the use of enriched foods (6).

In 1961 the Council and Board reiterated the desirability of meeting nutritional needs by the use of an adequate variety of foods, in so far as could be practical. Foods regarded suitable for the distribution of additional nutrients are those which have diminished nutritive content as a result of loss from refining or other processing, and those which are widely and regularly consumed. Nutrients added to such foods should be of the kinds and quantities associated with the class of foods involved. Addition of other nutrients may be favored when deemed by properly qualified judgment to be advantageous to public health. The foods endorsed have been listed previously in this book on page 223.

The consumer who becomes familiar with the policies of the Council on Foods and Nutrition of the American Medical Association and the Food and Nutrition Board acquires knowledge that will help protect him against exploitation of products which are overadvertised for their additional nutrients. In this instance, education is the only source of protection for consumers. Therefore, nutrition educators must keep posted with current policies of AMA and the NRC, relaying such information to the public.

Similarly, educators must alert consumers to the pitfalls of many advertising appeals which are based on emotional promises of ease and convenience, along with oversimplification and half-truths, and with impressive but ambiguous "scientific claims."

In addition to basic information and knowledge of authoritative sources, homemakers may need most of all to have for themselves a basic underlying philosophy that serves to direct their choices of foods in the ever increasingly complex market.

FOOD AND RADIOACTIVITY

Attention has frequently been focused on the potential hazards of radiation to our food supply and to the human race. It is true that some radioactive products of nuclear fission can be detrimental to man. Of the forty or more nuclides in fission material, those assessed as biologically important (either because of their yield or their physical half-life) are Strontium-90; Iodine-131; Cesium-137; and, to a lesser degree, Barium-140 and Strontium-89. When ingested, they cause radiation exposure throughout the alimentary canal, and when absorbed, they may concentrate in specific tissues.

The radioactivity of Strontium-90 disappears slowly. It affects plants, thereby finding its way into foods of animal origin, later to be absorbed in the human body, and finally deposited and retained in the bones near the blood-cell-producing tissue. Accumulating in high concentrations, it can cause bone cancers and possibly leukemia.

Cesium-137 is more mobile, hence it becomes more widely distributed through the body. It can subject the reproductive organs to radiation. Iodine-131 is largely concentrated in the thyroid (7).

That increased radioactivity of elements in our environment introduces new health hazards can scarcely be doubted. There is some indication, however, that the current degree of concern is out of proportion to the facts. There is also the unfortunate tendency to associate the hazards with milk, while actually all foods are affected. Milk happens to be a commodity most easily measured for even a minute level of radioactivity.

Some reassuring facts which may guide public thinking on this subject were summarized as follows by Hundley (8):

1. Radiation has always been with us. Fallout from nuclear explosions simply adds to this.
2. A great deal has been learned about the biological effects of exposure to radiation, but more information is needed.
3. The amount of radioactivity in milk, various foods, drinking water, and air is under constant "early warning" surveillance network. There are 60 stations for atmosphere testing; more than 60 for milk sampling, and 20 for total diet sampling. In addition we have networks for monitoring general air and water pollution, with a total of 343 stations.
4. Amounts of radioactivity in food generally and in milk specifically are well below the level at which any action to reduce radioactivity is indicated. There is at present no reason for the public to reduce consumption of milk or other dairy products because of fear of radioactive contamination.
5. The human body must have calcium. Evidence exists that animals on a good calcium intake absorb less Strontium-90, while calcium-depleted animals absorb more.

A major disruption of the dairy industry through fears of radioactive contamination would do more harm than good. Undoubtedly, some risks are involved in the use of atomic energy. However, this is a danger to which our government is fully alert. Therefore, there is no reason for public panic. In the event of a fallout emergency, steps would be taken to warn the public and protect our people from any serious hazards affecting food supplies.

NUTRITION IN THE SPACE AGE

Research designed to sustain man in space over a period of time will undoubtedly influence many aspects of life on earth, too. Maintenance of the individual in a good state of nutrition will be essential to success of the space probes. We may expect space research to result in much new information about nutritional needs of human beings under various physical and psychological conditions.

When man lives in his earthly environment, a *precise* knowledge of his needs is perhaps less essential than when he is faced with the many restrictions of space travel. The limitations imposed by an environment to which he has not had the benefit of generations of biological adaptation require new methods to sustain him.

The development of closed systems, whereby waste products may be converted into forms suitable for re-use by the body, is a matter of considerable interest. Much research has been begun in the development of concentrated forms of food suitable for space travel, along with the possibility of food substances which may be grown aboard space ships during travels to outer space.

*How do we
explain that
quantitative need
has been
overestimated?*

CHANGES IN NUTRITION KNOWLEDGE AND METHODS OF COMMUNICATING THEM

Keeping abreast of new developments in food research, technology, production, and distribution is a major challenge for the nutrition educator. A research worker in nutrition may limit his efforts somewhat to *depth* in a major field of interest, but the educator must employ considerable *breadth*. Review articles in the professional journals, along with conferences, workshops, and short courses, all provide help in keeping posted.

As a prerequisite to the full use of current data, the nutrition educator must have a good grasp of nutrition science and the current status of its application. A sound basic preparation in the supporting sciences is the necessary background for an effective, up-to-date specialist in nutrition education. In our present educational system, however, we find many people with less than adequate background in nutrition and science. They nevertheless must carry the responsibility of teaching nutrition for everyday living. The specialist must assume the responsibility of giving practical assistance to the nearly-lay teachers of nutrition, especially in interpreting new findings to them.

We must recognize problems of preparing people for revising their concepts in nutrition. How do we explain, for example, that the quantitative need of a nutrient has been overestimated in the past, or that a food once considered a good source of a certain nutrient is now not recognized as such? Or that the well-learned concept of iron as a blood builder is now regarded as oversimplified and only a fraction of the whole truth?

The reflections of such changes and uncertainties in the minds of people is expressed in the following statement by Will Durant (9):

And if the day should come when our dietitians will have at last made up their minds as to what they really know and believe, I should ask them to teach the principles of diet an hour in every school week for fifteen years, so that our people might make with some corporate intelligence the dietetic changes required by the passage from an outdoor and physical life to a mental and sedentary one.

Nutrition educators have a large body of well-established knowledge from which to draw. The everyday lessons of nutrition can be largely centered upon such data, but people must be receptive to new knowledge and willing to modify earlier information in the light of it. The research point of view, as described by Charles Kettering, suggests a basic philosophy that may generate a spirit of open-mindedness so important to nutrition education:

> Research is a high-hat word that scares a lot of people. It needn't. It is rather simple. Essentially, it is nothing but a state of mind — a friendly, welcoming attitude toward change. Going out to look for a change instead of waiting for it to come. Research, for practical men, is an effort to do things better and not be caught asleep at the switch. The research state of mind can apply to anything: personal affairs or any kind of business, big or little. It is the problem-solving mind as contrasted with the let-well-enough-alone mind. It is the composer mind instead of the fiddler mind. It is the "tomorrow" mind instead of the "yesterday" mind.

Nutritionists may at times be too eager to teach "what's new." Let us first be sure that we utilize the basic facts that have stood the test of time, for these form the background against which new information must be tested and evaluated.

Along with the constant flood of new information is a barrage of misinformation. This can take the form of outright deceit, half-truths, and misleading statements, all geared to garner a share of the consumer's food or health dollar.

The public must be helped to develop a discriminating attitude toward what they see and hear about food. They should learn to ask questions about the "authority" behind a statement; to consider it in the light of their own knowledge, experience, and common sense; to consult qualified people; to beware of promises of "easy" ways, cure-alls, and emotional appeals; they should learn to distinguish between associations and cause-and-effect relationships, and to realize that news headlines may be different from confirmed scientific facts. Nothing will help combat misinformation more effectively than sound knowledge of the basic facts of nutrition — which deal with the composition of foods and how they serve the needs of the body.

THE CHALLENGE OF CHANGE IN PHILOSOPHY AND OBJECTIVES

Nutrition education usually does not constitute a segregated program. It is incorporated in a health or home economics program at the primary, secondary, or college level. It may be part of an extension program or an adult education class. Wherever it is found, it does not operate as an isolate.

Therefore, in teaching nutrition it is important that the educator consider the basic philosophy and new developments of the specific professional group with which he is allied.

The home economics branches of the U.S. Office of Education and of the Land Grant College Association are currently engaged in curriculum projects designed to obtain agreement concerning basic concepts for home economics either in secondary schools or in universities. The effectiveness of the nutrition educator will be increased if she is aware of these developments as she plans her program.

The over-all aims of a profession provide a structure within which the nutrition educator may function. Such statements of purpose or philosophy as the "Task Force" report of the American Public Health Association; the "Scope" of the Cooperative Extension Service; and "New Directions in Home Economics" of the American Home Economics Association are excellent. The latter is a statement issued on the 50th anniversary of the American Home Economics Association. Included in it are "Twelve Competences" which were developed as guideposts for home economists. Nutrition educators concerned with families, especially the home economics educators, should seek to interpret the contribution that knowledge of nutrition has to make toward each of these competences or goals for family living.

Fundamental to effective living are the competences to:

- *establish* values which give meaning to personal, family, and community living; select goals appropriate to these values
- *create* a home and community environment conducive to the healthy growth and development of all members of the family at all stages of the family cycle
- *achieve* good interpersonal relationships within the home and within the community
- *nurture* the young and foster their physical, mental, and social growth and development
- *make* and carry out intelligent decisions regarding the use of personal, family, and community resources
- *establish* long-range goals for financial security and work toward their achievement
- *plan* consumption of goods and services — including food, clothing, and housing — in ways that will promote values and goals established by the family
- *purchase* consumer goods and services appropriate to an over-all consumption plan and wise use of economic resources
- *perform* the tasks of maintaining a home in such a way that they will contribute effectively to furthering individual and family goals.
- *enrich* personal and family life through the arts and humanities and through refreshing and creative use of leisure
- *take* an intelligent part in legislative and other social action programs which directly affect the welfare of individuals and families
- *develop* mutual understanding and appreciation of differing cultures and ways of life, and cooperate with people of other cultures who are striving to raise levels of living.

MEETING THE CHANGES — TODAY AND TOMORROW

Nutrition education is a challenging field of endeavor. It offers possibilities of tangible rewards for a job well done because, as the individual improves his dietary patterns, favorable results eventually appear in his over-all state of health and well-being.

This book has attempted to provide for the reader an over-all perspective on teaching nutrition by offering a careful look at the past, along with an assessment of nutrition education in the present era, and a look ahead.

The future of nutrition education depends upon the efforts, knowledge, and dedication of all those who are offered the challenge of teaching nutrition.

REFERENCES

1. Paolucci, B., "Reviewing Our Orbit." *Jour. Home Econ.,* 50 (No. 7) :499–502, Sept. 1958.
2. Sidwell, V. D., and Eppright, E. S., "Food Habits of Iowa Children — Breakfast." *Jour. Home Econ.,* 45 (No. 6) :401–5, June 1953.
3. Hinton, M. A., "Factors Related to the Eating Behavior and Dietary Adequacy of Girls 12 to 14 Years of Age." Unpubl. Ph.D. dissertation, Iowa State University Library, Ames, 1962.
4. 1960 White House Conference on Children and Youth, *Proceedings,* p. 94.
5. Hampton, M. C., Shapiro, L. R., and Huenemann, R., "Helping Teen-age Girls Improve Their Diet." *Jour. Home Econ.,* 53 (No. 10) :835–38, Dec. 1961.
6. Council on Foods and Nutrition, "General Policy on Addition of Specific Nutrients to Foods." *Jour. Amer. Med. Assn.,* 178 (No. 10) :1024–25, 1961.
7. Setter, L. R., "Radioactive Contamination of Food." *Jour. Amer. Diet. Assn.,* 39 (No. 6) :561–66, Dec. 1961.
8. Hundley, J. M., "Diet and Health." U.S. Dept. HEW, *Public Health Reports,* 77 (No. 4) :277, Apr. 1962.
9. Durant, W. J., "What Education Is of Most Worth?" *Sat. Eve. Post,* 208:14, Apr. 11, 1936.

Guide for Identifying Foods
in Food Groups

There have been many food guides developed throughout the years, some with as few as 2 or 3 food groups, others with as many as 13. Many different combinations of foods provide the essentials needed for an adequate diet, so at the end of a day the individual will have consumed an adequate diet regardless of which guide he has followed. The two guides most generally in use in the United States are commonly called "A Daily Food Guide for Fitness" (often referred to as the "Basic Four") and "The Basic Seven."*

FOOD FOR FITNESS — A DAILY FOOD GUIDE

1. **Meat Group**
   Recommended amount: 2 or more servings
   Beef, veal, pork, lamb, poultry, fish, eggs
   As alternates — dry beans, dry peas, nuts

2. **Vegetable and Fruit Group**
   Recommended amount: 4 or more servings
   A citrus fruit or other fruit or vegetable important for vitamin C
   A dark-green or deep-yellow vegetable for vitamin A — at least every other day
   Other vegetables and fruits, including potatoes

3. **Milk Group**
   Recommended amount:
   Children: 3 to 4 cups
   Teen-agers: 4 or more cups
   Adults: 2 or more cups
   See list of equivalents given under the "Basic Seven" for amounts that may be substituted for one serving of milk.

---

* Adapted from E. F. Phipard and L. Page, "A Guide to Eating," *Food*, The Yearbook of Agriculture, 1959, USDA, pp. 266–70.
   See also "Food for Fitness — A Daily Food Guide," Leaflet No. 424, USDA.

4. Bread and Cereal Group
Recommended amount: 4 or more servings
Whole grain, enriched, or restored

Plus
Other foods as needed to complete meals and to provide additional food
energy and other food values. The foods of the various groups are
identified under the "Basic Seven" plan.

THE "BASIC SEVEN"

1. Dairy Products
Recommended amounts of milk:
Children: 3 to 4 cups
Teen-agers: 4 or more cups
Adults: 2 or more cups
The standard serving of fluid whole milk is 8 ounces or one-half pint
or 1 cup. The approximate equivalents of 1 serving of whole milk in terms
of other dairy products and appropriate supplements are:

Whole milk (dry) .... 4 tablespoons
Evaporated milk .... 1/2 cup
Condensed milk .... 1/3 cup [1]
Skim or nonfat milk (fluid) ...... 1 cup plus 1 serving (slightly less than 2 teaspoons) of butter or fortified margarine [2]
Buttermilk (made from skim milk) .... See skim or nonfat fluid milk
Nonfat milk solids (dried skim milk) .... 4 tablespoons plus supplements suggested for fluid skim milk
Cheddar cheese .... 1 ounce (approximately 1-inch cube) [3]
Cottage cheese .... 1 cup plus 1 serving of butter or fortified margarine [4]
Butter .... 1 serving (about 1/2 tablespoon) plus 1 cup of fluid skim milk or its equivalent
Cream (light) .... 2 to 4 tablespoons plus 3/4 cup of fluid skim milk
Cream (heavy) .... 1 tablespoon plus 1 cup of fluid skim milk
Yogurt .... variable; approx. 2/3 cup if made from concentrated milk or with milk solids added

---

[1] Has extra calories equivalent to about 3 tablespoons of sugar.

[2] Green, leafy, and yellow vegetables may replace the fat as a supplement in low-calorie diets.

[3] Slightly low in calories, thiamine, riboflavin, and calcium, as compared with one cup of fluid milk.

[4] One serving is usually not more than 1/2 cup. To be made approximately equivalent to 1 cup of milk, this amount should be supplemented with one large serving of table fat plus one serving of green leafy vegetable, as turnip greens.

Include in total milk intake the approximate amounts of milk furnished by foods prepared with it, as:

Ice cream	Cream pie
Pudding	Cereal with milk
Cream soup	Cocoa

Allow about one-half cup of milk per serving from foods of these types.

2. Green, leafy, or yellow vegetables and yellow fruits

Recommended amount: 1 or more servings.

Foods included in this group contain the equivalent of at least 1,000 I.U. of vitamin A per 100 grams or per ½ cup as prepared for serving.

Dandelion greens	Collards	Cantaloupe
Spinach	Winter squash	Water cress
Carrots	Beet greens	Broccoli
Chard	Kale	Tomatoes
Sweet potatoes	Pumpkin	Mustard greens
Turnip greens	Apricots	

3. Vitamin C-rich fruits and vegetables

Recommended amount: 1 or more servings.

Foods included in this group contain at least 25 milligrams of vitamin C (ascorbic acid) in servings of about ½ cup.

Oranges	Lemons	Honeydew melon
Orange juice	Lemon juice	Cooked greens
Grapefruit	Cantaloupe	Broccoli
Grapefruit juice	Strawberries	Collards
Tangerines	Green peppers	Brussels sprouts
Tangerine juice	Tomatoes	Cabbage

4. Other fruits and vegetables

Recommended amount: 2 or more servings.

This group includes fruits and vegetables not in Groups 2 and 3. Although they are not rich sources of nutrients, they are helpful in supplying the total amount of vitamins and minerals needed. Some of the most frequently used are:

Potatoes [2]	Snap beans [1]	Rhubarb
Corn	Asparagus [1]	Raspberries [2]
Beets	Apples	Cherries [1]
Peas [1]	Bananas	Blackberries [2]
Lettuce (head)	Pears	Prunes [1]
Onions	Peaches [1]	Pineapple
Turnips [2]	Plums	Raisins

---

[1] These provide a substantial amount of vitamin A (in the form of carotene), but not in sufficient amounts to permit classification in Group 2.

[2] These provide vitamin C, but not in sufficient amounts to permit classification in Group 3. Because of amounts used by many people in the daily diet, potatoes become a significant source of vitamin C.

5. Protein-rich foods

Recommended amount: 1 or 2 servings.

Foods which provide at least 15 to 20 grams of protein in a 3- to 4-ounce serving are included in this group.

Beef steak, roast, hamburger	Chicken
Veal	Turkey
Pork chops or roast	Fish
Lamb chops or roast	Game
Organ meats, as liver and heart	

Foods which require 2 or 3 servings to be approximately equivalent to one serving of meat are listed below.

Eggs
Milk
Cottage cheese (1/4 cup)
Cheddar cheese (1 once or 1-inch cube)
Legumes, as navy or lima beans, dried peas, peanuts, and peanut butter

6. Bread and cereals

Recommended amount: 4 or more servings.
Foods included in this group are:

Bread	Macaroni	Popcorn
Biscuit	Noodles	Doughnut
Muffin	Rice	Sweet roll
Bun	Spaghetti	Cooky
Pancake	Vermicelli	Crackers
Waffle	All breakfast foods	Plain cake

7. Fat and sweet foods

Use as needed to complete food energy requirements.

Butter	Nuts	Jelly
Cream	Bacon	Candy
Oleomargarine	Salt pork	Sweet desserts not mainly
Salad dressing	Sugar	milk, eggs, or fruit
Gravy	Sirup	

Appendix B

Rating Diets

If careful records are kept of amounts and kinds of food eaten, the food energy and nutrient intake may be estimated by use of food composition tables. These calculated intakes may be compared with the Recommended Daily Dietary Allowances (see Appendix C immediately following).

The following classifications, although arbitrary, have proved to be helpful:

1. *Excellent* — Met 100 per cent of Allowances of all nutrients.
2. *Good* — Within range of 66 – 75 per cent and 100 per cent of Allowances of all nutrients.
3. *Poor to Fair* — One or a few nutrients less than 66 per cent of Allowances.
4. *Poor* — Several nutrients less than 66 per cent of Allowances.

Simple dietary scores unaccompanied by careful inspection and interpretation of individual diets are generally unreliable as estimates of the nutritional adequacy of a diet. The following is a method of scoring used by Maxine Armstrong Hinton in her doctoral dissertation.[1] Scores correlated fairly well with the average of percentages of nutrients meeting the Recommended Daily Dietary Allowances. Proper interpretation of the score requires inspection of the diets for the usage of food groups that are starred. Even with this precaution some very good diets may be classified as inferior and, perhaps less often, a poor diet may escape notice.

In general a qualitative estimate of diets for nutrients is to be preferred and — in the interpretation of adequacy — health, growth, and general evidences of nutritional status should be taken into consideration.

---

[1] M. A. Hinton, "Factors Related to the Eating Behavior and Dietary Adequacy of Girls 12 to 14 Years of Age." Unpubl. Ph. D. dissertation, Iowa State University Library, Ames, 1962.

Food Group	Value per Serving	Maximum Values Allowed for 7 Days
★ 1. Milk and equivalents	1	28
2. Eggs	1	7
3. Legumes	1	7
4. Beef, veal, fowl, lamb, fish	2	8
5. Pork	2	4
6. Liver	4	4
★ 7. Vitamin C-rich foods	1	7
★ 8. Vitamin A-rich or carotene-rich foods . . .	1	7
9. Other fruits	1	14
10. Other cooked vegetables	1	7
11. Raw vegetables	1	7
12. Irish potatoes	1	7
13. Whole grain and enriched cereals	1	28
14. Butter or margarine	1	4
Maximum number of points		139

To score your* diet for the week:

$$\frac{\text{total points}}{139} \times 100$$

To interpret your score:

Score 85 to 100: *Good to Excellent,* provided scores for items 1, 7, and 8 (starred items) are at least 21, 5, and 3, respectively.

Score 70 to 84: *Fair to Good,* provided scores for items 1, 7, and 8 are at least 14, 4, and 2, respectively.
Fair to Poor, if scores for items 1, 7, and 8 are less than 14, 4, and 2, respectively.

Score 60 to 70: *Fair,* provided scores for items 1, 7, and 8 are 14, 4, and 2 or better, respectively.
Poor, if scores for these items are less than 14, 4, and 2.

Below 60: *Poor.*

---

* Planned for teen-age girls. The method of scoring does not permit an estimate of adequacy of food energy intake. Therefore it should be used in conjunction with observations on weight for height and age, and for desirable weight gains.

Recommended Daily Dietary Allowances

The Recommended Daily Dietary Allowances are a guide for planning adequate diets for healthy individuals and population groups. The table was prepared by the Food and Nutrition Board of the National Academy of Sciences – National Research Council. Members of the Board are appointed from among the leaders in sciences related to food and nutrition. The Allowances are based on available research and the best judgment of the members of the Board and their advisers.

The amounts are not minimal, but are estimated to cover the needs and to provide a margin of safety for most healthy individuals within a category. The calorie allowances must be adjusted for persons who differ in size, age, or physical activity from the reference[1] man and woman or the children described in the table.

The table includes those nutrients for which sufficient information is available to permit breakdown by specified age categories. Other essential nutrients will probably be supplied if the allowances are fully met.

Diets that supply less than the Recommended Allowances are not always deficient for a given individual. Consideration of the nutritional state of the individual is important in assessing dietary adequacy.

Origin of the Allowances is described in Chapter 9. The Allowances were revised in 1945, 1948, 1953, 1958, and 1963.

---

[1] The "reference" man and woman are both aged 25 years, and the allowance as recommended for age 25 years represents estimates to cover the period from 18 to 35 years. In the early part of this age range, additional allowances may be needed for certain groups; for example: young men in military service.

Energy requirements decline progressively after the years of early adulthood. It is proposed that daily calorie allowances be reduced by 5 per cent per decade between the ages of 35 and 55 and by 8 per cent per decade from ages 55 up to 75. A further decrement of 10 per cent is recommended for age 75 and the years beyond.

FOOD AND NUTRITION BOARD, NATIONAL ACADEMY OF SCIENCES—NATIONAL RESEARCH COUNCIL

RECOMMENDED DAILY DIETARY ALLOWANCES[1], REVISED 1963

Designed for the Maintenance of Good Nutrition of Practically All Healthy Persons in the U.S.A.

(Allowances are intended for persons normally active in a temperate climate.)

	Age[2]	Weight	Height	Calories	Protein	Calcium	Iron	Vitamin A Value	Thiamine	Riboflavin	Niacin Equivalent[3]	Ascorbic Acid	Vitamin D
	(Yrs.)	(Lbs.)	(In.)		(Gm.)	(Gm.)	(Mg.)	(I.U.)	(Mg.)	(Mg.)	(Mg.)	(Mg.)	(I.U.)
Men	18–35	154	69	2,900	70	0.8	10	5,000*	1.2	1.7	19	70	
	35–55	154	69	2,600	70	0.8	10	5,000	1.0	1.6	17	70	
	55–75	154	69	2,200	70	0.8	10	5,000	0.9	1.3	15	70	
Women	18–35	128	64	2,100	58	0.8	15	5,000	0.8	1.3	14	70	
	35–55	128	64	1,900	58	0.8	15	5,000	0.8	1.2	13	70	
	55–75	128	64	1,600	58	0.8	10	5,000	0.8	1.2	13	70	
	Pregnant (2nd and 3rd trimester)			+ 200	+20	+0.5	+5	+1,000	+0.2	+0.3	+3	+30	400
	Lactating			+1,000	+40	+0.5	+5	+3,000	+0.4	+0.6	+7	+30	400
Infants[4]	0–1	18		lb.×52.3 ± 6.8	lb.×1.2 ±0.2	0.7	lb.×0.5	1,500	0.4	0.6	6	30	400
Children ...	1–3	29	34	1,300	32	0.8	8	2,000	0.5	0.8	9	40	400
	3–6	40	42	1,600	40	0.8	10	2,500	0.6	1.0	11	50	400
	6–9	53	49	2,100	52	0.8	12	3,500	0.8	1.3	14	60	400
Boys	9–12	72	55	2,400	60	1.1	15	4,500	1.0	1.4	16	70	400
	12–15	98	61	3,000	75	1.4	15	5,000	1.2	1.8	20	80	400
	15–18	134	68	3,400	85	1.4	15	5,000	1.4	2.0	22	80	400
Girls	9–12	72	55	2,200	55	1.1	15	4,500	0.9	1.3	15	80	400
	12–15	103	62	2,500	62	1.3	15	5,000	1.0	1.5	17	80	400
	15–18	117	64	2,300	58	1.3	15	5,000	0.9	1.3	15	70	400

[1] The allowance levels are intended to cover individual variations among most normal persons as they live in the United States under usual environmental stresses. The recommended allowances can be attained with a variety of common foods, providing other nutrients for which human requirements have been less well defined.

[2] Entries on lines for age range 18–35 years represent the 25-year age. All other entries represent allowances for the midpoint of the specified age periods, i.e., line for children 1–3 is for age 2 years (24 months); 3–6 is for age 4½ years (54 months), etc.

[3] Niacin equivalents include dietary sources of the preformed vitamin and the precursor, tryptophan. 60 mg. tryptophan represents 1 mg. niacin.

[4] The calorie and protein allowances per lb. for infants are considered to decrease progressively from birth. Allowances for calcium, thiamine, riboflavin, and niacin increase proportionately with calories to the maximum values shown.

* 1,000 I.U. from preformed Vitamin A and 4,000 I.U. from beta-carotene.

Appendix D

Body Measurements

DESIRABLE WEIGHTS FOR MEN AND WOMEN 25 YEARS AND OVER

Desirable weights as they appear in Table D.1 represent an estimate of what people should weigh by the criterion of greatest longevity; desirable weights are within a range of 15 to 25 pounds below average weights. No single value can be designated as the desirable weight for all persons of a specified height, since individuals vary in many respects. These tables are based on available anthropometric studies and data from "Build and Blood Pressure Study," 1959. The main determinant of body frame was body width as measured by chest breadth and hip width. If people kept their weight down to the average in their early twenties, they would be close to the desirable weights at ages over 30 years.[1]

---

[1] E. W. Lew, "New Data on Underweight and Overweight Persons." *Jour. Amer. Diet. Assn.*, 38:223–27, April 1961.

TABLE D.1

DESIRABLE WEIGHTS FOR MEN AND WOMEN OF AGES 25 YEARS AND OVER*
Weight in Pounds According to Frame (in indoor clothing).

Men

Height (with shoes on) 1-in. heels		Small Frame	Medium Frame	Large Frame
(ft.)	(ins.)			
5	2	112–120	118–129	126–141
5	3	115–123	121–133	129–144
5	4	118–126	124–136	132–148
5	5	121–129	127–139	135–152
5	6	124–133	130–143	138–156
5	7	128–137	134–147	142–161
5	8	132–141	138–152	147–166
5	9	136–145	142–156	151–170
5	10	140–150	146–160	155–174
5	11	144–154	150–165	159–179
6	0	148–158	154–170	164–184
6	1	152–162	158–175	168–189
6	2	156–167	162–180	173–194
6	3	160–171	167–185	178–199
6	4	164–175	172–190	182–204

Women †

Height (with shoes on) 2-in. heels		Small Frame	Medium Frame	Large Frame
(ft.)	(ins.)			
4	10	92–98	96–107	104–119
4	11	94–101	98–110	106–122
5	0	96–104	101–113	109–125
5	1	99–107	104–116	112–128
5	2	102–110	107–119	115–131
5	3	105–113	110–122	118–134
5	4	108–116	113–126	121–138
5	5	111–119	116–130	125–142
5	6	114–123	120–135	129–146
5	7	118–127	124–139	133–150
5	8	122–131	128–143	137–154
5	9	126–135	132–147	141–158
5	10	130–140	136–151	145–163
5	11	134–144	140–155	149–168
6	0	138–148	144–159	153–173

* Sources: *Weight Control—A Word to the Wives*, Publ. No. T.(c) 5040— (8–60) and *How To Control Your Weight*, Publ. No. (Y) 380 L.W. (360), Metropolitan Life Insurance Co., New York.
† For girls between 18 and 25, subtract 1 pound for each year under 25.

BODY MEASUREMENTS FOR CHILDREN

The weight-height-age tables for boys and girls (Tables D.2 and D.3),[2] compiled by Baldwin and Wood in 1923, were derived from records of 70,000 boys and 55,000 girls from 12 schools in the Northeastern and North Central States. Age is reported at the nearest birthday, height at the nearest inch, and weight at the nearest pound. Certain percentages of net weights were added for clothing, exclusive of shoes, coats, and sweaters:

For boys — 3.5 per cent of weights from 35 to 65 pounds and over.

For girls — 3 per cent for weights from 35 to 65 pounds, 2.5 per cent for weights from 66 to 82 pounds, and 2 per cent for 83 pounds and over.

---

[2] Discussions and tables from "Heights and Weights of Children and Youth in the United States," *Home Economics Research Report No. 2.* Inst. of Home Econ. and Agr. Res., USDA, October 1957, pp. 57–59. For sale by Supt. of Document, U. S. Govt. Print. Office, Washington 25, D.C. (Price 65 cents.)

TABLE D.2 WEIGHT-HEIGHT-AGE TABLE FOR BOYS OF SCHOOL AGE (Baldwin and Wood, 1923)

Height (ins.)	19 yrs.	18 yrs.	17 yrs.	16 yrs.	15 yrs.	14 yrs.	13 yrs.	12 yrs.	11 yrs.	10 yrs.	9 yrs.	8 yrs.	7 yrs.	6 yrs.	5 yrs.	Av. Wt. for Ht. (lbs.)	Height (ins.)
38														34*	34	34	38
39													38*	35*	35	35	39
40													39*	36*	36	36	40
41												39*	41*	38	38	38	41
42												41*	44	39	39	39	42
43												44*	46	41	41	41	43
44											46*	46*	48	44	44	44	44
45											48*	48	50	46	46*	46	45
46											50*	50	53	48	47*	48	46
47										50*	53	53	55	50	49*	50	47
48										53*	55	55	58	52		53	48
49										55	58	58	61	55		55	49
50									55*	58	61	61	63	57*		58	50
51									58*	61	64	64	66*			61	51
52								58*	61	64	67	67				64	52
53								61*	64	67	70	70				68	53
54							64*	64	67	70	72	72*				71	54
55							68*	68	70	73	76*	75*				74	55
56					80*	72*	71	71	73	77	79*					78	56
57					83*	74*	74	74	77	80	83*					82	57
58					87	78	78	77	81	84						85	58
59				90	90	83	82	81	84	87						89	59
60				96	95	86	85	85	88	91*						94	60
61			106*	103	100	90	89	89	92							99	61
62		116*	111	107	104	94	93	92	95							104	62
63	127*	123	118	113	110	99	97	96	100*							111	63
64	130*	126	121	117	115	103	102	101	105*							117	64
65	134	131	127	122	120	108	107	106								123	65
66	139	136	132	128	125	113	111	109								129	66
67	142	139	136	134	130	118	117	114*								133	67
68	147	143	141	137	134	122	119									139	68
69	152	149	146	143	139	128	124*									144	69
70	155	151	148	145	144	134										147	70
71	159	154	152	151	150	137										152	71
72	163	158	156	155	153	143										157	72
73	167	164	162	160	157*	148*										163	73
74	171	170	168	164	160*											169	74

TABLE D.2 SUMMARY

		6 yrs.	7 yrs.	8 yrs.	9 yrs.	10 yrs.	11 yrs.	12 yrs.	13 yrs.	14 yrs.	15 yrs.	16 yrs.	17 yrs.	18 yrs.	19 yrs.
Average height (ins.)	Short	43	45	47	49	51	53	54	56	58	60	62	64	65	65
	Medium	46	48	50	52	54	56	58	60	63	65	67	68	69	69
	Tall	49	51	53	55	57	59	61	64	67	70	72	72	73	73
Average annual gain (lbs.)	Short	3	4	5	5	5	4	8	9	11	14	13	7	3	
	Medium	4	5	6	6	6	7	9	11	15	11	8	4	3	
	Tall	5	7	7	7	7	8	12	16	11	9	7	3	4	

Source: As presented in "Mother and Child," supplement to July issue, 1923.
Starred items represent values based upon theoretical computations rather than exact averages.

TABLE D.3 Weight-Height-Age Table for Girls of School Age (Baldwin and Wood, 1923)

Height (ins.)	Av. Wt. for Ht. (lbs.)	5 yrs.	6 yrs.	7 yrs.	8 yrs.	9 yrs.	10 yrs.	11 yrs.	12 yrs.	13 yrs.	14 yrs.	15 yrs.	16 yrs.	17 yrs.	18 yrs.	Height (ins.)
38	33	33	33													38
39	34	34	34													39
40	36	36	36	36*												40
41	37	37	37	37*												41
42	39	39	39	39*												42
43	41	41	41	41												43
44	42	42	42	42	41*											44
45	45	45	45	45	42*	45*										45
46	47	47*	47	47	45	48*										46
47	50	49*	50	50	48	50	50*									47
48	52		52	52	50	52	53*	53*								48
49	55		54	54	52	55	56	56*								49
50	58		56*	56	55	58	59	61	62*							50
51	61			59	57	61	61	63	65							51
52	64			63*	60	64	64	65	67	71*						52
53	68			66*	64	67	68	68	69	73*	78*					53
54	71				67	70	70	71	71	77	83*					54
55	75				69*	74	74	74	75	81	88	92*				55
56	79				72*	76*	78	78	79	84	93	96*				56
57	84					80*	82	82	82	88	96	100*	101*			57
58	89						84	86	86	92	101	105	103*	104*		58
59	95						87*	90	90	97	105	108	108	109		59
60	101						91*	95	95	101	109	113	112	113	111*	60
61	108							99	100	106	112	115	115	117	116	61
62	114							104*	105	110	117	119	117	119	118	62
63	118								110	115	121	122	120	122	120	63
64	121								114*	120	124	125	123	125	123	64
65	125								118*	122	130	131	128	129	126	65
66	129									128*	133	135	133	133	130	66
67	133									131*	135*	137*	136	138	135	67
68	138										136*	138*	138*	140*	138	68
69	142										138*	140*	140*	142*	142*	69
70	144												142*	144*	144*	70
71	145														145*	71

		6 yrs.	7 yrs.	8 yrs.	9 yrs.	10 yrs.	11 yrs.	12 yrs.	13 yrs.	14 yrs.	15 yrs.	16 yrs.	17 yrs.	18 yrs.
Average height (ins.)	Short	43	45	47	49	50	52	54	57	59	60	61	61	61
	Medium	45	47	50	52	54	56	58	60	62	63	64	64	64
	Tall	47	50	53	55	57	59	62	64	66	66	67	67	67
Average annual gain (lbs.)	Short	4	4	4	5	6	6	10	13	10	7	2	1	
	Medium	5	5	6	7	8	10	13	10	6	4	3	1	
	Tall	6	8	8	9	11	13	9	8	4	4	1	1	

Source: As presented in "Mother and Child," supplement to July issue, 1923.
Starred items represent values based upon theoretical computations rather than exact averages.

COMPARING BODY SIZE ACCORDING TO RATE OF MATURING

The Bayley (1956) table of heights and weights of boys and girls, (Table D.4), takes into consideration the important point of maturation of the child. A wide spread of difference exists among children in the age at which the growth spurt of adolescence takes place. These data are based on more than 300 healthy California children who were measured repeatedly from birth to 18 or 21 years of age as a part of an extended growth study.[3]

Table D.4 is adapted from *Growth Diagnosis*, by Leona M. Bayer and Nancy Bayley, University of Chicago Press, 1959. Copies may be obtained, on request, from Ross Laboratories, Columbus 16, Ohio.

CHARTS ON GROWTH OF CHILDREN

The Jackson-Kelly charts of growth of children (Figs. D.1 and D.2) on pages 308 and 309[4] are useful in following the growth of individual children or groups of children. They are based on 13,000 height and 11,000 weight measurements of Iowa City, Iowa, children. The data were collected from 1920 to 1940 and compiled by Meredith at the Iowa Child Welfare Research Station.

The charts can be purchased from the Department of Pediatrics, State University of Iowa, Iowa City, Iowa.

---

[3] Discussion and tables from "Heights and Weights of Children and Youth in the United States," Home Econ. Res. Rept. No. 2. Inst. of Home Econ. and Agr. Res., USDA, October 1957, pp. 90–91.

[4] *Ibid.* pp. 68, 71, 72.

HEIGHTS AND WEIGHTS OF BOYS AND GIRLS RELATED TO THEIR RATE OF MATURING *

Boys

Age	Accelerated		Average		Retarded	
	Height	Weight	Height	Weight	Height	Weight
(yrs.)	(ins.)	(lbs.)	(ins.)	(lbs.)	(ins.)	(lbs.)
1......	30.9	23.8	30.7	22.9	29.3	23.4
2......	35.2	31.1	34.6	29.3	32.8	27.3
3......	38.6	35.5	38.0	34.6	36.2	30.6
4......	41.5	41.4	40.8	39.0	39.6	35.7
5......	44.5	45.9	43.7	52.8	42.3	40.3
6......	47.2	51.8	45.8	47.6	44.9	44.1
7......	50.0	56.9	48.7	52.9	47.0	48.5
8......	52.5	65.0	50.9	58.2	49.4	54.7
9......	54.9	74.5	53.1	66.8	51.8	60.2
10......	57.3	86.0	55.3	74.1	54.1	66.1
11......	59.6	97.2	57.5	82.2	55.8	73.4
12......	61.8	109.8	59.1	91.3	57.7	80.7
13......	65.6	124.8	61.4	101.4	59.4	90.2
14......	68.5	134.5	64.6	116.0	61.7	100.1
15......	70.7	147.9	68.1	133.8	64.2	112.2
16......	71.7	154.1	70.1	142.6	67.7	131.0
17......	71.7	155.9	70.5	149.7	69.5	143.1
18......	....	.....	70.9	154.1	70.5	150.8
19......	....	.....	....	.....	71.3	151.7

Girls

Age	Accelerated		Average		Retarded	
1......	30.6	24.0	29.1	21.5	28.3	21.2
2......	34.4	30.2	34.4	28.0	33.3	25.9
3......	37.8	34.7	37.5	32.4	36.7	30.6
4......	41.3	42.1	40.6	37.5	39.4	33.7
5......	44.4	48.1	43.1	41.2	41.7	37.9
6......	46.9	53.2	45.9	46.7	44.5	43.0
7......	49.2	57.3	48.1	52.9	47.2	47.6
8......	52.0	66.8	50.4	60.0	49.2	51.1
9......	55.1	78.5	52.7	66.4	51.5	59.7
10......	57.3	92.2	55.1	76.1	53.3	64.8
11......	60.4	108.9	57.5	86.6	55.5	69.9
12......	63.1	124.8	60.7	99.2	57.7	78.0
13......	64.3	131.2	63.0	112.4	59.8	86.9
14......	64.8	135.0	64.2	121.0	62.4	99.0
15......	65.0	138.7	64.8	128.8	63.8	108.5
16......	65.2	139.3	65.2	131.6	64.5	114.6
17......	65.2	137.6	65.3	132.3	64.8	119.3
18......	65.2	134.5	65.3	131.8	64.9	119.0

* Heights and weights at the chronological ages were interpolated from a large graph based on mean values calculated at 2 per cent intervals on mature height. There were 38 boys and 27 girls in the accelerated groups, 106 boys and 108 girls in the average groups, and 31 boys and 25 girls in the retarded groups.

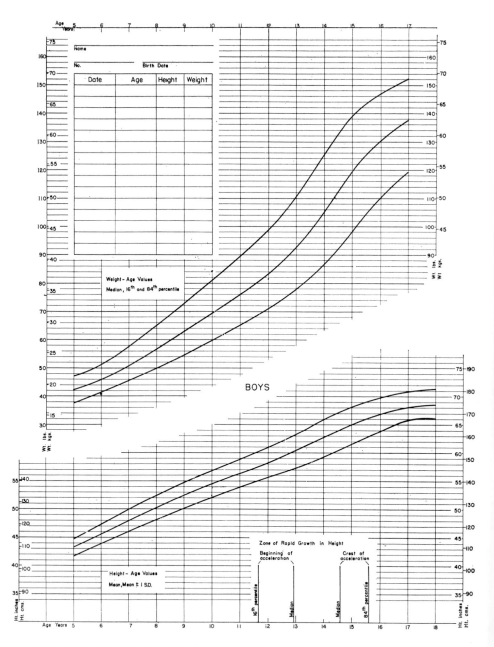

Fig. D.1 — Growth chart for boys aged 5 to 18 years. (Form 153-B, copy-righted 1943 by State University of Iowa.)

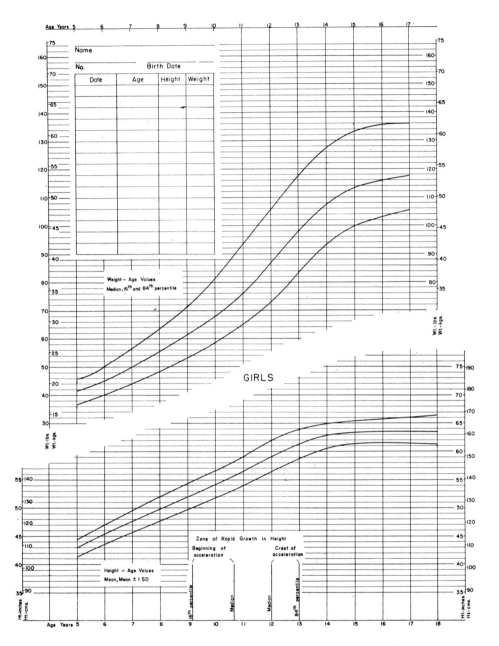

Fig. D.2 — Growth chart for girls aged 5 to 18 years. (Form 153-G, copyrighted 1943 by State University of Iowa.)

Appendix E

Explanation of Terms

Definitions used by people in the field of nutrition frequently have an emphasis unique to that profession. Listed below are many of what have become the "working definitions" accepted and employed in the specific field. These have been adapted from numerous authoritative sources.

Acne vulgaris — a simple uncomplicated condition resulting in a raised eruption on the skin due to inflammation, with accumulation of secretion, of the oil-secreting or sebaceous glands.

Allergy, food — hypersensitiveness to a substance in food which is ordinarily harmless in similar amounts for the majority of persons.

Amino acids — the nitrogen-containing acids obtained when protein materials are broken down chemically. The differences between proteins are largely a matter of the number, the kind, and the arrangement of such amino acids within the protein substances.

Amino acids, essential — amino acids which need to be included in the diet, i.e., which either cannot be synthesized in the body or not at a rate sufficient to meet the need.

Anemia — a reduction in the amount of hemoglobin in the blood or in the number of red corpuscles of the blood.

Appetite — the inclination or desire to eat; distinguished from hunger as the drive to eat.

Ascorbic acid — (see Vitamin C.)

Ash — the total mineral matter residue after ignition of a food; always either neutral or alkaline, since acid in excess of that which can be neutralized is volatilized.

Atherosclerosis — a degeneration of the blood vessels caused by a deposit of fatty materials along the lining of the wall of the blood vessel. Cholesterol is one of these fatty materials.

Bacterial action — changes produced by one-celled microorganisms such as those involved in fermentation, synthesis of vitamins, soil fertilization, decay of organic matter, and many diseases.

Calorie (large or kilocalorie) — the unit used to express food energy; the amount of heat required to raise the temperature of one kilogram of water one degree Centigrade.

Carbohydrates — a large group of chemical substances containing carbon, hydrogen, and oxygen; forms commonly seen are starch and various kinds of sugar.

Cardiovascular — pertaining to heart and blood vessels.

Carotene — provitamin A. A yellow-red plant pigment occurring in several forms; B-carotene is the most abundant form in common green leafy and yellow vegetables.

Cellulose — a constituent of the cell walls of plants forming the basis for vegetable fiber; chemically, a carbohydrate having about the same percentage composition as starch.

Cholesterol — the most common member of the group of sterols (complex, fatlike substances that can be dissolved in ether and other fat solvents); present in many foods and can be made within the body.

Congenital — existing at birth, referring to certain mental or physical traits, peculiarities, or diseases.

Connective tissue — (see Tissue.)

Dental caries — the progressive decay of tooth structures.

Emotional disturbances — an interruption of ability to resist forces which tend to arouse strong feelings; a disturbed mental state resulting in agitation and confusion.

Emotional stability — ability to resist forces which tend to arouse strong feelings or disturbed mental states.

Environment — the conditions and influences under which one lives. Everything that conditions the life process except the hereditary or genetic factors.

Fats — the name given to a group of chemical substances composed of the same three elements as carbohydrates, namely, carbon, hydrogen, and oxygen, but in different proportions; fats constitute a much more concentrated form of food energy. Fats have an oily texture and are not soluble in water.

Fatty acid — organic compound of carbon, hydrogen, and oxygen, which combines with glycerol to make fat.

Fermentative — relating to chemical change that takes place in an organic substance caused by certain fungi, bacteria, and enzymes, and is accompanied by evolution of gases often evidenced by hissing and bubbling.

Flour, enriched — white flour enhanced in thiamine, riboflavin, niacin, and iron value by changing the milling process to retain these constituents or by addition of the chemicals to white flour. The minimum levels specified in the standards of identity promulgated under the Food, Drug and Cosmetic Act are: thiamine, 2.0 mg.; riboflavin, 1.2 mg.; niacin, 16 mg.; and iron, 13 mg. per pound. Certain levels of vitamin D and calcium are permitted as optional ingredients. States which require enrichment of white flour have generally been guided by the federal legislation.

Food — any substance which may be used to yield energy; to build or renew body tissue; or to regulate body processes and internal conditions, so as to maintain a right internal environment for life.

Food energy value — refers to the carbohydrate, fat, and protein content of the diet, since these constituents release energy as they are broken down in the cells of the body; commonly expressed as calories, since heat is a measurable by-product of the energy released when the carbohydrate, fat, and protein are broken down.

Food, fortified — a food to which a vitamin or other dietary essential has been added in such an amount as to make the total content of the dietary essential larger than that contained in any natural (unprocessed) food of its class, for example, vitamin D milk and fortified margarine.

Food, utilization of — refers to the process by which ingested food is digested, absorbed, distributed, and assimilated by the cells of the body.

Fortified margarine — (see Margarine.)

Glycerol — serves as the backbone radical or framework of the fat molecule, permitting the attachment of three fatty acids.

Goiter, simple — enlargement of the thyroid gland, caused by an absolute or relative deficiency of iodine.

Hemoglobin — the red coloring matter of the blood found in the red blood cells; contains iron and is capable of uniting loosely with oxygen.

Heredity — the tendency of any living thing to reproduce the characteristics of its ancestors.

Hunger — a strong drive for food.

Ingestion — the introduction of food or drink into the stomach.

International Unit — a unit of measure established by a committee appointed by the Health Organization of the League of Nations, used for expressing the content of vitamins in foods and other materials; usually dropped when vitamin values can be conveniently expressed in weight but now used mainly for vitamins A and D. The recommended allowance for vitamin D for infants and children, including adolescents, and for women during pregnancy and lactation, is 400 International Units per day.

Iodized salt — (see Salt.)

Lactation — the period following childbirth during which milk is produced by the mammary glands of the breasts.

Lactic acid — a three-carbon organic acid formed as an intermediary in carbohydrate metabolism; produced by certain kinds of bacteria when acting on food residues, particularly milk.

Linoleic acid — one of the digestion products from certain fats; essential to body tissues; a polyunsaturated fatty acid which the body apparently cannot make and hence it must be provided by the food ingested.

Malnutrition — a condition of the body resulting from an inadequate supply or impaired utilization of one or more of the essential food constituents.

Margarine, fortified — margarine with vitamin A added. The margarine on the market in the United States is fortified with 15,000 I.U. of vitamin A per pound.

Maturation — the process of coming to full development, maturity, or adulthood.

Membrane, mucous — tissue lining the passages which lead into and out of the body and which secrete a clear viscid substance; examples are the digestive, respiratory, and urinary tracts.

Mental activity — the functional activity of the mind.

Metabolism — a general term to designate all chemical changes which occur to substances within the body after absorption. These changes include constructive (anabolic) and destructive (catabolic) processes.

Metabolism, intermediary — the transfers and chemical changes undergone by nutrients after digestion and absorption.

Milk, vitamin D — milk processed or produced to provide vitamin D; may be produced by three different methods:

    1) "fortified" milk, which is now more generally distributed than the other types, is that to which a vitamin D concentrate has been added;

    2) "metabolized" milk is produced by feeding the cows irradiated yeast; and

    3) "irradiated" milk has been exposed directly to ultraviolet rays.

    The standard amount used for fortification is 400 I.U. of vitamin D per quart of fresh or reconstituted milk.

Minerals — "inorganic elements." The following are known to be present in body tissues; calcium, cobalt, chlorine, copper, fluorine, iodine, iron, magnesium, manganese, phosphorus, potassium, sodium, sulfur, and zinc. These constituents, obtained from food, aid in the regulation of acid-base balance of body fluids and of osmotic pressure, in addition to the specific function of individual elements in the body. Some minerals are present in the body largely in organic combination, as iron in hemoglobin, and iodine in thyroxine; others occur in the body in inorganic form, as calcium salts in bone, sodium and chlorine as sodium chloride. The terms "minerals" and "inorganic elements" do not imply that the elements occur in inorganic form in food or body tissue.

Neuromuscular tremor — a trembling or shaking produced by nerve stimulation of contractile tissues of the body by which movements of the various organs and parts are affected.

Niacin, or nicotinic acid — a water-soluble heat-stable member of the vitamin B complex; needed for the use of the nutrients by the tissues. The antipellagric factor.

Nutrient — a substance which takes part in any of the three ways by which food nourishes the body. Some nutrients function in more than one of these ways.

Nutrition — the combination of processes by which the living organism receives and utilizes the materials necessary for the maintenance of its functions and for the growth and renewal of its components.

Nutrition, normal — a condition of the body resulting from the efficient utilization of sufficient amounts of the essential nutrients provided in the food intake.

Nutritional status — the condition of the body resulting from the utilization of the essential nutrients available to the body. Nutritional status may be good, fair, or poor, depending not only on the intake of dietary essentials but on the relative need and the body's ability to utilize them.

Nutriture — used interchangeably with nutritional status; the condition of physical health and well-being of the body as related to the consumption and utilization of food for growth, maintenance, and repair.

Obesity — excessive overweight due to the presence of a surplus of fat.

Overweight — an excess of more than 10 per cent above the desirable weight.

Physiological — relating to the normal vital processes of animal and vegetable organisms.

Plasma — the colorless fluid portion of the blood in which the cells are suspended.

Polyunsaturated — refers to a class of fatty acids that have more than one unsaturated linkage in the chain, each lacking 2 hydrogens. Saturated fatty acids have all the hydrogens the carbon chain can hold.

Precursor — a substance which is converted into another. For example, the carotenes are precursors of vitamin A.

Proteins — nitrogenous compounds which yield amino acids on hydrolysis; essential constituents of all living cells, and the most abundant of the organic compounds in the body.

Protein, complete — one which contains all of the essential amino acids, i.e., those which must be supplied preformed in food.

Protein, incomplete — one which is completely lacking in one or more of the essential amino acids which must be supplied preformed in food.

Protein, supplementary effect — the ability of one protein to supply amino acids in which another protein is deficient, so that from the mixture of the proteins an adequate intake of amino acids is secured.

Provitamin — a substance which may be converted into a vitamin; thus, the carotenes are provitamins A.

Pulses — edible seeds of various leguminous crops, as peas, beans, lentils, etc. Commonly used in combination with the term proteins, as "pulse proteins," meaning leguminous proteins.

Radioactive — giving off atomic energy in the form of radiations, such as in the alpha, beta, or gamma rays.

Riboflavin, or vitamin B_2 — vitamin of the B complex; soluble in water, not easily destroyed by heat but destroyed by visible light; a yellow pigment having a green fluorescence and essential for utilization of nutrients in the tissues.

Salt, iodized — table salt (sodium chloride) to which has been added one part per 10,000 of iodine as potassium iodide.

Serum — the colorless fluid portion of the blood that separates when blood clots.

Starvation — long-continued unsatisfied hunger; the condition of suffering or dying from lack of food.

Syndrome — a medical term meaning a group of symptoms that occur together.

Thiamine, or vitamin B_1 — vitamin of the B complex; soluble in water, destroyed by heat, essential for growth and the use of carbohydrate in the body.

Thyroid gland — a ductless gland lying in front of the upper part of the windpipe; furnishes an internal secretion which influences the rate of metabolism.

Tissue — a collection of cells or derivatives of cells, forming a definite structure. Examples are *adipose* or *fatty tissue,* a structure consisting chiefly of fat droplets; *muscle tissue,* composed chiefly of long, thin fibers or muscle cells embedded in a thin, delicate connective-tissue membrane.

Tissue, connective — a tissue holding together and in place other, usually more active tissues, as, for example, muscle fibers or the cells of the glands.

Tonus (tone) — a sustained state of partial activity such as exists in varying degrees in live muscles at all times.

Utilization of food — (see Food.)

Vascular — full of vessels that contain a fluid. In physiology, the blood and lymph vessels in the body.

Vitamins — substances that are: (*a*) distributed in foods in relatively minute quantities; (*b*) distinct from the main components of food (i.e., proteins, carbohydrates, fats, mineral salts, water), (*c*) needed for the normal nutrition of the animal organism, and (*d*) so essential the absence of any one will cause a corresponding specific deficiency disease. At least 8 of the 20 known vitamins are needed by man, or are of undoubted clinical significance.

Vitamin A value — the combined potency of a food or diet, represented by its content of vitamin A, carotene, and other plant precursors (of vitamin A).

Vitamin B complex — as originally used, this term referred to the water-soluble vitamins occurring in yeast, liver, meats, and whole-grain cereals, but some of the newer B complex vitamins — for example, folic acid and vitamin B_{12} — do not correspond to this distribution; includes a number of factors which have been identified, isolated, and synthesized, viz., thiamine, riboflavin, nicotinic acid, vitamin B_6, pantothenic acid, biotin, folic acid, inositol, and choline; vitamin B_{12}, which has been crystallized . . . and others which have been only partially demonstrated or indentified.

Vitamin C — a water-soluble vitamin easily destroyed by exposure to the oxygen of the air; a white crystalline solid with a sour taste; concerned specifically with the maintenance of cement-like substances which hold cells together throughout the body; deficiencies are manifest in ruptured blood vessels, loose teeth, and poorly calcified bones.

Vitamin D — designates a group of fat-soluble factors which help to utilize calcium and phosphorus.

Vitamin D milk — (see Milk.)

Vitamins, fat-soluble — vitamins A, D, E, and K, which are extractable from foods with fat solvents.

Vitamins, water-soluble — members of the B complex and vitamin C which can be extracted from foods with water as a solvent.

Using Nutrition Films

With Sample Lesson Plans

The use of films in teaching nutrition is an effective method of creating for the student a visual representation that can be related to or associated with daily life much more readily than can spoken or written words. The adage "One picture is worth a thousand words" may be an exaggeration, but it has merit in that a vivid mental image may be more easily recalled than words.

Following are a group of films readily adapted to nutrition classes, with sample lesson plans for five of them. Most of these films are available from Visual Instruction services at state universities (with a nominal handling charge) or may be ordered directly from the sources listed — most with no handling charge.

1. **And One To Grow On**   (16 mm. Color. 11 minutes.)
   A story of the foods needed to help children to "grow and go" from babyhood to adolescence.

   Emphasizes the importance of eating about one-third of the day's food at breakfast and the need to take time for a good school lunch.

   The mother's responsibility to provide and prepare a variety of of foods needed to meet the nutritional demands of her children is discussed.
   >   Source: Social Science Films
   >   2395 Hampton St.
   >   St. Louis, Mo.

2. **Babies Like To Eat**   (16 mm. Color. 11 minutes.)
   Excellent illustrations are given of how and when to introduce new foods to the baby. Emphasis is placed on the individuality of babies and the fact that happy babies like to eat.

   There is need for patience when helping the baby learn to drink from a cup or accept strange new foods, and understanding when the baby goes on food jags. Avoid making the baby the center of attraction.

   Inclusion of the same variety of food for the baby that the family is eating, prepared so the baby can handle it, is advocated.
   >   Source: Social Science Films
   >   2395 Hampton St.
   >   St. Louis, Mo.

3. *Hungry Angels* (16 mm. Color. 20 minutes.)
Guatemalan children (3), born the same day, show the dramatic fight for life when malnutrition (kwashiorkor) results from ignorance and superstition. Produced by INCAP.
> Source: Association Films, Inc.
> 347 Madison Ave.
> New York City, 17, N.Y.

4. *It's All In Knowing How* (16 mm. Color. 13 minutes.)
Especially recommended for use with adolescent boys and girls. Demonstrates how inadequate food intakes influence energy and personality. Emphasis is placed on the use of protective foods as sources of vitamins A, B complex, and C; and protein, calcium, and iron.
> Source: National Dairy Council
> 111 North Canal St.
> Chicago 6, Ill.

5. *The Fraud Fighters* (16 mm. Black and white. 17 minutes.)
This portrayal of the functions of the Pure Food and Drug Administration in the United States includes information about patent medicines, vitamins, foreign imported goods, coal tar dyes, cosmetics and other products in interstate commerce.

Animal experiments are shown which help to prove the merits of various foods, drugs, and cosmetics.

6. *Two Little Rats and How They Grew* (16 mm. Color. 11 minutes.)
A fifth grade group of boys and girls observed the needs of plants and animals (white rats) for growth.

The school lunch composed of protein food, fruit, vegetable, bread, butter, and milk was served to the children; their growth, as indicated by height and weight changes taken twice a year, was evaluated by the school doctor and nurse.
> Source: National Dairy Council
> 111 North Canal St.
> Chicago 6, Ill.

7. *The Medicine Man* (16 mm. Black and white. 27 minutes.)
This film, prepared by the American Medical Association, exposes some of the prevailing errors in "food faddism." It uses an effective dramatic device in exposing a self-styled medicine man who promotes homemade remedies at the expense of approved modern medical products.
> Source: Sterling Movies U.S.A., Inc.
> 43 West 61st St.
> New York City 23, N.Y.

8. *Weight Reduction Through Diet* (16 mm. Color. 15 minutes.)
Overeating is ascribed to family food patterns, loneliness, and unhappy social life. Overweight is portrayed as keeping one from appearing his best and possibly in preventing employment.

A group of college women, after a doctor's examination, ate as usual for one day and then calculated the calorie content of their food intake. Then weight-reduction diet patterns were made and explained for each subject. The reducing diets included a generous breakfast, and more protein and fat than most reducing diets.

Weight loss from 16–24 pounds was accomplished at a rate of approximately two pounds per week.

> Source: National Dairy Council
> 111 North Canal St.
> Chicago 6, Ill.

9. Something You Didn't Eat   (16 mm. Color. 9 minutes.)

A Walt Disney cartoon that illustrates in several ways the consequences of having inadequate quantities of certain groups of foods. It shows some early discoveries of the importance of (*a*) citrus fruits as cures for scurvy and (*b*) whole grains as cures for beri-beri. The results of poor diets for modern men and women are shown in an amusing manner, as are ways of securing adequate diets.

> Source: Motion Picture Service,
> USDA
> Washington, D.C.

10. Fundamentals of Diet   (16 mm. Black and white. 11 minutes.)

The introduction shows how young animals secure their first food. Rat-feeding experiments show what happens to animals that do not have sufficient quantities of protein, minerals, or vitamins A and D in their diets.

> Source: Encyclopedia Britannica, Inc.,
> Wilmette, Ill.

11. More Life in Living   (16 mm. Black and white. 11 minutes.)

Shows the effects of good and poor diets on general health, weight, and personality. Relationship between health and ability to participate in active sports is emphasized.

> Source: National Dairy Council
> 111 North Canal St.
> Chicago 6, Ill.

12. Whenever You Eat   (16 mm. Color. 10 minutes.)

Shows attractive high school boys and girls who are ambitious to succeed in such occupations as engineering, music, nursing, aviation, homemaking, and landscape architecture. Farming is not one of the occupations shown but many of the abilities emphasized are needed in farming. Some characteristics needed for each of these occupations are given and related to good health.

Menus for one day without milk, cheese, or butter are shown. A chart of food nutrients shows how these three meals fail to provide as much of each nutrient as is needed. When milk, cheese, and butter are added, more than the needed amounts of some nutrients are provided.

> Source: National Dairy Council
> 111 North Canal St.
> Chicago 6, Ill.

13. **What Makes Us Grow**   (16 mm. Black and white. 11 minutes.)
Made during World War II, this film emphasizes the importance to our country of the health of every one of us. The importance of each type of food in our meals is pointed out.
> Source: National Film Board of Canada
> 680 5th Ave.
> New York City 19, N.Y.

14. **Science Tells Why . . . Food Additives**
(Film strip. 80 frames. Color. 33⅓ r.p.m. transcription.)
Presents the reasons for using food additives; shows how they make possible a food supply greater in quantity and better in quality.
> Source: Manufacturing Chemists' Assoc., Inc.
> 1825 Conn. Ave., N.W.
> Washington 9, D.C.

15. **Food Through the Ages**
(Film strip. 82 frames. Color. 33⅓ r.p.m. transcription.)
A history of food preparation and processing; suitable for use in the elementary grades, but interesting to adults.
> Source: Manufacturing Chemists' Assoc., Inc.
> 1825 Conn. Ave., N.W.
> Washington 9, D.C.

SUGGESTED LESSON PLANS

Following are some suggestions for adapting five specific films to classes. The nutritionist will be able to devise procedures for adapting any film, keeping in mind the age, experience, and needs of members of the audience.

Something You Didn't Eat

Before showing the film, help students to evaluate their own diets as *good, fair,* and *poor.* A rating of 3, 2, or 1 may be assigned to each food group, using either 4 or 7 groups.

Questions To Answer When Viewing the Film

1. Why did men in the film become ill?
2. What foods cured the men who were ill?
3. How did the man and woman in the film show that their diets were inadequate?

Questions for Discussion After Viewing the Film

1. Why do we need food from each group in our diets every day?
2. Look at average scores for the diets of the students in our class.
   a. For which food groups is our rating *good* (3)?
   b. For which food groups do we rate *fair* (2)?
   c. For which food groups do we rate *poor* (1)?
   d. How does your individual score compare with the class score?
3. What may happen if we continue to omit or have too little of the foods for which we rated *poor* and *fair* in our diets?

Fundamentals of Diet

Questions To Answer When Viewing the Film

1. Why were white rats used for the feeding experiments?
2. What happened to the rat that did not get enough *(a)* protein, *(b)* minerals. *(c)* vitamin D, *(d)* vitamin A?

Questions for Discussion After Viewing the Film

1. Why did the rats need certain foods in their diets every day? To answer this question recall what happened to the rats and guinea pigs.
   a. Why did the eyes of one rat become red and sore? What could he have eaten to help prevent this?
   b. Why was one guinea pig larger and stronger than the other?
2. How are our needs similar to those of white rats? How are the nutritional needs of rats different from ours? (They grow 30 times as fast.)
3. Show a Food for Fitness or a Basic Seven chart. Why are foods divided into these groups? What may happen if we do not eat some foods from each of these groups?
4. During the year when there is little sunlight we need foods that are rich in vitamin D. How may vitamin D be obtained?
5. Study the report of the food for which our class rated *fair* or *poor*. Which foods did we learn about today?

More Life in Living

Questions To Answer When Viewing the Film

1. What did the boy who couldn't make the team eat?
2. What should he have eaten?
3. Why were these foods recommended?
4. Notice the different types of people in the film and try to remember what each of them ordered in the restaurant.

Questions for Discussion After Viewing the Film

1. Did the foods eaten by the people in the film seem to be related to the way the people looked or acted?
   a. The fat girl?
   b. The nervous woman?
   c. The boy who couldn't make the team?
   d. The family?
2. What foods should you eat each day to help you to be as attractive as possible?
   a. To have good teeth?
   b. To have good posture?
3. What foods should you eat sparingly if you are fatter than you want to be? (For older pupils.)
4. What kind of diet should you plan if you want to gain weight? What things may you need to do?
5. What foods should be eaten by all of us *every day*, regardless of our weight? (This question is intended to emphasize the importance of milk and cheese; eggs, meat; green or yellow vegetables; tomatoes, raw cabbage, oranges, or grapefruit.)

Whenever You Eat

Questions To Answer When Viewing the Film

1. What skills that were shown in the film are needed by farmers?
2. How does the lunch served at our school differ from the one shown in the film?
3. How do milk, cheese, and butter improve the three meals that are shown in the film?

Questions for Discussion After Viewing the Film

1. What work do you want to do when you finish school? How will your health influence success in the occupation you have chosen?
2. How did your three-day dietary fail to meet the standard recommended? How might continued lack of these foods affect you?
3. Using the school lunch menu for today, plan the other meals for the day. Check your menus against the food groups as given in appendix A.
4. When are we old enough to accept responsibility for our own health and especially our own way of eating?

What Makes Us Grow

Questions To Answer When Viewing the Film

1. How do the two foods for which our class scored lowest differ in nutrients from other foods?
2. Why should each one of us include these foods in our diets every day or several times a week?

Questions for Discussion After Viewing the Film

Place on the board the classification of food groups for which our class rated *good, fair,* or *poor* and also the average score for each food group.

1. Why is each of the food groups for which we rated *fair* or *poor* important in our diets?
2. What foods are classified under each of these food groups? (See Appendix A, pages 291–94.
3. How many of these foods do you eat every time they are served to you?
4. Are you refusing, at home or at school, most of the foods from a particular group?
5. As a class, which of these foods might we agree always to try to eat when they are served to us?

Care, Feeding, and Characteristics of Rats

GENERAL INSTRUCTIONS

Keeping records

If possible, secure white rats of weanling age (28 days). Be sure that cages are ready when rats arrive. Before the experiment begins, record each rat's age, weight, sex, and the diet you have planned for each one. Put this information on a label on each cage.

At the beginning of the experiment, establish a certain time to record information. It may be daily, two or three times a week, or weekly. Records should be made *at least* once a week.

Once a week discuss and analyze these records with students. After a week or two, students should be able to predict future progress or regression of rats. Stress the importance of keeping accurate figures.

Graphs are the easiest way to illustrate the weight and growth of rats. It is important to keep records so that students may see the relationship between food and growth.

Younger students will understand weight in terms of ounces and pounds. Older students may use grams as weight measurement.

Handling Rats

Rats respond to gentle handling. To pick up a rat, extend hand slowly toward rat's head. Hold it by placing thumb and forefinger under the rat's chin.

Poorly nourished rats are more irritable and may snap at fingers. It is wise to handle them with gloves. Explain to students that quick movements or pushing objects into cages may frighten the rats.

Set up a schedule with students so that there is a rotating plan for weighing rats, feeding rats, cleaning cages, and other details.

Feeding Rats

The main purpose of using white rats is to show the effects of diets of different natural foods which are commonly used in human dietaries. The experiments are planned to illustrate the importance of good food selection as shown by growth and external appearance.

This experiment includes three diets of natural foods which give striking results in growth and appearance of animals. The three diets are used to illustrate:

1. Effects on growing animals of diets completely lacking in milk and eggs, and inadequate in fruits and vegetables (Diet 1).
2. Effects of feeding the inadequate Diet 1 plus milk only (Diet 2).
3. Effects of feeding a fully adequate diet (Diet 3).

PERCENTAGE COMPOSITION OF 3 EXPERIMENTAL DIETS

Ingredients	Diet 1 (all foods dried) Inadequate	Diet 2 (all foods dried) Inadequate plus milk	Diet 3 (all foods dried except last 3) Adequate
	(per cent)	*(per cent)*	*(per cent)*
Meat	15	15	15
Beans (navy)	4	4	4
Potatoes (white)	10	10	10
Rolled oats	5	5	5
White flour	25	20	12
Butter	5	5	5
Lard	10	10	6
Sugar	20	10	5
Apples	5	5	5
Salt	1	1	1
Dried whole milk	0	15	15
Eggs	0	0	5
Lettuce	0	0	3
Carrots	0	0	4
Tomatoes	0	0	5
Total	100	100	100

Permit the rats on all 3 diets to eat as much as they desire. Be sure that they have plenty of food and water *at all times*. Give fresh food and water daily, except for week ends (see Week-end Care, next page). Remove foods not consumed.

Weighing Rats

Use balance gram scale if possible. Otherwise, use a small scale which records ounces. Check scale before weighing. Weigh container which is to hold rat. Then put rat into weighed container. Weigh container with rat in it. Subtract weight of container from total weight to obtain weight of rat.

Daily Cleaning of Cages

Each day, change newspaper in bottom pan of cages. Check, too, to be sure food containers are clean.

Weekly Cleaning of Cages

Wash cages weekly *(clean only one cage at a time — to prevent mix-up)*.

1. First put rat into coffee can and cover with screen or other material which admits air.
2. Clean cage, base, and cover using soap and water with mild disinfectant. Scrub with brush. Be sure food and water containers are clean. Rinse thoroughly.
3. Clean cupboard or other area which holds supplies for rats. Check to see that all needed supplies, cleaning equipment, and foods are available.

Handling Cages in Classroom

1. Keep cages in a place that will be good for the rats — they need light and air. Keep cages away from drafts. Keep rats away from *direct* light, in a quiet place, so they will not become nervous and excited.
2. Keep rats in a place where they can be observed but not where they will draw attention away from other studies.
3. Keep cages in a place where they will not be knocked over.
4. Be sure that rats are always returned to the proper cage. In the beginning, the rats will be about the same size and weight. It may be hard to tell them apart. Each cage will have an identifying card. When cleaning cages, remove only one rat at a time.

Week-end Care

Arrange with the janitor to find a place in the building which will be warm enough for the rats. They should have a temperature of about 70 to 80 degrees Fahrenheit. (Rats should be in a place where there is no danger of their being fed or handled by other people.) Just before the rats are placed in their week-end location, check to be sure each rat has plenty of food and water and is properly covered. Enough food should be provided so that some remains uneaten the following Monday morning.

Early Monday morning, return the rats in their cages to the classroom. Clean the cages.

Characteristics To Note in Rats

Well-Nourished Rat:	Poorly Nourished Rat:
Smooth, glossy coat	Shaggy, dull, possibly thin coat
Bright pink eyes	Crusty, speckled eyelids
Pink nose, feet, tail	Rough, dry, scaly ears, feet, tail
Smooth tail, free from roughness	Humped posture
Quick, alert movements	Pinched face
Easily handled, good-natured	Nervous, irritable, restless
Clean, tidy habits	Susceptible to "sniffles"

Appendix H

Landmarks in the Development
of World Nutrition *

1905 — David Lubin, an American, founded the International Institute of Agriculture in Rome, on a small scale comparable to Food and Agriculture Organization (FAO). Lubin was motivated by his belief that agricultural prosperity was the basis of economic prosperity.

1925 — Yugoslavia proposed that the Health Organization of the League of Nations examine and report on all of the aspects of the world food problems.

1935 — After a three-day debate in the Health Organization of the League of Nations on problems of production and distribution, it was decided to set up a committee of nutrition experts to draw up standards of human needs. Chairman, Sir Edward Mellanby; and representatives from the United States, Dr. W. H. Sebrell and Dr. Hazel Stiebeling.

1944 — Hot Springs Conference to consider ways and means of getting international cooperation to abolish hunger and raise the standard of living of the people working on the land; out of this conference arose the FAO, *the first organization* of the United Nations.

1945 — Food and Agriculture Organization formally organized in Quebec with 42 member nations (now approximately 80). Sir John Boyd-Orr, nutritionist and founder and head of the Rowett Research Institute, Aberdeen, Scotland, was elected the first Director-General. Motto "Fiat Panis" — Let there be bread. Headquarters, Rome, Italy.

1946 — WHO: World Health Organization

● First step toward establishment was taken at the United Nations Conference on International Organization, in San Francisco, April 25, 1945. Brazil accomplished insertion of the word "health" in the chapters of the U.N. Charter.

● Second step, Brazil and China proposed a joint declaration, unanimously approved, for establishment of an international health organization.

● U.S. Public Health Service and the Department of State took the lead in planning steps to make WHO a reality.

● At a conference in New York, July 1946, representatives of 61 nations signed the Constitution of the World Health Organization.

● This became an official organization of the United Nations when 26 members of the U.N. accepted the Constitution, on April 7, 1948. This date is now celebrated as World Health Day.

---

* Adapted from various documents.

- First Assembly met in June 1948 (56 states were active members). Headquarters, Geneva, Switzerland.
- Joint committees of FAO and WHO were formed prior to 1951. These combine emphasis of *FAO* on nutrition in relation to production, distribution, and consumption of food, and of *WHO* on nutrition in relation to the maintenance of health and prevention of disease.

1946 — UNICEF: United Nations International Children's (Emergency) Fund

- Created by the General Assembly of the United Nations December 11, 1946.

Purposes:
- to meet the emergency needs of children particularly in the war devastated countries, and

- to further improvement of child health generally. Headquarters, New York.

1946 — UNESCO: United Nations Education Scientific and Cultural Organization

- Established when 20th signatory to constitution deposited instrument of acceptance with the government of the United Kingdom.

Purpose:
- to promote collaboration through education, science, and culture in order to further justice, rule of law, and human rights and freedoms without distinction of race, sex, language, or religion.

1948 — Ford Foundation

- The study committee appointed agreed at the outset not to accumulate a comprehensive catalog of projects but to block out in general terms those critical areas where problems were most serious and where the Foundation might make the most significant contributions to human welfare.

Purpose:
- as stated in the charter, "to receive and administer funds for scientific, educational, and charitable purposes, all for public welfare."

The Ford Foundation will support activities in these five areas:
- Those that promise significant contributions to world peace and the establishment of a world order of law and justice.

- Those designed to secure greater allegiance to the basic principles of freedom and democracy in the solution of the insistent problems of an ever-changing society.

- Those designed to advance the economic well-being of people everywhere and to improve economic institutions for the better realization of democratic goals.

- Those designed to strengthen, expand, and improve educational facilities and methods to enable individuals more fully to realize their intellectual, civic, and spiritual potentialities; to promote greater equality of educational opportunity; and to conserve and increase knowledge and enrich our culture.

- Those scientific activities designed to increase knowledge of factors which influence or determine human conduct, and to extend such knowledge for the maximum benefit of individuals and of society.

1949 — INCAP: Institute of Nutrition on Central America and Panama

- Established with headquarters at Guatemala City and with membership that eventually included Costa Rica, El Salvador, Guatemala, Honduras, and Panama.

1950 — "Point Four" Act for International Development

- Created "to make available to peace-loving peoples the benefits of our store of technical knowledge."

Purposes:
- to foster capital investment in areas needing development;

- to develop a program of self-help by the peoples themselves for the under-developed areas; and

- to secure the growth of democratic ways of life, the expansion of mutually beneficial commerce, the development of international understanding and good will, and the maintenance of World Peace.

- President Truman's proposal was made in his inaugural address, January 20, 1949.

1954 — Public Plan 480 (PL480)

- Created to increase the consumption of United States agricultural commodities in foreign countries, to improve the foreign relations of the U.S. and for other purposes. (An act of Congress, passed July 10.)

- Under this program the United States by 1962 has given more than $10 billion worth of food and farm products to 40 countries, or sold it to them on special terms. The food has been used for a variety of purposes, including emergency relief, food reserves, and the speeding of economic and social development. The recipient government does not repay the United States in money, but is obliged to use the money for new developments, such as roads, dams, school buildings and similar projects in its own country.

1955 — International Seminar on Education in Health and Nutrition, held in Baguio, the Philippines, October 13 to November 3, 1955.

1955 — International Cooperative Administration

- Established under the Department of State by the Secretary of State to succeed Foreign Operations Administration, an outgrowth of Point Four.

1955 — ICNND: Interdepartmental Committee on Nutrition for National Defense

- Organized cooperatively by the Departments of Defense; State; Health, Education, and Welfare; Agriculture; and ICA.

Purpose:
- "to assess, to assist, and to learn."

- By 1963 this agency has worked in 22 different countries. Local specialists work side by side with personnel from the United States. Together they have defined the major nutritional problems, utilizing the best techniques now available for field studies, which encompass clinical examination, biochemical assessment, and dietary intake studies. As a result practical recommendations for improvement have been made.

1960 — Food for Peace Program

- "The United States Food for Peace Program seeks to use with imagination and compassion our excess of food for the benefit of mankind."

1961 — AID: Agency for International Development, replaced ICA

  • Statement of policy of the "Act for International Development of 1961" * :
    "It is the sense of the Congress that peace depends upon a wider recognition of the dignity and the interdependence of men, and the survival of free institutions in the United States can best be assured in a world-wide atmosphere of freedom.

    "To this end, the United States has in the past provided assistance to help strengthen the forces of freedom by aiding peoples of less developed friendly countries of the world to develop their resources and improve their living standards, to realize their aspirations for justice, education, dignity, and respect as individual human beings, and to establish responsible governments."

SIGNIFICANT QUOTES:
Nutrition on an international scale[1]

In the opinion of the writer, in this now small world, international cooperation to apply science to the promotion of the welfare of all mankind is the only alternative to war. There could be no better starting point of cooperation than on a food policy based on human needs. If a world food policy on that basis were adopted it would afford great satisfaction to those whose researches have established the health standard of needs, to know that as a result of their work a thousand million of their fellow men will be free from malnutrition and enjoy a fuller and longer life and that the necessary increased food production will contribute to economic prosperity of benefit to all nations. Thus the advance in the science of nutrition can be of greater benefit to mankind than the more spectacular advance in physics which released the hydrogen bomb.

Purposes of FAO [2]

The preamble to the Constitution of FAO tells in a few words the reason for its existence:
The Nations accepting this Constitution, being determined to promote the common welfare by furthering separate and collective action on their part for the purposes of raising levels of nutrition and standards of living of the peoples under their respective jurisdictions, securing improvements in the efficiency of the production of all food and agricultural products, bettering the condition of rural populations, and thus contributing toward an expanding world economy, hereby establish the Food and Agriculture Organization of the United Nations . . . through which the Members will report to one another on the measures taken and the progress achieved in the fields of action set forth above.

Summary of objectives:

  • To raise the levels of nutrition and standards of living of the peoples of their country and the world.

  • To secure improvements in the efficiency of production and distribution of all food and agricultural products.

  • To better the condition of rural populations.

  • To contribute to an expanding economy.

---

* Public Law 87–195, 87th Congress, S. 1983. Sept. 4. 1961, p. 1. Title later was changed to "Agency for International Development."

[1] Lord Boyd-Orr, *Borden's Review*, Mar.–Apr. 1954.

[2] Food and Agriculture Organization of the United Nations, Washington, D.C., Apr. 1946.

CONSTITUTION OF THE WORLD HEALTH ORGANIZATION [3]

THE STATES parties to this Constitution declare, in conformity with the Charter of the United Nations, that the following principles are basic to the happiness, harmonious relation and security of all peoples:

Health is a state of complete physical, mental and social well-being and not merely the absence of disease or infirmity.

The enjoyment of the highest attainable standard of health is one of the fundamental rights of every human being without distinction of race, religion, political belief, or economic or social condition.

The health of all peoples is fundamental to the attainment of peace and security and is dependent upon the fullest cooperation of individuals and States.

The achievement of any State in the promotion and protection of health is of value to all.

Unequal development in different countries in the promotion of health and control of disease, especially communicable disease, is a common danger.

Healthy development of the child is of basic importance; the ability to live harmoniously in a changing total environment is essential to such development.

The extension to all peoples of the benefits of medical, psychological and related knowledge is essential to the fullest attainment of health.

Informed opinion and active cooperation on the part of the public are of the utmost importance in the improvement of the health of the people.

Governments have a responsibility for the health of their peoples which can be fulfilled only by the provision of adequate health and social measures.

ACCEPTING THESE PRINCIPLES, and for the purpose of cooperation among themselves and with others to promote and protect the health of all peoples, THE CONTRACTING PARTIES agree to the present Constitution and hereby establish the World Health Organization as a specialized agency of the United Nations within the terms of Article 57 of the Charter of the UN.

---

[3] Source: *Amer. Jour. of Publ. Health*, 36, (No. 11):1315, Nov. 1946.

SOME FACTORS IN THE FRAMEWORK OF GOOD NUTRITION *

Country	Acres per Person	Per Cent of Arable Land	Per Cent of People-Farmers	Average Income per Person[1]	Calories per Person per Day	Infant Mortality[2]
Brazil......	41.2	2.2	58	112	2300	..
Canada....	247	3.9	16	870	3020	38
Denmark...	2.4	64.4	23	689	3220	29
Egypt......	11.8	2.5	65	100	2350	130
India......	2.2	40.0	66	57	1620	116
Italy.......	1.6	51.5	39	235	2480	64
Iraq.......	21.1	5.3	..	85	1930	..
Greece.....	4.2	26.4	58	128	2490	..
U.S.A......	12.4	24.7	11	1453	3160	29

* Source: Gove Hambidge, *Story of FAO*, Van Nostrand, 1955.
[1] In terms of U.S.A. dollars, 1949.
[2] Infants under 1 yr. of age per 1,000 live births (data added from other sources).

DISTRIBUTION OF POPULATION ACCORDING TO NATIONAL AVERAGE SUPPLIES OF CALORIES AND ANIMAL PROTEIN *

Calorie Supplies and Animal Protein	Per Cent of Total Population[1]	
	Prewar	Recent postwar
Calorie Levels		
Over 2700..........................	30.6	27.8
2700–2200..........................	30.8	12.7
Under 2200.........................	38.6	59.5
Animal Protein Levels		
Over 30 grams......................	22.1	17.2
30–15 grams........................	18.9	24.8
Under 15 grams.....................	59.0	58.0

* Source: *Second World Food Survey*, p. 11. Food and Agriculture Organization of the UN, Rome, Nov. 1952.
[1] Comprising approximately 80 per cent of the world's population.

PERCENTAGE INCREASE REQUIRED IN GROSS SUPPLIES FROM THEIR 1952 LEVELS TO
MEET 1960 TARGETS*

	Far East	Near East	Africa	Latin America	Europe	North America and Oceania	USSR	World
Cereals....	22	29	33	23	16	16	14	19
Starch roots....	16	66	16	14	21	−13	− 1	12
Pulses.....	48	61	48	68	56	13	24	47
Sugar.....	35	16	31	8	6	9	11	15
Fats......	..	88	..	..	16	4	32	..
Fruit......	..	68	..	..	48	39	39	...
Vegetables	..	14	..	..	39	34	34	..
Meat.....	47	43	33	28	23	20	20	30
Eggs......	24	88	67	55	30	12	12	39
Fish......	68	40	75	26	11	18	18	47
Milk[1]....	32	31	41	36	16	25	25	33
Estimated percentage population increase by 1960...	10	15	15	18	8	14	16	11

* Source: *Second World Food Survey*, p. 25. Food and Agriculture Organization of the UN, Rome, Nov. 1952.

[1] Includes all milk products, except butter, as fresh milk equivalent.

INTERNATIONAL NUTRITION [4]

Human groups move farther from savagery and closer to civilization as science makes it possible for larger numbers to live on more plentiful food, in more comfortable conditions, with more time free for activities about those required for existence. Scientific knowledge did not happen; it was gleaned by continuing and patient effort, by study and experiment. In the realm of food, as in all others, support of such effort has paid rich dividends in human welfare. But knowledge of the scientists and technologists is not sufficient. To put it into action, there must be widespread understanding and support by the people. And when people do have the facts, they usually come to sound conclusions and take wise actions.

Obviously, nutritional science bears a large responsibility for future generations of men the world over. It has hardly begun to face the colossal major problems. But it has solved the immediate and local ones, for America at least. And it has begun to spread its newfound knowledge, as is shown by the improved nutrition of most Americans. At the moment, its immediate problem is to disseminate that knowledge so that every man, woman, and child not only has a sound understanding of what good nutrition is but also acts on it. The greatest need of American nutrition today — and that means American health, too — is public education.

[4] Source: *Food for Life,* p. 302. Edited by Ralph Gerard, Univ. of Chicago Press, 1952.

Appendix I

Nutrition Education Reference List*

General References

1. Aldrich, C. K., "Prescribing a Diet Is Not Enough." *Jour. Amer. Diet. Assn.* 33(No. 8):785, 1957.
2. Dixon, J. P., "Meeting Human Needs." P. 259 in *Goals for Americans,* ed. by the President's Comm. on Natl. Goals, Prentice-Hall, 1960.
3. Ellis, M., "Make Every Week Nutrition Week." *Jour. Home Econ.* 48(No. 4):275, 1956.
4. Eppright, E. S., and LeBaron, H. R., "Our Responsibilities to Children and Youth." *Jour. Amer. Diet. Assn.* 38(No. 4):354, 1961.
5. Everson, G. J., "Bases for Concern About Teen-ager's Diets." *Jour. Amer. Diet. Assn.* 36(No. 1):17, 1960.
6. Hamilton, L. W., and Lowenberg, M. E., "Food Patterns in Relation to Breakfasts." *Jour. Home Econ.* 49(No. 10):796, 1957.
7. Harris, M., and Roehm, G., "Teaching Nutrition Toward a Measured Goal." *Jour. Home Econ.* 49(No. 6):419, 1957.
8. Hill, M. M., "Planning for Nutrition Education in Elementary Schools." *Jour. Home Econ.* 52(No. 4):259, 1960.
9. Hunscher, H. A., and others, "The Life Cycle and Its Diet." *Jour. Home Econ.* 49(No. 2): 101, 1957.
10. Knutson, A. L., and Newton, M. E., "Behavioral Factors in Nutrition Education." *Jour. Amer. Diet. Assn.* 37(No. 3):222, 1960.
11. McCann, M. B., and Trulson, M. F., "Our Changing Diet." *Jour. Amer. Diet. Assn.* 33(No. 4):358, 1957.
12. McCully, H., "Creative Cooking." *Jour. Home Econ.* 48 (No. 2):98, 1956.
13. MacKinnon, C. F., "Changing Food Habits—The Dietitian's Dilemma." *Jour. Amer. Diet. Assn.* 31 (No. 6): 566, 1955.
14. Meredith, A., "Nutrition Counseling for Patients in a Community." *Jour. Amer. Diet. Assn.* 33(No. 2):108, 1957.
15. Potgieter, M., and Morse, E. H., "Food Habits of Children." *Jour. Amer. Diet. Assn.* 31(No. 8):794, 1955.
16. Roth, A., "The Teen-age Clinic." *Jour. Amer. Diet. Assn.* 36(No. 1):27, 1960.
17. Semrow, E. H., "The Forward Look in Nutrition Education." *Jour. Home Econ.* 48(No. 9):685, 1956.
18. Simons, A. A., "An Elementary Challenge in Nutrition Education." *Jour. Home Econ.* 52(No. 10):846, 1960.
19. Smey, J., "Nutrition Education in the Elementary Schools." *Jour. Home Econ.* 50(No. 5):335, 1958.
20. Swanson, P., *Calcium in Nutrition.* National Dairy Council, Chicago 6, Ill., 1963.

* Prepared by Helen Barbour for use in a workshop held at Oklahoma State University.

21. Thigpin, L. W., and Mitchell, I. A., "Integrating Nutrition Into Nursing Education." *Jour. Amer. Diet. Assn.* 33(No. 4):378, 1957.
22. Whitehead, F. E., "How Nutrition Education Can Affect Adolescents' Food Choices. I. With and without one year's nutrition instruction. II. With and without two years' nutrition instruction." *Jour. Amer. Diet. Assn.* 37(No. 4):348, 353, 1960.
23. ———, "Nutrition Education for Children in the U.S. Since 1900." Parts I and II. *Jour. Amer. Diet. Assn.* 33(No. 9):880 and 885, 1957.

Human Values

1. Barbour, H. F., "Relationships of Values and Process Concepts of Selected Students to Generalizations in Nutrition." Unpubl. Ph.D. dissertation, Iowa State University, Ames, 1953.
2. Brown, M. W., "The Growth of Values in Childhood and Old Age." *Jour. Home Econ.* 52(No. 6):407, 1960.
3. Cassell, J., "The Social and Cultural Implications of Food and Food Habits." *Amer. Jour. Publ. Health* 46:732–40, 1957.
4. Davidson, C. S., and others, "The Nutrition of a Group of Apparently Healthy Aging Persons." *Amer. Jour. Clin. Nutr.* 10:181–99, Mar. 1962.
5. DiVesta, F. J., "Process Concepts and Values in the Social Adjustment of Adolescents." Unpubl. Ph.D. dissertation, Cornell University Library, Ithaca, N.Y., 1948.
6. Dressel, P. L., "Factors Involved in Changing the Values of College Students." Unpubl. report, Michigan State University, 1961.
7. Eddy, E. D., Jr., "Impact of the Curriculum on Values." *School and Society* 88(No. 2167) Jan. 30, 1960.
8. Fults, A. C., "Examining Socioeconomic Values in Terms of Family Welfare." *Jour. Home Econ.* 51(No. 4):284, 1959.
9. Hawkes, G. R., "A Study of the Personal Values of Elementary School Children." Unpubl. Ph.D. dissertation, Cornell University Library, Ithaca, N.Y., 1950.
10. Lee, D., "The Individual in a Changing Society." *Jour. Home Econ.* 52(No. 2):79, 1960.
11. Maslov, A. H. (Editor), *New Knowledge in Human Values.* Harper Bros., 1959.
12. Mockmore, B. M., "Lasting Values in a Changing World." *Jour. Home Econ.* 50(No. 10):751, 1958.
13. Pease, D., and Swanson, L. V., "Middle Childhood and Pre-Adolescence Deserve Study, Too." *Jour. Home Econ.* 50(No. 1):33, 1958.
14. Queen, G. S., "Culture, Economics, and Food Habits." *Jour. Amer. Diet. Assn.* 33(No. 10):1044, 1957.
15. Woodruff, A. D., "A Study of Directive Forces in Individual Behavior." (Private ed.) Ph.D. dissertation, University of Chicago, 1941.
16. ———, and DiVesta, F. J., "The Relationships Between Values, Concepts, and Attitudes." *Educational Measurements* 8:645–59, 1948.

Teaching Methods and Ideas

1. Beeuwkes, A. M., "Educational Television—Nutrition's New Opportunity." *Jour. Amer. Diet. Assn.* 33(No. 5):477, 1957.
2. ———, "Teaching Nutrition—Progress and Problems." *Jour. Amer. Diet. Assn.* 35(No. 8):797, 1959.
3. Bergevin, P., "Telling vs. Teaching—Learning by Participation." *Jour. Amer. Diet. Assn.* 33(No. 8), 1957.
4. Boulden, J. B., "Creative Thinking." *Jour. Amer. Diet. Assn.* 36(No. 6):565, 1960.
5. Browne, J. H., "Programs To Fit Changing Health Needs." *Jour. Amer. Diet. Assn.* 35(No. 9):789, 1959.
6. Burgess, A., "Nutrition Education in Public Health Programs—What We Have Learned." *Jour. Amer. Publ. Health* 51:1715–26, 1961.
7. Cartier, F. A., "Blazing New Trails in Thinking." *Jour. Amer. Diet. Assn.* 34(No. 2):125, 1958.
8. Cate, H., "Developing Ability To Solve Family Dietary Problems." *Jour. Home Econ.* 49(No. 1):32, 1957.

9. Cody, E., and Carrington, E. M., "Retraining a Child To Eat." *Jour. Amer. Diet. Assn.* 33(No. 6):605, 1957.

10. Edwards, M., "Pretesting Determines Student Nurses' Need for Cookery Class." *Jour. Amer. Diet. Assn.* 31(No. 1):54, 1955.

11. Eppright, E. S., "Vitalizing Nutrition Teaching." *Jour. Home Econ.* 43:89–92, 1951.

12. Galdston, I., "Motivation in Health Education." *Jour. Amer. Diet. Assn.* 25:745, 1949.

13. ———, "Nutrition From the Psychiatric Viewpoint." *Jour. Amer. Diet. Assn.* 28:405, 1952.

14. Hager, W. H., "Educating Women for a Changing World." *Jour. Home Econ.* 49(No. 9):619, 1957.

15. Hankins, J., "Are Teachers Prepared To Teach Nutrition?" *Jour. Amer. Diet. Assn.* 35(No. 8):802, 1959.

16. Harper, W. A., "TV: New Force in Education." *Jour. Home Econ.* 49(No. 10):784, 1957.

17. Hawkins, M., "Teaching Aids That Teach." *Jour. Home Econ.* 49(No. 4):281, 1957.

18. Howard, P. B., and Davis, P. H., "My Job and Yours. Dolls Show Golden Opportunities." *Jour. Home Econ.* 51(No. 10):878, 1959.

19. Kreitlow, B. W., "Teaching Adults Democratically." *Jour. Amer. Diet. Assn.* 3(No. 8):788, 1957.

20. Lane, L., "You and Your Public Image." *Jour. Home Econ.* 52(No. 7):514, 1960.

21. Lantis, M., "The Child Consumer." *Jour. Home Econ.* 54:370–75, May 1962.

22. Leverton, R. M., "Teaching Nutrition to Teen-agers." *What's New in Home Economics,* 25:52, Jan. 1961.

23. Lewin, K., "Forces Behind Food Habits and Methods of Change." *The Problems of Changing Food Habits,* National Research Council Bulletin, 108:35–65, 1943.

24. Lison, T. R., "Our Professional Ethics." *Jour. Home Econ.* 48(No. 10):769, 1956.

25. Lucke, D. M., "Teaching Methods in Non-Laboratory Classes." *Jour. Home Econ.* 48(No. 3):173, 1956.

26. Lyng, A., "Using Science in Our Profession." *Jour. Home Econ.* 52(No. 10):821, 1960.

27. McClaskey, W. R., "Brainstorming." *Jour. Home Econ.* 49(No. 9):705, 1957.

28. McCormack, A. M., "An In-Use Approach to Nutrition Teaching." *Jour. Home Econ.* 50(No. 1):47, 1958.

29. Miller, J. G., "Know the Behavioral Sciences." *Jour. Home Econ.* 52(No. 5):327, 1960.

30. Moore, B. M., "Time, Tension, and Mental Health." *Jour. Home Econ.* 49(No. 10):759, 1957.

31. Norman, E. C., "Group Discussion in Changing Food Habits." *Jour. Amer. Diet. Assn.* 34(No. 11):1187, 1958.

32. Paarlberg, D., "Food-for-Peace." *Jour. Home Econ.* 52(No. 10):803, 1960.

33. Pease, D., and Pattison, M., "Observation: A Method of Learning About Children." *Jour. Home Econ.* 48(No. 10):755, 1956.

34. Petersen. E. L., "Demonstrations Aid in Teacher Education." *Jour. Home Econ.* 48(No. 10):786, 1956.

35. Radke, M., and Klisurich, D., "Experiments in Changing Food Habits." *Jour. Amer. Diet. Assn.* 23:403, 1947.

36. ———, and Caso, E. K., "Lecture and Discussion-Decision as Methods of Influencing Food Habits." *Jour. Amer. Diet. Assn.* 24:23, 1948.

37. Raiman, E. S., "Telling Is Not Teaching." *Jour. Amer. Diet. Assn.* 37(No. 2):118, 1960.

38. Schroeder, W. P., "Learning-by-Doing Through Teaching." *Jour. Amer. Diet. Assn.* 37(No. 6):577, 1960.

39. Schubert, G. W., and Dalrymple, J. I., "Problems and Needs of Young Homemakers: Implications for High School Home Economics." *Jour. Home Econ.* 51(No. 5):365, 1959.

40. "Science and Food: Today and Tomorrow." Food Protection Comm., Food and Nutr. Board, Natl. Acad. of Sciences, Symposium, *Proceedings,* Dec. 8, 1960, NRC Publ. No. 877.

41. Spader, M., "Nutrition Education for Senior Citizens." *Jour. Home Econ.* 52(No. 1):43, 1960.
42. Stone, D. B., "Nutrition: The Forgotten Art." *Nutr. Revs.* 19:1–2, 1961.
43. Strong, D. H., "Science Requirements in Home Economics." *Jour. Home Econ.* 51(No. 6):461, 1959.
44. "Teaching Aids in Production." Symposium, *Jour. Home Econ.* 49(No. 5):343, 1957.
45. "Teaching Aids in Use." Symposium, *Jour. Home Econ.* 49(No. 6):423, 1957.
46. "Teaching Posters Feature Nutrition This Month." *Jour. Home Econ.* 51(No. 10):902–3, 1959.
47. Venable, T. C., "Nutrition Education—What Is the Problem?" *Jour. Amer. Diet Assn.* 33(No. 6):600, 1957.
48. Young, C. M., "Teaching the Patient Means Reaching the Patient." *Jour. Amer. Diet. Assn.* 33(No. 1):52, 1957.

Attitudes Toward Food and Eating

1. Babcock, C. G., "Attitudes and the Use of Food." *Jour. Amer. Diet. Assn.* 38(No. 5):546, 1961.
2. ———, "Food and Its Emotional Significance." *Jour. Amer. Diet. Assn.* 24:390, 1948.
3. Breckenridge, M. E., "Food Attitudes of Five- to Twelve-year-old Children." *Jour. Amer. Diet. Assn.* 35(No. 7):704, 1959.
4. Bryan, M. S., and Lowenberg, M. E., "The Father's Influence on Young Children's Food Preferences." *Jour. Amer. Diet. Assn.* 34(No. 1):30, 1958.
5. Dudley, D. T., Moore, M. E., and Sunderlin, E. M., "Children's Attitudes Toward Food." *Jour. Home Econ.* 52(No. 8):678, 1960.
6. Fathauer, G. H., "Food Habits—An Anthropologist's View." *Jour. Amer. Diet. Assn.* 37(No. 4):335, 1960.
7. Glaser, A., "Building Food Acceptance in Nursery School Children." *Jour. Home Econ.* 49(No. 1):47, 1957.
8. Hamburger, W. W., "The Psychology of Dietary Change." *Amer. Jour. Publ. Health* 48:1342–48, 1958.
9. Hawkins, M., ". . . The Highest Possible Level of Health." *Jour. Home Econ.* 50(No. 6):416, 1958.
10. Jones, L., "New Techniques." *Jour. Home Econ.* 50(No. 5):340, 1958.
11. Lee, D., "Cultural Factors and Dietary Choice." *Amer. Jour. Clin. Nutr.* 5:166, 1957.
12. Pilgrim, F. J., "What Foods Do People Accept and Reject?" *Jour. Amer. Diet. Assn.* 38(No. 5):439, 1961.
13. Taylor, M. M., "Food Taste Patterns of Junior High School Students." *Jour. Home Econ.* 50(No. 9): 719, 1958.
14. Vawter, H. J., and Konishi, F., "Food Acceptance by Soldiers Under an *ad libitum* Regimen." *Jour. Amer. Diet. Assn.* 34(No. 1):36, 1958.
15. Young, C., Waldner, B. G., and Berresford, K., "What the Homemaker Knows About Nutrition. IV: Her Food Problems, Shopping Habits, and Sources of Information." *Jour. Amer. Diet. Assn.* 32:429, 1956.

Dietary Survey Methods and Calculation of Food Intakes

1. Adelson, S. F., "Some Problems in Collecting Dietary Data From Individuals." *Jour. Amer. Diet. Assn.* 36(No. 5):453, 1960.
2. Bowes, A. deP., and Church, C. F., *Food Values of Portions Commonly Used.* 9th ed. revised by Church, C. F., and Church, H. N., Lippincott, 1963.
3. Burchinal, L. G., and Hawkes, G. R., "Home Interviews With Families." *Jour. Home Econ.* 49:167, 1957.
4. Caplow, T., "The Dynamics of Information Interviewing." *Amer. Jour. Soc.* 62:165, 1956.
5. Donelson, E. G., and Leichsenring, J. M., "A Short Method of Dietary Analysis." *Jour. Amer. Diet. Assn.* 18:429, 1942.
6. French, C. M., Iokal, M., and Khan, M. N., "A Nutritional Survey of the Armed Forces of Pakistan, Dietary Studies." *Jour. of Nutr.* 68(Suppl. 1) July 1959.
7. Hunscher, H. A., and Macy, I. G., "Dietary Study Methods. I. Uses and Abuses of Dietary Study Methods." *Jour. Amer. Diet. Assn.* 27:558, 1951.

8. Leichsenring, J. M., and Wilson, E. D., "Food Composition Table for Short Method of Dietary Analysis" (2nd review). *Jour. Amer. Diet. Assn.* 27:386, 1951.
9. Medlin, H. S., "The Art of Questioning." *Natl. Educ. Assn. Jour.* 44:236, 1955.
10. *Nutritional Data*, 3rd ed. H. J. Heinz Co., Pittsburgh, Pa.
11. *Recommended Daily Dietary Allowances.* National Research Council—Food and Nutrition Board, Publ. 589, 1958.
12. Trulson, M. F., and McCann, M. B., "Comparison of Dietary Survey Methods." *Jour. Amer. Diet. Assn.* 35:672, 1959.
13. Young, C. M., and Trulson, M. F., "Methodology for Dietary Studies in Epidemological Surveys. II. Strengths and Weaknesses of Existing Methods." *Amer. Jour. Publ. Health* 60:803, 1960.
14. Yudkins, J., "Dietary Surveys: Variation in the Weekly Intake of Nutrients." *British Jour. of Nutr.* 5:177, 1951.

Importance of Fat in the Diet

1. Brewer, W. D., and Arnrich, L., "The Role of Fat in the Diet." *Jour. Home Econ.* 50(No. 4):269, 1958.
2. Brown, H. B., "Fashioning a Practical Vegetable-oil Food Pattern." *Jour. Amer. Diet. Assn.* 38(No. 5):536, 1960.
3. ———, and Spodnik, M. J., "Meat for Low-fat Diets." *Jour. Amer. Diet. Assn.* 38(No. 5):540, 1961.
4. Coons, C. M., "Fatty Acids in Foods." *Jour. Amer. Diet. Assn.* 34(No. 3):242, 1958.
5. Groom, D., "Atherosclerosis and Diet." *Jour. Amer. Diet. Assn.* 35(No. 9):919, 1959.
6. Hansen, A. E., "Essential Fatty Acids in Infant Feeding." *Jour. Amer. Diet. Assn.* 34(No. 3):239, 1958.
7. Hardinge, M. G., and Crooks, H., "Fatty Acid Composition of Food Fats." *Jour. Amer. Diet. Assn.* 34(No. 10):1065, 1958.
8. Meredith, A. P., "Living With the Vegetable-oil Food Patterns." *Jour. Amer. Diet. Assn.* 38(No. 5):543, 1961.
9. Okey, R., Scheier, G., and Reed, M., "Food Restriction and Cholesterol Metabolism. Effect on Cholesterol Metabolism of Limiting the Time Food Is Accessible." *Jour. Amer. Diet. Assn.* 36(No. 5):441, 1960.
10. "The Role of Dietary Fat in Human Health." Committee on Fats in Human Nutrition, National Research Council, Publ. 575, 1958.
11. Stefanik, P., and Trulson, M. F., "Modifying the Fatty Acid Content of the Diet." *Jour. Amer. Diet. Assn.* 34(No. 6):591, 1958.
12. Vail, G. E., "Cooking With Fats High in Polyunsaturated Fatty Acids." *Jour. Amer. Diet. Assn.* 35(No. 2):119, 1959.
13. Van Itallie, T. B., and Hashim, S. A., "Diet and Heart Disease—Facts and Unanswered Questions." *Jour. Amer. Diet. Assn.* 38(No. 5):531, 1961.
14. Wilcox, E. B., and Galloway, L. S., "Serum Cholesterol and Different Dietary Fats." *Jour. Amer. Diet. Assn.* 38(No. 3):227, 1961.

Food Additives

1. Burns, M., "Popularizing the Food Additive—Story." *Jour. Home Econ.* 52(No. 5):342, 1960.
2. DeEds, F., "Chemicals in Foods." *Jour. Amer. Diet. Assn.* 35(No. 1):19, 1959.
3. Fenton, F., "Food Additives and Labeling: The Responsibility of the Consumer." *Jour. Home Econ.* 52(No. 9):747, 1960.
4. Horst, R. L., "The Food Additives Amendment." *Jour. Home Econ.* 52(No. 9):743, 1960.
5. Larrick, G. P., "Explaining the Food Additive Law to the Homemaker." *Jour. Home Econ.* 52(No. 9):744, 1960.

6. Schultz, H. W., "Chemicals in Foods." *Jour. Amer. Diet. Assn.* 34(No. 5):492, 1958.
7. Williams, C. S., "Food and Drug Administration's Consumer-Consultant Program." *Jour. Home Econ.* 52(No. 9):772, 1960.

Food Fads and Fallacies

1. Friedman, L., "Evaluating Protein Quality for Advertizing." *Jour. Amer. Diet. Assn.* 35(No. 6):574, 1959.
2. Janssen, W., "Food Quackery—A Law Enforcement Problem." *Jour. Amer. Diet. Assn.* 36(No. 2):110, 1961.
3. Mitchell, H. S., "Food Fads—What Protection Have We?" *Jour. Home Econ.* 53(No. 2):100, 1961.
4. Nielson, J. P., "Effect of Processing and Handling on Foods." *Jour. Amer. Diet. Assn.* 34(No. 12):1313, 1958.
5. Todhunter, E. N., "The Food We Eat." *Jour. Home Econ.* 50(No. 7):510, 1958.

Weight Control References

1. Ayers, W. M., "Changing Attitudes Toward Overweight and Reducing." *Jour. Amer. Diet. Assn.* 34(No. 1):23, 1958.
2. Berryman, G. H., "Simple Obesity: A Current Review." *Jour. Amer. Diet. Assn.* 31(No. 4):347, 1955.
3. Bowser, L. J., and others, "Methods of Reducing. Group Therapy vs. Clinic Interview." *Jour. Amer. Diet. Assn.* 29(No. 12):1193, 1953.
4. Brozek, J., "To Be or Not To Be—Fat (and how to tell if you are)." *Jour. Amer. Diet. Assn.* 29(No. 4):344, 1953.
5. Conrad, S. W., "Resistance of the Obese to Reducing." *Jour. Amer. Diet. Assn.* 30(No. 6):581, 1954.
6. Darling, C. D., and Summerskill, J., "Emotion Factors in Obesity and Weight Reduction." *Jour. Amer. Diet. Assn.* 29(No. 12):1204, 1953.
7. Fryer, J., and others, "Satiety Values of Isocaloric Diets for Reducing. With special reference to glucostatic theory of appetite control." *Jour. Amer. Diet. Assn.* 31(No. 9):868, 1955.
8. Hamburger, W. W., "Appetite in Man." *Amer. Jour. Clin. Nutr.* 8:569, 1960.
9. ———, "The Psychology of Weight Reduction." *Jour. Amer. Diet. Assn.* 34(No. 1): 17, 1958.
10. Harrison, H. E., "Vitamin D and Calcium Requirements." *Jour. Amer. Diet. Assn.* 31(No. 5):483, 1955.
11. "Heavy and Light Eaters." Editorial in *Nutr. Revs.* 20:11–13, 1962.
12. Leverton, R. M., "The Merry-go-round of Reducing Diets." *Jour. Amer. Diet. Assn.* 29(No. 4):333, 1953.
13. Lew, E. A., "New Data on Underweight and Overweight Persons." *Jour. Amer. Diet. Assn.* 38(No. 4):323, 1961.
14. Mayer, J., "An Experimentalist's Approach to the Problem of Obesity." *Jour. Amer. Diet. Assn.* 31(No. 3):230, 1955.
15. ———, and Stare, F. J., "Exercise and Weight Control. Frequent Misconceptions." *Jour. Amer. Diet. Assn.* 29(No. 4):340, 1953.
16. Munves, E. D., "Dietetic Interview or Group Discussion—Decision in Reducing." *Jour. Amer. Diet. Assn.* 29(No. 12):1197, 1953.
17. Sebrell, W. H., Jr., "Weight Control Through Prevention of Obesity." *Jour. Amer. Diet. Assn.* 34(No. 9):920, 1958.
18. Simmons, W. D., "The Group Approach to Weight Reduction. I. A review of the project." *Jour. Amer. Diet. Assn.* 30(No. 5):437, 1954.
19. Simon, J., "Psychologic Factors in Dietary Restriction." *Jour. Amer. Diet. Assn.* 37(No. 2):109, 1960.

20. Suczek, R. F., "The Group Approach to Weight Reduction. II. Psychologic aspects of obesity and group weight reduction." *Jour. Amer. Diet. Assn.* 30(No. 5):442, 1954.
21. Young, C. M., "Helping the Overweight Individual." In *Weight Control* — a collection of papers presented at the weight control colloquium — Iowa State University, Ames. Iowa State University Press, 1955.

Recommended Books

1. Bowes, A. deP., and Church, C. F., *Food Values of Portions Commonly Used.* 9th ed., revised by Church, C. F., and Church, H. N. Lippincott, 1963.
2. Callahan, D., and Payne, A. S., *The Great Nutrition Puzzle.* Scribner, 1956.
3. Chaney, M. S., *Nutrition.* 6th ed. Houghton Mifflin, 1960.
4. Cooper, L. F., Barber, E. M., Mitchell, H. S., and Rynbergen, H. J., *Nutrition in Health and Disease.* 13th ed. Lippincott, 1958.
5. Fleck, H., and Munves, E., *Introductory Nutrition.* Macmillan, 1962.
6. *Food.* The USDA Yearbook of Agriculture, 1959. Supt. of Documents, U.S. Govt. Print. Office.
7. Kain, I. J., and Gibson, M. B., *Stay Slim for Life.* Doubleday, 1958.
8. Leverton, R. M., *Food Becomes You.* Iowa State University Press, 1960.
9. McHenry, E. W., *Basic Nutrition.* 2nd ed. in prep. Lippincott, 1962.
10. Martin, E. A., *Nutrition in Action.* Holt, Rinehart, Winston, 1963.
11. ———, *Nutrition Education in Action.* Holt, Rinehart, Winston, 1963.
12. ———, *Robert's Nutrition Work With Children.* University of Chicago Press, 1954.
13. Mowry, L., *Basic Nutrition and Diet Therapy for Practical Nurses.* Mosby, 1962.
14. Nasset, E. S., *Food and You.* 1st ed., C C Thomas, 1951. 2nd ed., Barnes and Noble, 1958.
15. ———, *Your Diet, Digestion, and Health.* 2nd ed. rev., Barnes and Noble, 1961.
16. Proudfit, F., *Normal and Therapeutic Nutrition.* 12th ed. Macmillan, 1961.
17. Sherman, H. C., and Langford, C. S., *Essentials of Nutrition.* 4th ed. Macmillan, 1957.
18. Spock, B., and Lowenberg, M., *Feeding Your Baby and Child.* Pocket Books, 1955.
19. Tanner, J. M., *Growth at Adolescence.* C C Thomas, 1962.
20. Taylor, C. M., *Food Values in Shares and Weights.* 2nd ed. Macmillan, 1959.
21. ———, and others. *Foundations of Nutrition.* 5th ed. Macmillan, 1956.
22. Watt, B. K., and Merrill, A. L., *Composition of Foods — Raw, Processed, Prepared.* Agr. Handbook No. 8. U.S. Govt. Print. Office, 1950.
23. Wilson, E. D., and others, *Principles of Nutrition.* Wiley, 1959.

Index